EPONYMISTS IN MEDICINE

Richard Bright
1789-1858

Physician in an Age of
Revolution and Reform

Diana Berry and Campbell Mackenzie

Editor-in-Chief: Hugh L'Etang

Publication of this volume was supported by an
educational grant from Fresenius Health Care Group,
whose help is gratefully acknowledged

Royal Society of Medicine Services Limited

Royal Society of Medicine Services Limited
1 Wimpole Street London W1M 8AE
7 East 60th Street New York NY 10022

© 1992 Royal Society of Medicine Services Limited

British Library Cataloguing in Publication Data
A catalogue record for this book is available from the British Library

ISBN 1-85315-188-2

Design by Mehmet Hussein/Medilink Design

Phototypeset by Dobbie Typesetting Limited, Tavistock, Devon

Printed in Great Britain by Henry Ling Ltd at the Dorset Press, Dorchester, Dorset

Contents

Acknowledgements

The authors have received invaluable assistance from many sources during the writing of this book and would wish to express their sincere gratitude.

Firstly special thanks to the many descendants of Dr Richard Bright who have given so generously both of their time and hospitality and have willingly shared with us important family letters, manuscripts, pictures and memorabilia for inclusion in the book:

Dr and Mrs Peter Baker and Mrs Baker Senior, Mrs Joan Astley, Major and Mrs L. Athill, Mr and Mrs Charles Bright, Mrs E. Lloyd, Mrs Peggy Gibbs, Dr and Mrs Dennis Gibbs and Countess Annabel Ferrers.

We would make particular mention of Pamela Bright, the Doctor's great-great-niece, whose continued encouragement, enthusiasm and generosity of spirit has lightened those dark moments of doubt and considerably eased our task.

Secondly, we are most grateful for the co-operation and help we have received from the following institutions, libraries and museums and their willing members of staff:

The Royal College of Physicians of both Edinburgh and London, particularly Mr A. Milne and Mr G. Tate, The Royal Society of Medicine, The Wills Librarian, Mr Andrew Baster and Mr Jo Dawes of the Gordon Museum both at Guy's Hospital, London, Bristol University Medical School Library and Chief Librarian Mr Clive Ward, The Wellcome Institute, The Royal Pharmaceutical Society and Archivist, Mr Nigel Tallis, L'Academie des Sciences, Institut de France and Archivist, Madame Claudine Pouret, The British Library and The Bodleian Library Oxford, Bristol Central Library, Bristol Records Office, Bristol City Museums and Art Gallery, Mr T. J. Gooch, Royal Devon and Exeter Hospital, Jennifer Oldershaw and Pauline Glover of Southmead Medical Information and Library Services, Mr Nick Bowyer and the and the staff of Medical Illustration, Southmead Hospital, Bristol, The Sue Ryder Foundation and Bi-Design, Bristol for graphic work.

We would also wish to thank the following for their help and support: Dr Conrad Swan, the York Herald of Arms, Dr Bela Szebenyi, Mr Clive Charlton, Dr Christopher Gardner-Thorpe, Dr Andrew Wawn, Mrs Barbara Wright, Mr Gerald Hart, Mrs Barbara James and the secretarial staff of the Renal Unit at Southmead Hospital.

We are most grateful to the Fresenius Health Care Group, who generously agreed to contribute towards the publication of this book.

Finally, thanks are due to our long-suffering families who have borne the inevitable disruption occasioned by frenetic literary output!

Illustrations

Biographical sketch

1789	Born 29 Queen Square, Bristol
1790	Moved to Ham Green
1795-1808	Schooling in Bristol and Exeter
1808-1810	Preclinical studies in Edinburgh
1810	Expedition to Iceland
1810-1813	Clinical years in Guy's and Edinburgh
1811	Elected to Guy's Physical Society
1813	MD Thesis on Contagious Erysipelas
1814-1815	Travels in Hungary: Congress of Vienna
1815	Battle of Waterloo—tended wounded
1815	*Travels through Lower Hungary* published
1816	Assistant Physician at Willan Fever Hospital
1817	Contracted typhus
1818	Further travels in Europe—meets the French school
1820	Associated physician at Guy's: Elected FRS
1822	Marriage to Martha Babington
1823	Birth of William Richard Bright—Martha's death
1824	Full Physician at Guy's
1826	Marriage to Elizabeth Follett
1827-1831	Reports on Medical Cases Vols I and II
1832	Elected FRCP
1833	Goulstonian Lecturer: Abdominal and Renal diseases
1837	Appointed Physician Extraordinary to HM Queen Victoria
1838	Awarded Monthyon Medal Institute of Science, Paris
1837	Lumleian Lecturer: Diseases of the Brain
1844	Retires from Guy's
1849	Attends Queen Adelaide
1853	Receives Doctorate of Civil Law (Oxon)
1858	Died Savile Row: buried Kensal Green

Contemporary events

1789	French Revolution
	Mutiny on the Bounty
1793	Execution of Louis XVI
1799	10% income tax introduced by Pitt
1760-1830	Industrial Revolution
1805	Battle of Trafalgar
1810	Accession of George IV
	Corn Law riots
1812	Lord Liverpool—Prime Minister
1815	Congress of Vienna
	Battle of Waterloo
1816-1830	Pandemic of cholera
1819	Peterloo Massacre
1825-1835	Growth of trade unions
1828	Duke of Wellington—Prime Minister
1829	Metropolitan Police Force
1830	Accession of William IV
1830-1850	Age of railways and steamships
1831	Bristol riots
1832	Earl Grey—Prime Minister
	Reform Act
	British Medical Association founded
1833	Abolition of Slavery
	Factory Act
1836	Registration of births, marriages, deaths compulsory
1837	Accession of Queen Victoria
1839	Rowland Hill: introduction of postage stamp
1840	Marriage of Queen Victoria and Prince Albert
	Introduction of penny post
1841	Sir Robert Peel—Prime Minister
1846	Lord John Russell—Prime Minister
1848	Public Health Act
1852	Lord Derby—Prime Minister
1853-1856	Crimean War
1859	Charles Darwin published *Origin of the Species*

Contemporaries

MEDICINE

William C Wells	1710-1801
Edward Jenner	1749-1823
James Parkinson	1755-1824
Thomas Beddoes	1760-1808
Sir Astley Cooper	1768-1841
John Blackall	1771-1860
Sir Charles Bell	1774-1842
Guillaume Dupuytren	1777-1835
John Cheyne	1777-1836
René Laennec	1781-1826
Humphry Davy	1788-1829
Robert Adams	1791-1875
Pierre Rayer	1793-1867
Robert Graves	1795-1853
Thomas Addison	1793-1860
Thomas Hodgkin	1798-1866
Armand Trousseau	1801-1867
Sir Dominic Corrigan	1802-1878
Claude Bernard	1813-1875

THE ARTS

Ludwig van Beethoven	1770-1827
William Wordsworth	1770-1850
Sir Walter Scott	1771-1832
Samuel Taylor Coleridge	1771-1834
Robert Southey	1774-1843
Joseph M W Turner	1775-1851
John Constable	1776-1837
Stendhal	1783-1842
Lord Byron	1788-1824
Gioacchino Rossini	1792-1868
Percy Bysshe Shelley	1792-1822
John Clare	1793-1864
Honoré de Balzac	1794-1850
John Keats	1795-1820
Franz Schubert	1797-1828
Victor Hugo	1802-1885
Nathaniel Hawthorne	1804-1864
Benjamin Disraeli	1804-1881
Alfred, Lord Tennyson	1809-1892
Elizabeth Gaskell	1810-1865
Charles Dickens	1812-1870
Robert Browning	1812-1889

Foreword

Dr Richard Bright was a Guy's man, a brilliant clinician and on the roll of honour of famous doctors he takes his place as the most outstanding English physician of the first half of the 19th century; during his own lifetime he became a legend in medical centres throughout Europe.

In its prime his life was dominated by medicine in all its many facets, in the wards and consulting rooms with his patients, teaching his students, or 'young friends' as he called them, addressing learned societies and post-graduate meetings, attending to the medico-political needs of Guy's Hospital and the Royal College of Physicians and finally in the *post mortem* room, where his correlation of clinical signs in life with morbid anatomy after death left a legacy of original observations. Not least of these were the seminal works on the clinico-pathological aspects of renal disorders which led to the eponymous title of 'Bright's Disease'. He was the first of the famous Guy's triumvirate of Bright, Addison and Hodgkin to receive this accolade, but sadly it has become the least remembered eponym amongst today's medical students. The decline in the teaching of the history of medicine in our medical schools is to be deplored and if eponyms can help to encourage pride in our medical heritage then let us retain them. Bearing this in mind, it is therefore fitting and appropriate that Bright should be included in the early volumes of the Eponymist Series published by the Royal Society of Medicine, lest we forget his enormous contributions not only to renal but to all other aspects of medicine. His position as the 'father of modern renal medicine' is unassailable.

We understand that his diaries and much of his correspondence were destroyed shortly after his death but, happily, extant letters provide a tantalising insight into his persona and general philosophy of life. From his medical writings, which are so intimately composed, it is possible to gain an impression of the professional man and his relationship with his colleagues, students and patients.

Pamela Bright, the doctor's great-great niece, has written an excellent account of his life, centred largely around his family. He has had many other distinguished biographers down the years since his death, many of them from the staff of Guy's Hospital, some from the great tradition of American medical historians, and a few well-known renal Physicians, perhaps inspired by his example to write about their renowned predecessor. Those who eulogise about Dr Bright are sometimes said to be in danger, in their interpretation of his writings, of extrapolating beyond the data—an eagerness which would not have won with his approval! We have, therefore, attempted to take a more critical look at what he wrote. It has to be remembered that as an inveterate seeker after the truth, he faithfully recorded findings before and after death, in patients with a variety of diseases, yet he was never tempted to over-theorise about the signficance of his findings.

It has to be assumed that most of what Bright wrote has been reproduced in some form or other, mainly in celebration of notable anniversaries. The first of these was the centenary in 1927 of the publications of Volume 1 of the *Medical Reports* which contained the revolutionary work on the kidney; secondly, in 1958 the centenary of his death, and thirdly and more recently, the anniversary of the bicentenary of his birth which was held in 1989.

Some of the quotes have become fairly hackneyed with use but they have stood the test of time and are often the best ones, thus we have unashamedly used many in the compilation of this volume. Bright was a broadly educated man of many talents outside medicine and it is probably true to say that most subjects he touched, he adorned.

This biography is an extended version of the booklet *Dr Richard Bright—A man of many parts* which was published for the members of the Dr Richard Bright Society to mark the 200th anniversary of his birth in 1789.

Diana Berry
Campbell Mackenzie

To Pamela Bright with warm affection—
well met on 'The Road to Xanadu'

Richard Bright, 1789-1858.

Introduction

'Like Ulysses he had seen the manners and cities of many men and following Goethe's precept he had taken pains to develop his powers in every direction.'

Heroes of Medicine
The Practitioner 1901; **67**, 562-65

In the Bright Oration delivered at Guy's Hospital on July 8th 1927, Dr W S Thayer spoke of Richard Bright as a man 'Happy in his birth and in the surroundings and conditions of his early life'. He further described him as an 'artist, a linguist, a man of scholarly taste'. How easy for one born to privilege to have lost something of 'the common touch', to have enjoyed his place in society with little regard for those less fortunate. Thayer, however, went on to praise Bright for his modesty, his simple high-mindedness. He saw him as one who was, in the true sense of the word, a gentleman possessed of the 'megalopsychia' of Aristotle, a greatness of soul, a magnanimity which allowed him to 'move among men high and low, with courtesy and sympathy and charity'.

Bright, the third son of Richard Bright, a wealthy Bristol merchant and banker and his wife Sarah, was born on September 28th 1789 at 29 Queen Square, Bristol. In August of that same year the French Assembly had approved the final version of the Declaration of the Rights of Man: 'Men are born free and remain free with equal rights' was the startlingly new concept embodied in the first article. A few weeks later the women of Paris marched to Versailles and in answer to the Queen's suggestion 'Qu'ils mangent de la brioche' they forced King Louis to return to Paris and ultimately to his death in 1793 at the cutting edge of Dr Guillotine's humanitarian invention.

It was a time of harsh social contrast and unrest which was confined not only to France; for in England also there were rumblings of discontent. Some years later Blake was to write of a 'rich and fruitful land' in which:

'Babes (were) reduc'd to misery,
Fed with cold and usurous hand.
. . . so many children poor?
It is a land of poverty.

A revolution that was, on the one hand, geographically distant had, on the other, the power to touch and significantly influence the intellectuals and radical thinkers on this side of the channel where appalling slum conditions bred of the Industrial Revolution had turned many urban areas into ghettoes.

Richard Bright was indeed a man fortunate in the circumstances of his birth and in the material and emotional security provided by an affluent upper middle-class family whose over-riding concern was the well-being of their offspring. The 'surroundings and conditions of his early life' certainly provided him with the opportunities and the encouragement which paved the way for his later successes.

Yet despite intense social unrest the optimism of that time is encapsulated in Wordsworth's:

> 'Bliss was it in that dawn to be alive
> But to be young was very heaven.'

for it was also the birth of a golden age of invention, of great literary, musical and artistic achievement and of scientific discovery in which Bright was to play a significant part.

The tradition of naming medical and surgical problems after doctors whose observations first clarified their essential clinical features was well established. The work of Heberden, Paget and Graves, Bell, Stokes and Adams provides an example of such recognition.

Drs Wells and Blackall had come close to an accurate description of renal disease, bringing together the triad of dropsies, albuminuria and kidney derangement, and were themselves almost worthy of eponymous recognition but this was reserved to Bright whose careful observations of the living and diligent cataloguing of the many *post mortem* specimens of diseased kidneys which he saw provided the necessary links in the chain of indisputable symptoms and manifestations that could definitely be attributed to impaired renal function.

Richard Bright's interests and undisputed talents, however, were not confined to medicine, but rather like so many of his contemporaries, he displayed that all-round quality of polymathy which the ancient Greeks strove to attain and which nowadays has become increasingly elusive in a world of burgeoning technological advances which demand an exclusive and undivided attention.

In contrast, apart from his life in medicine the Doctor was also a keen traveller and linguist and his extensive journeyings in Hungary provided the impetus for a book on that country which remains to this day one of the best and most informative travel guides.

He was also a keen artist and his ability in this field was put to excellent use in his medical work as well as in more pleasant outlets such as the fine illustrations which appear in his book *Travels through Lower Hungary*. Similarly pleasing examples may be found in Sir George Mackenzie's book *Travels in the Island of Iceland* for as a student he had the opportunity to indulge in the world of exploration when he joined Sir George on his expedition to Iceland in 1810. Bright's task was to describe, document and illustrate the flora and fauna of the island. The journey also provided him with a chance to augment his collection of mineralogical specimens, for geology was yet another interest and one which later gave him membership of the Royal Society.

As we have seen he was born into an age of revolution and throughout his lifetime he witnessed the progress of much needed social and political reform. In his own chosen field of endeavour he was innovative in his approach and provided the impetus both for new ways of thinking and for beneficial changes in practical aspects of patient care.

Bright was both an artist and a scientist yet Dr Wilks claimed he was 'not generally regarded as a brilliant man' and that 'he had little powers of exposition', which may tempt us to pose the question 'Was the character of the artist predominant? Was it merely the finely tuned powers of perception and observation which produced a life's work worthy of both national and international recognition?' Whatever the conclusions to which one is ultimately brought, it remains an unassailable fact that his was an invaluable contribution to the expanding body of medical knowledge and the understanding of disease.

Chapter 1

Bristol—City of the Merchant Venturers

> Majestic Bristol: to thy happy port
> Prolific Commerce makes its lov'd resort:
> They gallant ships with spacious sails unfurl'd
> Waft to thy shore, the treasures of the world!
> *Romaine Joseph Thorne, 1794*

In 1817 Richard Bright, recovering from a serious attack of typhus fever, revisited the Bristol of his boyhood. Sights once so familiar— the quayside, the beauty of the Avon Gorge and surrounding hills and woodland, the chance to renew acquaintance with old friends— such simple pleasures filled him with quiet content and hastened his complete recovery.

The 'golden age' of the Merchant Venturers
The visitor to Bristol in the 1990s who strolls along the city quays may find it hard to picture the tall-masted West Indiamen making their passage slowly up river for now the city docks are home to countless small pleasure craft, houses line the Merchant's Quay, Rownhams Mead and the Bathhurst Basin, Cannon's Marsh provides an international exhibition centre and Brunel's pride the SS 'Great Britain', rescued from a watery grave off the Falkland Islands, will eventually offer dining and conference facilities as opposed to transatlantic passage. Yet despite these changes bearing the stamp of the late twentieth century, the eighteenth century city of the Merchant Venturers with the fine terraces of 'Clifton on the hill' is still much in evidence and whilst the Society has long since lost the power and influence of its 'golden age' it still maintains an interest in its educational and charitable foundations.

When Richard Bright's grandfather, Henry Bright, came to Bristol in 1732 to commence his apprenticeship in the firm of Richard Meyler & Co. the city's reputation as a centre for maritime trade was already well-established. Her port was the second most important in the country, despite the fact that the ever-increasing tonnage to be cleared led to overcrowding and even damage to visiting vessels. As the committee of the Council pointed out in 1755 'no human prudence could prevent the growing danger to ships, without provision be made for further room.'[1]

Bristol's prosperity was obviously closely dependent on the adequacy of the accommodation she could offer to visiting ships. The problems attendant on having a dock area some miles up the mouth

St Augustine's Parade around 1815, by Samuel Jackson (1794-1869).

of a heavily tidal river became increasingly evident and prompted a series of proposals for the urgent construction of a floating harbour and general enlarging of the quays. Yet it was to be many years before any such improvements were made. Richard Bright's father was much involved with matters relating to the Docks and personally drew up plans for their enlargement.[2]

Although the ultimate responsibility for improvements lay with the Corporation, the Society of Merchant Venturers was also under some obligation in the matter as it had been granted the lease for wharfage collection in return for undertaking to construct and maintain the dock and quays.[3]

Bristol and the triangular trade

The city's mercantile ventures were not confined to overseas trading for the greatest number of vessels visiting the city were involved in local coastal and river trade—only one third of the thousand ships registered as entering and sailing in the year 1788 were destined for transatlantic voyages. In economic terms, however, the most important commerce for Bristol was that undertaken with the plantation colonies—the sugar, tobacco, mahogany and other plantation crops developed with European capital and produced through the labour of the negro slaves captured and brought to the plantations from the coast of Africa. Some of the ships trading out of Bristol were engaged in direct voyage to the colonies carrying necessities for the plantations whilst others engaged in a triangular crossing—first to the coast of Africa where slaves were taken in exchange for cotton, linen, brass, spirits and weaponry, then on to the West Indies to unload the human cargo and take on the produce of the plantations eagerly awaited in the northern hemisphere.

By the 1750s Bristol had become the predominant port for the slave trade and the Bright family fortunes were to a large extent dependent on commerce of this kind.

The Reverend Henry Bright—churchman and academic

Richard Bright's grandfather Henry provided the foundations upon which the family's position and future as the Brights of Bristol was built. Prior to taking up his apprenticeship in Bristol Henry Bright had lived at the family home in Colwall, Worcestershire. Relatively little is known about Dr Bright's great-grandfather who was lord of the manor of Brockbury and who died in 1726 leaving his widow Mary Bright and six children. At the time his second son, Henry, was only ten years old. We do, however, know that the Brights of Colwall were descended from the Reverend Henry Bright of Balliol College, Oxford who was for forty years Master of King's School, Worcestshire and a prebend of Worcester Cathedral. In the year 1600 he purchased Brockbury Manor and several other properties in the neighbourhood of Colwall. Some years later his son Henry purchased Colwall Mill which remained in the family for many years eventually passing, along with other property, to Richard Bright senior, Dr Richard Bright's father.

Richard Bright's ancestors were country people, of solid yeoman stock, yet they maintained an interest in scholarly and intellectual pursuits very much in the tradition of the Reverend Henry Bright, Master of King's School. This cultivation of the intellect was much evident in Bright's own father, who occupied a prominent place in the scientific and literary life of Bristol in the late eighteenth and early nineteenth century.

Richard Meyler, to whom Bright's grandfather Henry was apprenticed, was a cooper by trade, descended from Thomas Meyler, a shoemaker, whose family had settled in Pembrokeshire in the early seventeenth century. As a cooper, Meyler went to Bristol to develop his business interests. He imported tallow and timber from the Baltic. This trade soon blossomed into an involvement with ships and ship building. He supplied casks for wine and cider and as his business grew he participated in shipping and trading in the West Indies via the triangular African route.

Ham Green becomes the family home

As Meyler's business ventures prospered and he became more affluent he took the opportunity of purchasing some acres of land at Ham Green on the Somerset side of the river Avon. There

The Bright Family Portraits

Henry Bright
(grandfather)

Richard Bright (senior)

Sarah Bright (mother)

Lowbridge Bright
(uncle)

(Courtesy of the Bright and Gibbs families.)

he built a fine mansion for himself and his family. Situated about four miles out of the city of Bristol, the land was close to the village of Pill, traditionally the home of the pilots who navigated the great ships' pathway up the river Avon or out to sea at the commencement of their long voyages. Some fifty years later Meyler's great-grandson the young Richard Bright would enoy the freedom of Ham Green's fine gardens and meadows beyond and watch eagerly as distant sails heralded the arrival of a long-awaited vessel.

It is interesting at this point to note how in 1966, just over a hundred years after Bright's death, the Bristol Renal Dialysis Unit was opened at Ham Green Hospital, barely fifty yards from the Bright family home.

Grandfather Bright's business ventures prosper

It was to Richard Meyler then that Henry Bright owed his early success in business. He took up his apprenticeship in 1732 and by 1740 he was responsible for a large part of Meyler's affairs both in Bristol and in the West Indies. In that same year he made his first visit to the islands, first to Nevis and then on to St Kitts where he opened a store. Within two years he had moved to Kingston, Jamaica, where he worked as Meyler's agent selling goods on commission. He was soon trading on his own account but also, as was common in the eighteenth century, he developed partnerships in different ventures with other merchants.

Henry Bright returned to Bristol in 1746 to marry Richard Meyler's only daughter Sarah, but the following year he resumed his business interests in Kingston whilst his wife remained at home living either with her parents at Ham Green or at 29 Queen Square, which Meyler had purchased as a wedding present for his daughter and son-in-law. When Henry finally returned permanently to Bristol in 1751 the Meyler and Bright families lived together sharing the properties in Queen Square and Ham Green.

It was fortunate that Henry Bright's business ventures prospered for his widowed mother, brothers and unmarried sister all required his financial support. Family letters written at that time speak of debts and general family problems.[4] His eldest brother Robert was made bankrupt in 1756 and it was Henry who dealt with his creditors and organised his travel to the West Indies so that he could start afresh in a law practice in Jamaica. Robert died there in 1758 and was buried near another brother, Francis, who had been in partnership with Henry Bright and had died in 1754. At the time of Robert's death Henry Bright did all that he could to help his brother's widow and surviving children: he gave a home to Robert's eldest son Lowbridge and brought him up with his own son Richard and he later found him employment in his banking business, the Old Bank.

Richard (senior) and Lowbridge Bright were always very good friends and in later years Dr Richard Bright shared this affection for his well-travelled, kindly uncle whose great passion was his superb art collection which included paintings by some of the finest Old Masters such as Vandyck, Rembrandt and Velasquez.

Of Henry Bright's remaining brothers, William went to sea whilst Allan Bright was an able businessman who on the death of William and Elizabeth Watkins took over the firm of pewterers and brass founders which they had established and in which he had originally been apprenticed. Unfortunately he had little real interest in such commercial affairs and instead he retired to his country estate, Welland Court, near Worcester.

A time for celebration

In 1754 Henry and Sarah Bright had the pleasure of accouncing the birth of their son Richard. On his first birthday his grandmother Mary Bright wrote from Colwall and sent some country fare with which the event was to 'be kept'

> '. . . to my granson Dick a gammon of bacon to keep his birthday with and do wish he may live to be as old a man as either of his great granfathers . . .'[4]

These surviving letters provide a picture of the contrasting concerns of the country life compared with that of the city, and country produce is clearly considered to be of superior quality for chickens are sent at Christmas time both for the Brights and for Mr Meyler.

Warrington Academy—the Dissenter's school

Dr Richard Bright's father was, like his son, born at 29 Queen Square, Bristol. The houses backed on to the bustling quays whilst the more formal solemn front facades looked out over the square which to this day remains one of the most impressive in the country. The family home was adjacent to the 'Hole in the Wall' Inn, so named because in the late eighteenth century a look-out was kept at a spy-hole to warn of the approach of the dreaded press-gang seeking hands to crew His Majesty's Men-of-War. It was also the inspiration for the inn in Robert Louis Stevenson's *Treasure Island* from whence the treasure seekers were to 'sail on the noonday tide.'

When the time came for Richard Bright (senior) to go away to school there was unfortunately no place for him that year at Harrow but his parents were quite happy to send him instead to Warrington Academy. This was one of the four Dissenting schools and in its spirit of liberal thought and willingness to embrace innovation in education the Academy fostered in Richard Bright senior not only a deep interest in the Sciences but also in Literature and the Arts especially Music. A poem written by Dr Aikin's daughter celebrates the liberal spirit of the Academy:

(a)

(a) 29 Queen Square, birth place of Dr Richard Bright (reproduced by kind permission of the Redcliffe Press Ltd) and (b) Ham Green House—the Bright family residence (watercolour by Sarah Bright, sister of Dr Richard Bright).

(b)

'Lo! there the seat where science learned to dwell,
where liberty her ardent spirit breathed.'

At the Academy he was much influenced by the ideas of Joseph
Priestley whose chemical experiments were part of the new thrust
to push forward the barriers of knowledge through measured
experimentation and close observation. Scientific pursuits always
remained an important part of his life and as his own son grew up
with the evidence of his father's interests all around him we may
assume the influence this had on his ultimate choice of career.

Fellow students at the Academy included representatives of the
Estlin family, Malthus, the economist and essayist, the Gaskells,
the Aikins, and the Wedgwoods who as a family were to become
patrons to the poets Coleridge and Wordsworth.

As a centre renowned for liberal ideas and educational innovation
the Academy also attracted many famous visitors such as Joseph
Banks whose tales of tropical flora and fauna, strange new lands
and peoples and fearful voyaging with Captain Cook kept the
students in thrall. Benjamin Franklin who once told Priestley he
'collected fire very copiously from the air' involved them in his
curious experiments with electricity whilst George Watts introduced
innovative thoughts and researches into animal behaviour.

During his years at the Academy Richard Bright (senior's) close
friend was Samuel Heywood and he often visited the Heywood family
home in Manchester. Surviving letters request his father's
permission to absent himself from the Academy for the last two
weeks of the term in order to travel with them in Ireland. His
affection for Benjamin Heywood's daughter grew over the years and
eventually blossomed into a more serious relationship that was to
lead to marriage.

A further letter from Richard Bright (senior) to his father, dated
Warrington, December 4th 1772 displays some of the preoccupation
with pecuniary considerations so evident in his own son's letters
written some forty years later! He is considering a Christmas visit
to London and the possible expenses to be incurred:

'. . . should I go it will bring some expences with it, which till
since I wrote my last letter I did not consider, the one is another
suit of cloaths for what will do perfectly well in Bristol will hardly
do to go in to any public place in London. The other is a pair of
lace Ruffles; but indeed by getting both those things now will
prevent my wanting them when I come to Bristol in the summer.
I shall want these things the more as the family which I shall
be in is a very genteel one and sees a good deal of company. But
should I go you may be assured Sir, that I shall go into no
unnecessary expences.'

In the same letter he mentions the fact that 'this Day the last sheet of Miss Aikin's poems was printed'—perhaps this included the one written in celebration of the 'liberal spirit' so evident at Warrington?

Branching out—setting up the family bank

As we have already seen, the Bright family fortunes were much bound up with the West Indies trade but as a trading city where large sums of money changed hands on a regular basis, business opportunities in banking were also an attractive proposition. Henry Bright took advantage of this opportunity and in the year 1769, in partnership with five other prominent Bristol Merchants, including Edward Harford, he opened a bank which was known as 'The Harford Bank'.[5] It had its premises in Small Street in a large mansion house which had once belonged to Bristol's famous philanthropist and Merchant Venturer, Edward Colston.

Henry Bright's son Richard was to continue in banking, being first in partnership with Deane, Whitehead and Co (formerly the Harford Bank) and then in 1756 with Levi Ames, John Cave, Joseph Harford and George Daubeney in Ames, Cave and Co. at 15 Corn Street which was known as the 'The New Bank'.

The cultural and intellectual life of the city

Although the Bristol of the Merchant Venturers was predominantly concerned with trade and commercial undertakings the intellectual and cultural life of the city was not neglected.

Education in Bristol was provided in the endowed schools such as The Grammar, The City School, Colston's and Queen Elizabeth's Hospital but there was keen competition from privately run schools, particularly those of non-conformist persuasion such as that provided by the Unitarian minister Dr John Prior Estlin. Richard Bright senior strongly supported the Reverend Estlin's educational establishment, sending his own sons, including the young Richard Bright, to benefit from the Doctor's enlightened and forward looking approach to learning.

As for the Arts, drama in the city was first provided as early as 1729 in a small theatre which was erected at Jacob's Well. It was said to be convenient for 'coaches as well as the Ropewalks leading to the Hot Well' but in fact roads leading to the theatre were completely without lighting—a boon to would be local villains!

In the second half of the eighteenth century however, when many of the wealthy families such as the Brights took up residence in Queen Square and the surrounding neighbourhood, the inconvenience of the Jacob's Wells theatre became more evident and early in 1764 it was decided that a theatre that would be worthy of the city should be erected. A group of fifty prospective proprietors, of which Henry Bright was one, was formed; each contributed £50 towards the theatre project. A further sum of £1,400 was subscribed

by other admirers of the dramatic arts, allowing for the purchase
of some old properties in King Street. The new theatre was completed
by the spring of 1766 but it was not until 1778 that the Royal Licence
was granted, allowing the theatre to adopt its existing name the
Theatre Royal.[6]

A civic library had been provided for the city as early as 1613 by a
prominent Bristol Merchant, Robert Redwood, but again, the second
half of the eighteenth century saw this collection augmented by a
private venture known as the Bristol Library Society, which was
founded in 1772. The Society was able to use the Library building
in King Street and in the early days it was open to all who wished
to use it. Prominent educated families among the merchant class
including Unitarian and Quaker families such as the Brights took
advantage of the facility, and literary and scientific figures such as
Coleridge, Southey, Beddoes and Humphry Davy also benefitted from
the wider choice of books.

Bristol had been one of the earliest cities to have its own press
and during the eighteenth century news was disseminated on a
weekly basis by newspapers such as *Felix Farley's Bristol Journal*,
Bonner and Middleton's *Bristol Journal*, *The Bristol-Gazette*, and
the *Bristol Mercury*.

The Brights hold civic office
During the eighteenth and nineteenth centuries the merchants
of Bristol, represented by the Merchant Venturers Society were
a powerful body of men whose decisions influenced not only
the commercial but also the social and cultural life of the city.
The Bright family traditionally held office both in the civic order
and in the Society of Merchant Venturers. Henry Bright was a
sheriff of the city in 1753 and Lord Mayor in 1771. Richard Bright
(senior), like his father Henry, was also a member of the Merchant
Venturers, becoming Master of the Society in 1792. He was elected
Lord Mayor in 1796 but his refusal to serve required him to pay
a fine of £400![7]

Bristol was fortunate in having a number of societies and
intellectual institutions which were well-supported by the Bright
family. The Anchor and Dolphin Societies provided outlets for the
social and charitable interests of the Merchant Venturers Society.
The Dolphin was started in 1749 and was predominantly Tory whilst
the birth of the Anchor Society in 1769 provided a social venue for
those whose allegiance was to the Whigs—interestingly enough
Richard Bright (senior) was a member of both!

The Philosophical and Literary Institution which opened in Park
Street gave scope for scientific lectures by people such as Humphry
Davy and for some of a more literary nature by Hannah More and
Dr Lant Carpenter who tutored Dr Richard Bright during his school
years in Exeter.

In contrast to these academic pursuits a rather more low-brow entertainment was provided by the Bristol bare-knuckle fighters. For a quarter of a century 'The Bristol Men' dominated the national boxing championships with such famous figures as Jack Broughton, Bill Stevens and Jem Belcher drawing vast crowds of those who professed themselves followers of 'The Fancy'.[8]

Attempts to reform slave trade

Whilst Bristol had a reputation as an important city for the slave trade its prosperity was also much influenced by a valuable local commodity—coal. The Kingswood mines provided the local industries such as the foundries, sugar refineries, glasshouses and potteries with all their fuel requirements. Yet despite the importance of these industries and the trade wealth which they could generate, the efforts of reformers to secure the abolition of slavery met with strong resistance from local merchants. First moves towards abolition came in 1788 with a Bill brought before Parliament designed to prevent overcrowding on the slave ships and thus to lessen the suffering of the unfortunate human cargo. Public opinion supported such moves and in Bristol demand grew for the complete abolition of the trade.

A local support committee was formed under the chairmanship of Joseph Harford one of Richard Bright (senior's) banking partners but the city's West India planters and merchants were horrified and held an opposition meeting at Merchant Venturer's Hall in April 1789, the year of Dr Richard Bright's birth to defend this traffic 'on which the welfare of the West India islands and the commerce and revenue of the Kingdom so essentially depend'.

This meeting was supported by the majority of the corporation and Aldermen including Richard and Lowbridge Bright. It is interesting to reflect on how Dr Richard Bright might have responded to such demands for the abolition of this cruel trade for as a young man he showed great concern and humanitarian feelings, particularly evident in his denunciation of the appalling conditions in which prisoners were kept not only in England, but also in Hungary which he visited in 1814. Unfortunately we have no evidence of his reaction to the trade upon which much of the family fortune had been built.

Liberal ideas meet harsh opposition

Perhaps rumblings of the kind that prompted anti-slavery meetings in Bristol and other cities allied to a heightened public awareness and conscience in response to the evident inhumanity of this trade in human lives was symptomatic of an increasing social unrest which, fuelled by the spirit of revolution, was first to free the American colonies and later to topple the French Monarchy. In Britain, amongst the educated radical thinkers there was much sympathy with revolutionary idealism, a belief that the rule of the People would allow the desires and needs of common man to prevail bringing an end to war and the creation of a brotherhood of nations.

Those who saw the apparent ease with which the French revolutionaries rid themselves of the yoke of ancient privileges and their attendant inequalities hoped for the introduction of parliamentary reforms which would allow for the establishment of an enlightened democracy, and ultimately provide for a just and representative legislature. Sadly, the later excesses of the Jacobins and the extremes of force employed by the revolutionaries in France to achieve their visions of freedom, equality and 'The Rights of Man', spread alarm amongst the more moderate. The 1780s saw some attempts by Prime Minister Pitt to achieve the beginning of Paliamentary reform with the Bills of 1782 and 1785 which he unsuccessfully attempted to introduce. However the outbreak of revolution and consequent war with France convinced him that reform would be dangerous and instead a number of repressive Acts such as the suspension of Habeas Corpus were pushed through Parliament.

On September 28th, 1789 Richard and Sarah Bright's third son, Richard, was born into an age of revolution in an England of gross social inequality. Much of his working life in medicine was to bring him face to face with the harrowing outcome of urban poverty and disease and it is certainly to his credit that in his professional duties he attempted to alleviate the suffering of patients from all walks of life.

Chapter 2

Growing up in an Age of Revolution

'When France in wrath her giant-limbs upreared,
And with that oath, which smote air, earth and sea,
Stamped her strong foot and said she would be free,
Bear witness for me, how I hoped and feared!'
Samuel Taylor Coleridge

After leaving Warrington Academy Richard Bright (senior) took up his responsibilities in the family business although he still maintained his abiding interest in the Sciences and the Arts. His cousin Lowbridge encouraged such pursuits and made it possible for him to visit other cities such as London and also Birmingham which was the birthplace of the Lunar Society whose membership included the Wedgwoods, James Keir, James Watt and Erasmus Darwin. He also made several visits abroad and in Paris met Lavoisier, later guillotined during the Terror, and also Benjamin Franklin, then Ambassador to France. Franklin had lost favour in England after his involvement in the publication of the Hutchinson letters which fuelled an already volatile situation and culminated in the American War of Independence.

Following his marriage to Sarah Heywood, Richard Bright (senior) seems to have found a great sense of fulfilment in his domestic life. Naturally he was much involved with his business transactions and also with the city of Bristol and all its ancient traditions and customs. Within two years of his marriage his first son Henry was born soon to be followed by a daughter Phoebe and in 1787 a second son named Benjamin after his grandfather, Benjamin Heywood.

An age of revolution, a time of hope
The year 1789, which saw not only the birth of the young Richard Bright but also the outbreak of the French Revolution, was for many a time of great hope. Representatives of a broad spectrum of human endeavour, literary men and men of science alike dared believe that they were witnessing the dawn of a new era. In the mercantile city of Bristol, however, the outbreak of the French Revolution caused relatively little stir although it did inspire the Corporate body to celebrate the 4th November, centenary of the Glorious Revolution which had abolished for ever the concept of the Divine Right of Kings. The expenditure of £177.11s.8d, chiefly on liquor, ensured a fitting honour to the memory of King William III and the start of Parliamentary democracy.

Richard Bright as a child with his mother Sarah Bright. (By kind permission of Lady Ferrers.)

Life in the prosperous city continued with little outward change. The Brights celebrated the birth of their third son and Richard Bright (senior) was concerned with plans for enlarging the docks and also with caring for his growing family.

The rise of 'Clifton on the hill'
The last decade of the eighteenth century did, however, bring a boom in building projects in the city, particularly in Clifton for this was a much favoured area being elevated some several hundred feet above the bustling world of commerce and industry focused on the docks below.

On his arrival in Bristol, Humphry Davy's first letter to his mother extols the beauty of 'Clifton on the hill':

> Clifton is situated on the top of a hill commanding a view of Bristol and its neighbourhood, conveniently elevated above the dirt and noise of the city. Here are houses, rocks, woods, town and country on one small spot; and beneath us the sweetly flowing Avon, so celebrated by the poets'[1]

A few years later Jane Austen was to express great relief and a 'happy feeling of escape' on leaving Bath to visit in Bristol particularly Clifton where she stayed. By the 1790s, however, it had already become the tendency for wealthy and successful businessmen to distance themselves even further from the city: it became fashionable to set up home in the Gloucestershire countryside beyond the Downs and across the Avon Gorge in Somersetshire. Perhaps it was in anticipation of this fashion for a more rural life or with the desire for a healthier environment for his children, that in the year following the birth of his third son, Richard Bright (senior) decided to move his young family to the ancestral home at Ham Green which he had inherited from his mother.

Ham Green provided an ideal setting for him to indulge his keen interest in horticulture and also to demonstrate his considerable talents in farming and husbandry. He collected seeds and plant samples from many parts of the world and experimented with their growth. He introduced new varieties of trees and shrubs sending mulberry cuttings and Spanish olive trees to his West Indian estates in the hope of cultivating additional crops.

At Ham Green he also kept his fine and growing collection of geological specimens some of which were later donated to the Bristol Institution which he helped to found in 1820, and after his death the remainder of his collection went ultimately to the British Museum. He was made an honorary member of the Geological Society of London soon after its foundation in 1807.

The peace of the countryside was also ideal for the pursuit of other creative ideas, notably those relating to his interest in chemistry which had been fostered by his friendship with Joseph Priestley. The arrival in Bristol of Dr Beddoes with his plans for the Pneumatic Institute to alleviate the suffering of chest patients and the work of his assistant the young Humphry Davy who experimented in the use of nitrous oxide provided further stimulus for Richard Bright (senior's) own inventive pursuits in which he later involved his son Richard.

Ham Green—a childhood idyll
Ham Green also provided an environment full of wonder for the Bright children for here were fields and wooodland running down

The Laboratory (watercolour by Sarah Bright). The building still stands in the grounds of Ham Green House.

to the river. From the gazebo they watched the tall ships slip by on the tide. They would have seen their father's own vessels, perhaps the 'Avon', the 'Ocean' or the 'Hero' making their passage to the open sea. The gardens, orchards, stables and paddock provided further places for childhood adventures. Here they could collect fine butterfly specimens, fungi, fossils and bones. The children also loved to visit the Pill cottagers, many of them old sailors who provided a bottomless fund of sea sagas and tales of the exciting journeyings of the merchant ships now patiently awaiting pilotage up river.

The Brights were an extremely hospitable family and the house was often filled with friends and other visitors who happily availed themselves of the opportunity to broaden the limits of their knowledge that was afforded by the fine library in which

Richard Bright (senior) housed, amongst other volumes, a fine collection of the best in contemporary writing. This included examples of works by Edmund Burke, Dr Erasmus Darwin and Joseph Priestley. Although something of an extravagance, he also supported the local press subscribing to such papers as *Felix Farley's Bristol Journal*, the *Bristol Gazette* and the *Bristol Mercury*.

Richard and Sarah Bright sought in every way possible to promote the interests of their offspring and as Dissenters they took special care to provide for their instruction in the religious tradition that was so dear to them. Bible reading was a part of the day-to-day life of the family and the children would have been encouraged to learn the psalms by heart.

These were the happy surroundings, the fortunes of birth which provided the young Richard Bright with his earliest memories including the birth of two younger sisters, the one surviving only a few months, the other his sister Sarah who would in later years bring comfort and practical support to him and his tiny son William after the death of his beloved first wife Martha.

War with France—the beacons are lit

Gradually something of the cares and terrors of the outside world, of a nation close to war with its neighbour and not far from a similar revolutionary ideology began to invade the peace and tranquility of life at Ham Green.

In the year 1793 beacons were lit on the declaration of war with France. In the same year, Joseph Priestley, for so long a close friend and certainly an inspiration to Richard Bright (senior), became a victim of those who feared change and greater religious freedom. On the pretext of 'defending Church and King' a Birmingham mob raised to the ground Priestley's Meeting House, ransacked and destroyed his home and irreplaceable laboratory.[2] Priestley was eventually driven to leave England and to attempt to rebuild his life in America. As a close friend, Richard Bright (senior) was sad at the loss but did all in his power to facilitate the scientist's departure in the hope that his reputation and undisputed success in the field of chemistry would flourish in a new spirit of freedom and would at last gain recognition and reap the deserved rewards.

Around this time the children also experienced some extremes of nature with the drought of 1794 followed by one of the harshest winters. The joy of learning to skate on the frozen lake was tempered by an awareness of the intense suffering experienced by the poorest workers on the estate who lacked both food and fuel. Their father's philanthropic response provided a fine example of the caring attitude of the Dissenter in respect of those bound up with him both as equals and in more lowly station as farm labourer or, as we are given to understand, plantation slave.

The Kingsroad, Lamplighters and the Great Western Lightship (watercolour by Sarah Bright).

'Unwillingly to school'

At last the day came for the young Richard Bright to experience the harsher world outside the perimeter of the family home. In 1795 he was sent to join his elder brothers at the school of Dr John Prior Estlin which was in the Reverend's own house on St Michael's Hill, Bristol.

Dr Estlin had been at Warrington Academy with Richard Bright's father who was later instrumental in securing for him the Ministry of Lewins Mead Unitarian Church, Bristol. Dr Estlin was well-travelled and an excellent linguist, this, added to his undoubted intellectual prowess and fund of general knowledge made him eminently suitable to undertake the education of the Bright sons. England was at that time cut off from the Continent by war but through Dr Estlin the students gained experience of contemporary German scientific experimentation and advances and also of the new literature emerging from revolutionary France.

Despite the good intentions of the kind Doctor, school brought its share of unhappiness for the young schoolboy. It is unlikely that Dr Estlin's establishment shared anything in common with the horrors of 'Dotheboys Hall' but equally certain that its comforts were minimal. Richard Bright's brothers Henry and Benjamin helped him 'survive' his first year and their letters home to sister Sarah testify to the sparsity of creature comforts, the frugality of daily fare and the usual unpleasant character traits as evident in the 1790s in a schoolboy population as they remain to this day.

Long hours were spent in memorising passages from the classics and in draughty classrooms in the study of the sciences, mathematics, botany and geography. Reading aloud and the acting out of comic drama also formed part of the curriculum—physical activities were also encouraged—paper chases and kite flying being particularly popular with Dr Estlin.

Sundays were devoted to worship in Dr Estlin's church at Lewins's Mead. For Dissenters this was one of the most important places of worship and services were attended by some of the most influential of the merchant class and Unitarian businessmen. Bristol at that time was a small and decidedly intimate community and on Sunday evenings Dr Estlin and his wife were happy to welcome to their home some of the city's most interesting intellectuals, amongst whom were included the poets Coleridge, Southey, and Robert Lovell—dedicated representatives of liberal ideology and supporters of moves for political reform.

The 'closeness' of the community meant that most prominent families were acquainted and few, if any, events or happenings went unremarked, so that a local newspaper felt quite at liberty to comment on Mr Coleridge's sartorial and toiletry shortcomings:

> Mr Coleridge would do well to appear with cleaner stockings in public, and if his hair were combed out . . . it would not depreciate him in the esteem of his friends.'[3]

The Pantisocrats

For those such as Coleridge and Southey who were moved by the revolutionary spirit the search for a new social order was at its height and Dr Estlin's Sunday evening gatherings, set aside as they were for debate and philosophical exchanges, provided a forum for the development, amongst other things, of their pantisocratic dreams. Coleridge and Southey had first met in Oxford. Southey, like Coleridge, felt the burden of his family situation and lack of money. He considered British society to be intrinsically corrupt and with Pitt's suspension of Habeus Corpus he believed a revolution to be close at hand. He had already considered following Priestley's example and emigrating to America. In discussion with Coleridge the idea of a land where Godwinian principles of shared property and ideal Communism could be pursued appeared a most seductive scheme and thus the idea of Pantisocracy was born.

Southey's poetic description of their future life:

> 'When Coleridge and I are sawing down a tree we shall discuss metaphysics; criticise poetry when hunting buffalo, and write sonnets whilst following the plough . . .

provides a foretaste of the paradisial idealism so evident in the famous Manifesto which was to burst upon Europe some fifty years later!

In the interests of achieving their goal Coleridge had joined Southey in Bristol where they were busily engaged in drumming-up 'conscripts' and even more importantly, some funding for the realisation of their dream. Southey believed there to be: 'No mercantile place so literary as Bristol,' and certainly the 1790s saw a gathering in the city of some of the finest literary figures of the time. William Hazlitt and Charles Lamb were frequent visitors and Wordsworth, Coleridge and Southey had a close association with Bristol that lasted about four years. The city and its surrounding countryside also provided inspiration for the artists of the time such as Muller, Danby, Jackson and Pocock. Neither was science neglected for not far from Bristol, in the village of Berkeley, Edward Jenner was completing his work on a vaccination against smallpox. In the wider world of the Arts, Beethoven was composing some of his finest music, Blake was writing his 'Songs of Experience', whilst the artistic prowess of Constable and Turner was as yet in its infancy. It was indeed a 'golden age' in many realms of human endeavour. Against this backdrop the young Richard Bright experienced the second of Shakespeare's 'seven ages.'

A growing awareness of the outside world

There was obviously a variety of events and relationships in Richard Bright's early life which had a major influence on a developing personality. The year 1798 brought rumours of an invasion by Napoleon. Richard Bright (senior) was voted into the Volunteers and was soon made a sergeant responsible for the training of others, which involved him in some lengthy periods away from home. His young son was anxious at these absences and it appears that the entire city of Bristol lived in fear of the tramp of foreign forces upon its native soil, particularly when the city bells were heard to strike at an unaccustomed hour. The 'painted devils' of Georgian England were 'bad Boneys' as opposed to 'reds under the beds!'

In that same year the harvest again failed and Richard Bright (senior) enlisted his young son's help in more peaceful pursuits, that is in the practical and clerical tasks involved in his research into the development of a chemical substance that could replace wheat. The boy's powers of observation were precise and his father also involved him in another project which at the time he was undertaking with his friend James Watt. Together they were working on the development and further refinement of an air pump which was to be employed in the administration of therapeutic gases which Dr Beddoes was hoping to use in his new chest clinic the 'Pneumatic Institute' which opened in Dowry Square, Bristol in 1799.

The Pneumatic Institute.

Dr Beddoes, described in a recent biography as 'an accomplished chemist, mineralogist, geologist and physiologist'[4] was a keen advocate of liberal ideology and had certainly been very outspoken in his revolutionary views. Such outspokeness appears to have stood in the way of the full development of his professional reputation; he was never able to break free of the suspicions which surrounded these political beliefs.[2] Small wonder that in one of the last letters he wrote to Humphry Davy he described himself as one who had 'scattered abroad the Arena Fatua of knowledge, from which neither branch, nor blossom, nor fruit has resulted'—like Gerald Manley Hopkins a century later, he was 'Times eunuch'.

However disillusioned Beddoes felt with regard to his life's work succeeding generations have admired and valued his undoubted achievements and, perhaps, even more importantly, his breadth of vision. Such pioneering zeal extended into the question of educational philosophy. Beddoes's ideas were of a somewhat *avant garde* nature for he wished to see a move away from authoritarianism.

He was also aware of the socio-political advantages to be derived from universal education: 'a well-digested system of public instruction [would] secure the peace of society more efficiently than the gallows and the bayonet.' Such ideas, were, of course, in the established tradition of Locke and Rousseau. Closer to home, his father-in-law, Richard Edgeworth and his colleague, Thomas Day, shared such views and amongst the teaching materials which Beddoes recommended were fictional works by Dr Aikin's daughter, Mrs Barbauld. Education, was as we know, highly valued by the Dissenters and we must assume that if they found time for discussion of such matters, Beddoes' ideas would probably have won approval with Richard Bright's father.

Of course, at this time, Beddoes' pre-occupation was with his work in alleviating the suffering of the consumptive patients under his care at the clinic. In 1798 at his request, Humphry Davy the young chemist from Penzance, came to Bristol. Dr Beddoes put him in charge of the laboratory at the Pneumatic Institute and the young man's exploits and experiments with the gases provided matter enough for lively discourse; he soon became the talk of the town though not always in favourable terms.

Science and the Arts—indivisible cultures

In late Georgian times and well into the Victorian era there was no obvious division between the Sciences and the Arts. The two cultures were indivisible—scientist, artist and humanist shared common ground and communicated in a common language. They assumed a vision for their activities based on the common bonds of human values. It was in this spirit that the poets Coleridge, Southey and Wordsworth became willing 'guinea pigs' in Davy's rather notorious experiments with purified nitrous oxide and 'drunk' on inhalations they made their way up Clifton Hill lost in hysterical laughter. Davy's own records tell of its agreeable effect.[1] He felt:

'. . . a more high degree of pleasure from breathing nitrous oxide than I ever experience from any cause whatsoever—a thrilling all over me most exquisitely pleasurable. I said to myself I was born to benefit the world by my great talents . . .'

The effect of the gas on other friends is chronicled in his 'jeu d'esprit' entitled *The Pneumatic Revellers* including as *dramatis personae* Dr Beddoes, the Rev Barbauld, his wife Mrs Barbauld and Robert Southey. On drinking the gas Mrs Barbauld exclaims:

'Blithe as when I skipped with Lissy
Crowned with many a pretty flower
Beddoes! how I long to kiss y'
In my trembling moonlight bower . . .'

Sir Humphry Davy. (Reproduced by kind permission of the Bristol Art Gallery).

Moved to even dizzier heights Southey proclaims:

> '. . . I spurn, I spurn
> This cumbrous clod of earth, and borne on wings
> Of lady-birds, all spirit, I ascend
> Into the immeasurable space.'

Humphry Davy provides us with an excellent example of that indivisible bond between Science and the Arts. His friend Southey was quick to recognise that Davy would have excelled in any branch of Art or Science to which he had directed his intellect and talent. He had:

> 'all the elements of a poet and only wanted the art.'

Coleridge declared that if he had not been the greatest chemist he would have been the greatest poet of his age. Dr Richard Bright similarly displayed all the attributes of the artist as well as that of the scientist.

Another Guy's man who exemplifies such a bond is, of course, the poet Keats who, having passed his exams with credit, was a dresser at the hospital from 1815–1816 at which point he decided to devote his time entirely to the writing of verse. It is interesting to reflect how narrowly in terms of time the two doctors missed sharing a professional environment. Keats House at Guy's remains to this day, a monument to the poet.

Dr Thomas Beddoes. (Reproduced by kind permission of the National Portrait Gallery).

Dr Beddoes' theories and experimentation into the treatment of consumption also included a curious belief that patients would be helped by inhaling the breath of cows which were to be brought into the bedrooms of the unhappy sufferers for this purpose. As the animals were readily available on the Downs such experiments were reputedly carried out despite the protests of the landladies.[5] We may find such practices bizarre in the extreme but ultimately they seem less injurious to the patients' well-being than the excessive purging and blood-letting which characterized medical treatment some forty years later.

Of the Bright family's social involvement with either Beddoes or Davy we have scant evidence, though apparently Humphry Davy taught the Bright children to salmon fish with fly bait.

'Taking the Waters'—the heyday of the Hotwell Spa
At this time the relationship between Richard Bright and his father was very close. The latter was much involved with the Hotwell Spa and his son often accompanied him on visits there. Those who came to "take the waters" expected other entertainments which could compete with those offered in Bath. A contemporary account tells how:

'After quaffing the salutary beverage, those who are inclined have the advantage during rainy or cold weather of walking under a colonnade, in a crescent form with a range of shops. There is likewise a fine gravelled parade about 600 feet long, by the side of the river, shaded with trees, and here during the heat of the day, the company may retire, and be amused with the ever-varying scenes of ships passing and repassing. Little excursions are frequently taken down the river in boats, sometimes accompanied with music, which re-echoed by the rocks, has a delightful effect. Companies sometimes sail as far as Portishead, where they land and dine in the cool and shady woods, and, from different stations in the vicinity, enjoy delightful views of Bristol Channel the steep and flat Holmes islands, and the opposite Welch mountains'.[2]

Perhaps some of Bright's later interest in the curative powers of mineral waters may be attributed to the experience he gained at that time albeit that the numerous unmarked graves in the Hotwells Strangers' Graveyard may raise doubts in our minds as to the true efficacy of 'taking the waters'! At the time the young boy apparently found the visits extremely tedious and in later years remarked that the one thing of value that he had gained was 'instruction I remember, in the feelings of pity!' Even at such a tender age these feelings of pity allied to the experience of Beddoes' work in attempting to relieve the worst symptoms of the consumptive were surely instrumental in laying the foundations of Richard Bright's later development as a doctor.

The birth of a lifetime's friendship

At Dr Estlin's school it was some time before the young Richard Bright developed any particular friendships. His most important was that forged with Henry Holland (son of Dr Peter Holland of Knutsford) who was later to share both the same profession and a lifetime's friendship.

Henry Holland, even as a fifteen year old, was an extremely charismatic figure. A slim, fair-haired young man with piercing blue eyes, his command of the social arts made him well-prepared to undertake the role of Head Boy. In contrast, the fourteen year old Richard Bright was reserved, rather unattractive physically and lacking in self-confidence. The readiness with which Henry Holland responded to his overtures came as something of a surprise; the relationship was encouraged by Richard Bright's father. The Hollands of Cheshire were Dissenters who shared the same Whig sympathies, in addition the boy was related to the philanthropist Josiah Wedgwood and in school holidays was under the care of Dr Aikin, Richard Bright (senior's) former school-fellow and friend.

The two boys shared a developing interest in natural phenomena. Holland helped Bright augment his collection of geological specimens and the latter aided and encouraged him in the study of the river life of the Avon. Little could they know at that time that a few years hence they would have an opportunity to recapture those moments of boyhood pleasure in the expedition to Iceland which they undertook in 1810 with Sir George Mackenzie of Coul. The friendship with Henry Holland was to dominate Richard Bright's life for three school terms at the end of which Holland left the school to work in the office of a mercantile house in Liverpool.

Richard Bright was now made Head Boy and although he responded well to this responsibility his lethargy and lack of interest in both his studies and leisure pursuits hitherto so dear to him gave cause for concern. In view of his subsequent reputation as somebody with a high energy level we can only assume that he was suffering from one of the problems of adolescence, although it has also been suggested that he may have had glandular fever. Dr Estlin wrote to his father expressing his anxiety at the boy's long silences whilst Mrs Estlin felt certain that he was 'sickening for something'.

By Christmas of that year the boy's health gave such cause for concern that his parents sent for Dr Lovell, the family doctor. He was at a loss to account for the symptoms of lethargy, pallor and general lack of enthusiasm for all the activities which the young student had previously enjoyed. It was thought that a change of air would be beneficial and Devon seemed a suitable choice. It was decided that he should lodge and continue his schooling at the house of the Reverend Lant Carpenter in Exeter.

At Exeter with the Reverend Carpenter
The Reverend's household offered little to raise the boy's flagging spirits. Mrs Carpenter, newly wed, appeared to resent the intrusion of her husband's pupils and the atmosphere in the home was rigorous and puritanical; there was none of the warmth and joy which filled the house at Ham Green. It seems that Lant Carpenter was something of a zealot though his nervous disposition often led to bouts of complete exhaustion. At one point during Richard Bright's time with him the school had to be closed early in the summer to allow the Reverend to take a period of rest and relaxation in Teignmouth.

Richard Bright spent three years, 1805-1808 at the Carpenters' school. The Reverend was an exacting tutor but perhaps our young scholar achieved some recompense when he was at last invested with the office of teacher. His friend Henry Holland had once enjoyed such status at Dr Estlin's school but the modest Richard Bright had thought such an honour for himself to be quite unattainable.

The Christmas holiday of 1805 brought a respite from studies and a well-deserved holiday at Ham Green. The war with France continued but this did not mar the festive season. The house was gaily decorated and a series of visitors came to call including the artist Nicholas Pocock who was well pleased with the success of the Water Colour Society he had just formed.

A challenging career—the choice is made
It appears that at some time during this holiday Richard Bright (senior) discussed with his son a possible choice of future career. He wrote at length to the Reverend Carpenter seeking to know the genesis of his son's enthusiasm for medicine and also discussing the boy's academic achievements. It is interesting to note that he did not consider him to be in any sense a brilliant scholar but that notwithstanding other admirable character traits such as 'goodness of principles', 'desire of improvement' and 'steadfastness of judgement' will ensure his success—his son's achievements bore testimony to the correctness of his judgement:

Ham Green January 13, 1807
'I have taken pains since Richard's return to us to discover whether his wish to pursue a profession rather than a trade, and if a profession, then medicine, rather than either of the others, was the effect of any accidental influence or founded on a serious and deliberate preference—I conclude from the result of our conversations, that the latter is the case—I am therefore inclined to let him pursue his studies, with a view in due time to qualify him for that profession, and as he certainly did not in the earlier part of his education qualify himself so well in the preparatory parts of knowledge as might be expected at his age, for one so destined,

it is my wish as well as his own that he should continue under your instruction for another year. . .

'I have with much pleasure looked over the proofs he brought with him of his diligence, his improvement, during the last half year, which coupled with the testimony you gave of his progress in Latin and Greek are highly satisfactory to me—I doubt not the least anything you say regarding the increasing power of his mind, and I must flatter myself that altho he may never show great brilliancy of genius, yet that with the goodness of his principles, his desire of improvement—and a steadfastness of judgement he will henceforth make a respectable figure in his profession.[5]'

At this time the young boy's professed interest in following a career in medicine filled his father with some degree of disquiet. He considered his son's retiring nature to be more suited to the church and felt the 'odium, the envy, the narrow-mindedness', which in his belief characterised medicine, were pitfalls he would find insurmountable.

He knew that his son had both moral courage and honesty yet he doubted he had the drive to succeed in what was then, as it remains to this day, a competitive and demanding profession. Despite his father's misgivings Richard Bright had set his heart on medicine and he worked hard at his studies, determined to succeed. Dr Carpenter's ill-health caused some delay in the completion of his studies but the young student at last left Exeter in June 1808. Later that year he followed in his elder brother's footsteps enrolling at the University of Edinburgh for the continuation of his studies.

Chapter 3

Student Days in Edinburgh

'Breathes there the man with soul so dead
Who never to himself hath said,
This is my own, my native land.'
Sir Walter Scott

Standing in the shadow of the Scott Memorial today the guide's introduction before embarking with his 'foreign pilgrims' on a tour of Edinburgh Old Town, reminds us that all those famous men that we had perhaps mistakenly claimed as sons of south of the border had had their roots planted firmly in Scottish soil!

The blossoming of 'Auld Reekie'

Looking back to the early 1800s and to the Edinburgh of Richard Bright it is true to say that even though they may not have been born in Edinburgh, many eminent figures, representative of both the Arts and the Sciences, did in fact make it their home, if only for a brief time. This was the Edinburgh of Walter Scott, Francis Jeffrey, Henry Brougham, Sydney Smith and Francis Horner to name but a few—a city of intellectuals, of philisophers and literary men—a city built on the intellectual and cultural foundations laid some decades earlier by David Hume, Adam Smith, Henry Mackenzie and Robert Burns.

The final years of the eighteenth century saw the Continent closed by the war with France. The 'Grand Tour' was hazardous if not impossible and Edinburgh became the 'Mecca' for aspiring young men who were sent there to improve their education and broaden their knowledge of the world:

'Any man who can afford to wear a decent coat and live in a garret upon porridge or herrings may, if he pleases, come to Edinburgh and pass through his academical career just as creditably as is required or expected.'

The customs and manners of the North were in marked contrast to those of the South and visitors could experience the pleasure and stimulus of foreign travel without the hazards and inconveniences. Academically too Edinburgh had much to offer with the reputation of such illustrious and inspiring professors as Joseph Black, John Playfair and Dugald Stewart, the philosopher, honoured to this day with an impressive classical monument high on Calton Hill which fittingly commands a fine view of the Old Town.

In the last decade of the twentieth century the city of Edinburgh has made a tourist attraction of the tortuous wynds and closes of the old town but these are no longer the 'stinking, reeky mass of stones and lime and dung' that forced the young Carlyle to escape to Arthur's Seat—'A mountain close beside us where the atmosphere is pure as a diamond, and the prospect grander than any you ever saw.'[1] The Parliament House still provides in its impressive hall a setting against which the black-gowned and bewigged Learned Counsellors pace in earnest discussion of the finer points of the Law.

We have no surviving evidence of Richard Bright's first impressions on his arrival in the city. We do, however, know that he did not have to suffer the miserable living conditions and penury of some of the students native to Scotland whose 'abstemiousness and parsimony, their constant attendance to study and their indefatigable industry' Mr Topham had described as almost 'bordering on romance' particularly in that their lives contrasted so vividly with some 'foreign students' who were leading a life of 'unrestricted dissipation.'[1]

Richard Bright fell into neither of these categories. His father had accepted for him the offer of lodgings at 21 Hill Street in the New Town. This was the home of The Reverend Robert Morehead. It is probable that he hoped that a period spent living as part of the clergyman's family might influence his young son to follow a career in the church which his father, as we know, considered much more suited to Bright's disposition than that of medicine. This however, was not to be the case for the Reverend Morehead was well-respected in the intellectual clubs of Edinburgh and many of his close friends lectured in medical subjects.

Enrolling in the Faculty—meeting the 'famous men'

Number 21 Hill Street is outwardly little changed from those days although it is now used as offices rather than as a private dwelling house. Conveniently situated close to Castle Street the house is south facing with well-proportioned rooms which let in warmth and sunlight. To the young student this must have provided a marked and pleasing contrast with the austere surroundings to which he had been accustomed at Dr Carpenter's establishment in Exeter. He quickly became acquainted with Edinburgh and under the tactful guidance of the Reverend Morehead he went to all the right places and met with the right people. From his brother Benjamin he had letters of introduction which were no doubt useful to him in the task of completing his enrolment which appears in the Faculty Register for 1808/10. He bought tickets entitling him to attend a course of lectures on political economy by Professor Dugald Stewart, on

natural philosophy by Professor Playfair, and on mathematics by
Sir John Leslie.

The work of Dugald Stewart, John Playfair and Sir John Leslie
dominated the academic scene for many years, as the comments of
students both pre- and post-Richard Bright bear testimony. Henry
Cockburn found that Dugald Stewart's lectures were 'like the
opening of the Heavens. His noble views, unfolded in glorious
sentences, elevated me into a higher world . . . I was admitted to
all the glories of Milton and Cicero and Shakespeare. They changed
my whole Nature.'[1]

As a professor he had excited an interest in philosophy previously
unknown either in Scotland or England and despite his politics
bearing the influence of the new ideas emerging from France, his
fame as a lecturer drew to Edinburgh many pupils of wealth and
nobility. From him Richard Bright learned the principles of political
economy, statistics and free trade. The philosophical theories of
Malthus, Franklin and Mirabeau were particularly fascinating to
an emergent intellect.

In his autobiography, the distinguished physician Sir Robert
Christison, some eight years younger than Richard Bright, wrote
of John Playfair as being a 'charming teacher—so simple, unaffected
and sincere in manner, so chaste in style, so clear in demonstration.'[2]
John Playfair's lectures on natural philosophy and literature fed
Richard Bright's interest in geology and he greatly enjoyed the

Edinburgh old town with Salisbury Crags and Arthur's Seat in the background

excursions organised by his tutor to the Salisbury Crags, up the
volcanic steps to Arthur's Seat and then down to the waters of Leith.
Other excursions took them to the Braid Hills and the Pentlands
and as far afield as Blackhope Scaur. They examined the mineral
wealth with exactitude and on their return many happy hours were
spent in the scrutiny of gathered specimens.

Hutton versus Werner—the great controversy

At this time there was a good-humoured controversy raging between
Playfair, who was an advocate of the Huttonian theory that the
Earth's crust originated through the action of fires, and the opposing
view favoured by Dr Robert Jameson which was the Wernerian
theory of the Earth's origins being aqueous. Richard Bright had the
opportunity of studying both theories. He studied geology, chemistry,
physics and ethnology for at this time these subjects had important
connections with medicine as fossilized bones and minerals were used
by physicians in the treatment of their patients.

Christison's comments on Sir John Leslie suggest that he 'presumed
too much on the aptitude of the youthful and untrained mind for
mathematical reasoning'. Christison's 'fastidiousness was shocked',
too, by Sir John's winding up of the life of Pythagoras: 'thus died this
illustrious philosopher at the advanced age of the square of nine.'
But despite these misgivings he concluded that 'Leslie made
mathematicians'. This was certainly true for Richard Bright for at
the end of the session he was awarded the top prize in mathematics.

Edinburgh, as we can see, was indeed a place fertile with new ideas,
the academic standards were high and Richard Bright, being a keen
student, took full advantage of the opportunities offered. Dugald
Stewart and John Playfair both had a good rapport with their students.
They invited them into their own homes and did much to broaden
their horizons and stimulate them with exciting new ideas.

In those days a student's life was isolated and lonely. Tutorials
and collegiate life are a modern phenomenon, but in Richard Bright's
time a student worked to get a place in his class, scribbled down
notes as best he could then returned to his lodgings and endeavoured
to make sense of the information he had gathered. This way of living
was not too onerous for the young man from Bristol accustomed as
he was to the rigidity of Dr Carpenter's timetable and his own
preference for solitude and hard work.

The Edinburgh School required its students to undertake pre-
medical studies in the Sciences and Humanities. With the award
of his first degree Richard Bright was now able to embark on a degree
in medicine commencing in the autumn of 1809.

Boerhaave—the great tradition

The first medical professors instituted in Edinburgh were Sir Robert
Sibbald and Dr Archibald Pitcairn in 1685 but they were titular

professors only and in no way involved in the establishment of a medical school. The Royal College of Physicians possessed an exclusive right to the practising of medicine but was barred from teaching in Edinburgh. The regular teaching of different branches of 'physic' first started in the city in the year 1720. Dr Alexander Munro (primus) was instituted as professor and he began a course

Dr Hermann Boerhaave.

of lectures on anatomy and surgery. The opening of the Infirmary gave students the opportunity of hearing a set of clinical lectures, and the ability of the professors in various branches of the science augmented the growing reputation of the University's School of Medicine. A major influence on the development of Edinburgh's medical school was the University of Leyden and the work of the renowned physician Boerhaave. Munro had been a pupil of his as had John Rutherford who lectured in the Practice of Medicine. His manner of introducing lectures illustrates the influence of Boerhaave and his insistence on clinical experience: 'I shall examine every patient appearing before you,' he explained, 'that no circumstance may escape you. I shall give you the history of the disease, enquire into the cause of it, give my opinion as to how it will terminate, lay down the indications of cure which will arise or, if any new symptoms happen, acquaint you of them that you may see how I vary my prescriptions. If at any time you find me deceived in giving my judgement, you will be so good as to excuse me for neither do I pretend to be, or is the Art of Physic, infallible . . .'.[3] It is interesting to note that a century or more later the young Dr Bright was giving similar emphasis to clinical observations. In the autumn of 1809 when he entered the Medical Faculty of the University of Edinburgh he enrolled for a course of lectures in chemistry with Charles Hope, anatomy with Alexander Munro (tertius) and medicine with Dr Andrew Duncan.

Andrew Duncan was an excellent teacher and a man of great foresight and dedication to his profession. After his return from China in 1769 where he had gone as Company Surgeon with the East India Company Ship 'Asia' he decided to settle down in Edinburgh where he hoped to obtain a lectureship. One of his first steps towards achieving this goal was the setting up of a private extra-academical course on therapeutics. In 1773 he commenced publication of *Medical and Philosophical Commentaries*, a journal devoted to medical subjects. In the same year he founded a supper club known as the Aesculapian Society.

One of the innovations for which Andrew Duncan is best remembered was the setting up of a public dispensary which served the double purpose of providing free out-patient medical care for the poor and also a teaching clinic for medical students. His later, equally successful efforts at establishing a lunatic asylum were no doubt prompted by his concern over the death in 1774 of the poet Robert Fergusson who met his end in the most miserable conditions afforded by a charity workhouse. The asylum was granted a Royal Charter in 1807 the year prior to the commencement of Richard Bright's studies in Edinburgh.[4] Dr Prout, later a contemporary of Bright's at Guy's, described Andrew Duncan as 'A man of singularly clear vision, boundless energy and great perseverance.' Richard Bright was clearly fortunate in having him as his tutor for, though few of his contemporaries shared Duncan's view, he too considered practical work of great importance. In those days patient contact was in no way compulsory, but Duncan's pupils gained first hand experience in the city dispensary in Richmond Street and also in the lunatic asylum housed in Morningside. These experiences and the emphasis on practical training obviously impressed Bright for in later years when he had students of his own, he was determined that their studies should have a practical orientation in addition to the theoretical: he was also before his time in insisting that laboratory facilities be made available.

In contrast to Andrew Duncan's tutorials Bright found Alexander Munro's teaching as dry as the bones and hard facts which formed

Dr Andrew Duncan.

the material of his lectures. Dr Prout, later his colleague at Guy's sums up Munro's shortcomings: 'he was insufferably careless and lazy' and 'in all he did and said his manner betrayed an impassioned indifference, as it if were all the same to him whether his teaching were acceptable or not. Munro's plan of adhering to the traditions of his predecessors was to read his grandfather's notes.'

Robert Christison, similarly critical was of the opinion that: 'A lecturer who seldom shows himself in his dissecting room will scarcely be looked up to as an anatomist.' The general consensus seems to have been that it was Andrew Fyfe, Munro's 'prosector' in charge of the dissecting room who in a sense brought the subject 'alive' for the students. He was an excellent anatomist and took pains to pass on his wealth of knowledge. Apparently there was no dearth of material, though from whence it originated is not made clear! The activities of the resurrectionists such as the notorious Burke and Hare team had not yet come to light.

Charles Hope, described by Sir Astley Cooper as a 'man of reading, a gentleman and dignified and very eloquent' gave lectures which in Prout's words were characterised by 'uncommon clearness of expression, and an unexampled splendour and success in experimental demonstrations.'[5]

Richard Bright in common with other students enjoyed Hope's lectures but was disappointed at the lack of laboratory facilities as the working benches were unfortunately available only to the professor's assistants. On balance though he appears to have been fortunate as regards the quality of tuition he received.

Dedication to work—a pattern for the future
The day-to-day routine of Richard Bright's life changed little, being characterised only by increasing dedication to his studies. University life provided none of today's organised outlets for student relaxation—there was no-one to monitor the allocation of the student's time and physical exercise was sacrificed to the need for concentrated mental effort—indeed the only hint we get of Richard Bright indulging in physical as opposed to mental effort was in his running frantically to and from his classes! He found, as in a way his father had feared, that medicine was a demanding discipline. The Reverend Morehead noted the strain in his face and manner, but try as he might he was unable to find suitable diversions to alleviate the young man's anxiety.

The winter of 1810 brought no respite as his energies were directed exclusively to his studies. He wrote to his father that he had purchased a 'lancet and a tongue scraper' clearly hoping that he might add some practical experience to the study of medicine which as we know was almost entirely theoretical. However, during the Christmas break he was entrusted with a midwifery case in some rat-infested hovel in the High Street—a matter perhaps more

Henry Holland. (Reproduced by kind permission of the Hakluyt Society, London.)

of convenience to his tutor in view of the festive season than of a considered opportunity to afford 'hands-on' experience for the young student.

As the Spring gradually brought life to the city and surrounding hill sides the young doctor caught its infectious lightening of the spirit—his thoughts soared beyond the confines of his books and crowded lecture rooms—he was restless and longed for travel. A fine opportunity to satisfy these longings was provided through the offices of his friend Henry Holland who was largely instrumental in arranging that they should both accompany Sir George Steuart Mackenzie of Coul on his expedition to Iceland the purpose of which was to undertake mineralogical research and to attempt an assessment of the theories of Werner and Hutton. Edinburgh

University provided a forum for debate and allegiance to the contrasting theories—Bright's tutor John Playfair was, as we have already seen, a firm supporter of the Huttonian proposition that rocks were igneous in origin and had been formed from within the earth by heat acting under pressure on debris from pre-existing rock formations. His ideas provided a cyclical rather than a progressive explanation for the possible origin of rocks.

The Wernerian theory which was supported by Robert Jameson who had studied under Werner at Freiburg, proposed that all rock formations in their complex stratifications had been produced by chemical or mechanical precipitations from aqueous solution and suspension. Wernerians claimed that water had once covered the surface of the earth and that its surface features were deposited during that period.[6] Sir George Mackenzie supported the Huttonian theory and hoped that his expedition to Iceland would provide specimens and then evidence to confirm the thesis.

It was in February 1810, at a meeting of the Royal Society of Edinburgh, that Sir George first suggested to Henry Holland that he might like to join the proposed expedition. Henry Holland needed little persuasion to take up the offer and for Richard Bright this was a glorious opportunity both to fulfil his desire for travel and to allow him to develop his own interest in geology.

Chapter 4

Iceland—
from Arthur's Seat to Snaefellsjokul

> And ice, mast high came floating by
> As green as emerald . . .'
> *Samuel Taylor Coleridge*

Richard Bright's expedition to Iceland in the company of his friend Henry Holland and Sir George Mackenzie provided his first experience of foreign travel and despite the many hardships encountered this journey stimulated the growth of a developing 'wanderlust'. Unfortunately we have little in the way of a direct account of his response to these new and challenging situations which he encountered, apart from his report of the ascent of Snaefellsjokull which appears in Sir George Mackenzie's work. For the rest we have decided to rely on his friend Henry Holland's journal which, since it represents the impressions of youth, we have chosen as our main source of information, augmented where necessary by further detail from Sir George Mackenzie's book which also contains sketches made by Richard Bright in the various places they visited.

A journey to a 'strife-riven land'
Before embarking on an account of the expedition it would seem appropriate to look briefly at the prevailing political and economic climate in this island which was unable to escape the effect of the strife general to Europe which resulted from the Napoleonic Wars, particularly in so far as Britain was involved. As Andrew Wawn points out in his introduction to Henry Holland's journal:

'. . . any projected voyage to Iceland in 1810 was a voyage to a land whose turbulence was not confined to the geysers and volcanoes—by 1810 Iceland had become an anxious, enfeebled and to an extent, strife-riven land. This stemmed in part from a succession of wretched winters and subsequently disappointing harvests'.[1]

The worst problem however for the Icelanders was caused by French attempts to isolate Britain and thus force other countries of strategic importance such as Denmark to ally themselves to France. For their part, the British Government demanded that the

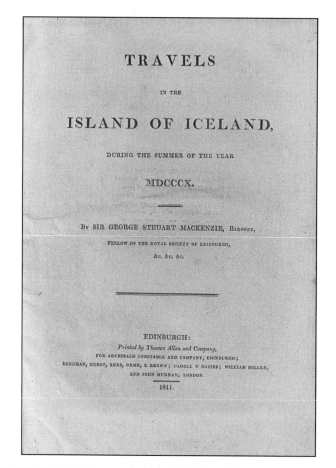

Frontispiece to Travels in the Island of Iceland, *together with map of Iceland*

Danes accept a defence alliance with Britain. Denmark, at this time, viewed France as a more invincible ally and the British answer was to bombard Copenhagen and to set up a naval blockade. It is easy to see how disastrous this was for the Icelanders, dependent as they were on the Danish trading vessels.

In the final pages of his book *Travels in the Island of Iceland* published in 1811 Sir George Mackenzie expressed a belief that in his writing:

'. . . enough will be found to excite compassion in every British breast, for the calamitous situation of an innocent and amiable people, at that critical period when oppression or neglect may overwhelm them in misery. The distracted state of Europe will not, I trust, be considered as a reason that Britain should disregard their wants or withold relief.'[2]

For Sir George Mackenzie a solution to the problem is overwhelmingly simple:

'The possession of Iceland would not be burdensome to England. An exuberant and inexhaustible supply of fish from the sea and the rivers, would alone repay the charitable action of restoring freedom to the inhabitants whom under the fostering care of a benevolent government, might soon improve their soil and their own condition'.[2]

When Richard Bright visited Hungary some four years later he found plenty in the plight of the peasants to 'excite compassion' yet nowhere did he suggest the annexation of that country as a solution to the problems! Again one can only lament the paucity of extant Bright journals or correspondence and resort to imagining his reactions to the wide variety of experiences catalogued in the rather dry, literal style of his friend Henry Holland.

Setting sail—the adventure begins
All arrangements having been made, Sir George Mackenzie's expeditionary party set sail from Leith on Wednesday 18th April, 1810, in the sloop 'Fingal' bound for Stromness. Here they had an appointment to take passage in the 'Elbe' in which they would sail to Iceland. Unfortunately the vessel did not arrive at the appointed time and the start of their journey was thus delayed for a week. They spent their time in exploration of the surrounding countryside which they found to be of some mineralogical interest. They were entertained at the Manse by Mr Clouston the minister. Before tea they were handed 'glasses of brandy and cinnamon water—and the same process was repeated after tea.'

The 'Elbe' appeared in Stromness on the evening of Wednesday the 25th April and the following Friday was 'set for the recommencement of the voyage northwards'. Their plan was again thwarted, this time by a strong south-easterly wind so that it was midday Saturday before they finally set sail.

The 'Elbe' was a vessel of some 350 tons and had cabin accommodation which Henry Holland described as 'particularly good'; Liston, her Captain, he found to be an 'active, intelligent man'. The ship carried a miscellaneous cargo for Phelps & Co., whose agent, Mr Fells, was a fellow passenger.

Early on the voyage was marked by a most unfortunate incident which occurred on the morning of May 3rd. A violent squall of wind from the north-east produced a swell that caused such heavy pitching of the vessel that an elderly seaman was thrown from the mizzen-top-sail to the deck below. The injured man was carried conscious to his berth—Richard Bright and Henry Holland examined him as carefully as circumstances would allow. He appeared to have no external injuries or fractures. He was bled and fell into a fitful sleep but sadly despite all efforts to save him he died some hours later in the day. This accident had a profound effect on the young student doctor—he felt his inadequacy in the face of these practical demands on his medical knowledge and it seems likely that his loathing of the sea stemmed from that unfortunate incident which revealed these shortcomings. The gales continued throughout the night and Holland describes how the next day:

'the heavy swell consequent upon the preceeding gale from the N E rendered the motion of the ship exceedingly unpleasant—Sir George Mackenzie and Mr Bright continued in bed during the whole of the day and both very unwell.'[1]

On Saturday May 5th the dawn light revealed the first glimpse of the coastline of Iceland—high mountains, snow-covered apart from the sheer cliffs that fell precipitate to the sea: 'Not a single sign of animal or vegetable life appeared upon the land—everything was gloomy, barren and desolate.' The coast of the Guldbringe Syssel revealed the volcanic nature of the area: 'the occurrence here and there of jets of smoke or vapour—and still more the bursting forth of a thick mass of sulphurous vapour from a cleft in the rocks, all afforded the strongest testimonies to this fact.'[1]

By Sunday evening the 'Elbe' had safely rounded Cape Reykjanes and a gun was fired for a pilot to come aboard but it was the next morning before the request was answered. For the first time they met the natives of Iceland for some local fishing boats crowded around the 'Elbe', which purchased the catch of one of the trawlers paying 'four shillings for 16 or 18 cod of very large size.'

First impressions

That afternoon their ship entered the bay of Reykjavik where she finally dropped anchor some half a mile from the shore. Shortly afterwards the party took the long boat and were landed on the beach where they were welcomed by the Bishop, Geir Jonsson Vidalin. Dr Klog, the 'Lands physicus' or Principal Medical Officer of the island was also one of the reception party.

Their fellow traveller Olafur Looptson, who had been engaged by Sir George Mackenzie as guide and interpreter, was welcomed with great cordiality. He had previously studied medicine with Thomas Klog but having been shipwrecked off the island of Lewis he had eventually met up with Sir George Mackenzie and continued his medical studies in Edinburgh under Sir George's benevolent patronage.

Aboard the Elbe they had already observed in the fishermen who had come aboard, the custom of 'Salutation by the lips among individuals of the male sex'. As Henry Holland observes they now 'had the most ample opportunity of witnessing the repetition of this practice'.

Their first couple of days in Reykjavik were to be taken up with practical concerns such as the finding of suitable accommodation. Holland had accompanied Dr Klog on his rounds and was amazed by the extreme poverty of the Icelandic cottages. Whilst awaiting embarkation in Stromness the expeditionary party had been struck by the 'wretchedness of the cottages' in Orkney but Holland described those in Iceland as wearing 'all the characters of rudeness in a much higher degree'. The cottagers themselves he found to be far 'superior to their habitation'.

A visit to the Bishop, who received them with great friendliness and hospitality, did little to reassure them as to the overall standard of housing. The Bishop's abode was not 'distinguished externally from those around it' and its 'cleanliness could not be applauded— it was clear that a long period had elapsed since either water or broom had visited the flooring and walls.' It was, however, impractical to remain sleeping aboard the 'Elbe' and they were all quite relieved when the problem was resolved by the fact that the Governor, Count Trampe, was away in England and they would thus be able to have the use of some vacant rooms in the Governor's house, with which they were very well satisfied.

Setbacks delay start of expedition

The finding of suitable accommodation was particularly fortunate since their departure from Reykjavik seemed likely to be delayed for some time as a disease had decimated the island's horse population on which they would be dependent for travel and the transport of baggage. They were also advised that snow and lack of forage for such horses as they could procure would make their journey quite impossible until at least the beginning of June. Fortunately Reykjavik and the surrounding area provided plenty of diversions in the early days of their visit and they had time to learn something of the customs of the people of Iceland.

One of their first excursions was to Vidoe, a tiny island in the Bay of Reykjavik. Here they were received by Mr Steffensen, a propertied gentleman and former Governor of Iceland. The tiny island derived great wealth from the vast number of Eider ducks which used it as a breeding ground.

They were invited to dine, their repast consisting of sago soup, a sirloin of beef, sugared fritters and sago jelly in cream. Later in the day they were served coffee 'succeeded by a prodigious tureen of hot punch, which [they] were not allowed to quit till the last drop was exhausted.'

Diseases of the island
On Thursday 10th May, they were able to move into the Governor's house and, baggage safely stowed, they met with Dr Klog to undertake the inoculation of some local children with cowpox using the two cowpox crusts which they had carried from Leith.

The next day the sailor from the 'Elbe' who had died during the course of the voyage from Stromness was buried with a simple ceremony conducted by the Minister for Reykjavik. We are not told how his body had been preserved during the interim period nor why he had not been buried at sea.

The everyday diet of the Icelanders was rather monotonous and indeed as Henry Holland pointed out in his *Diseases of the Island of Iceland* was a contributory factor to the many diseases of the skin which he encountered. The Icelanders ate virtually only rye bread, all other types being extremely scarce; they had fish in abundance but scarcely any fresh vegetables or fruit.

During their enforced delay in Reykjavik the party took several exploratory walks along the coast where they gathered many specimens, particularly of the crusts which formed the mouth of the hot springs. They saw seals and a wide variety of water fowl including the Eider ducks.

Meeting the local dignitaries
They also gave a ball for 'the good people of Reykjavik' which amounted to some 60-70 people including such important guests as the acting Governor, the Bishop and his lady and 'all the other fashionables of the place'. They had hoped to see examples of Icelandic dress fashion and of local dances and were disappointed to find that with the exception of three elderly matrons the rest were dressed in gowns similar to the English 'in the middle classes of life'.

The accompaniment to the dances made up of one fiddle, the Government drum and a pair of triangles provided tunes of a 'miserable description and miserably played'. The 'assembly' did not break-up until half-past four in the morning, candles having been snuffed at three. Holland describes how whilst 'the dancing went forwards, the elders of the party were smoking and drinking punch in an adjoining room. Some of them left the house a little less steadily than they entered in', particularly, it seems, the Right Reverend Father, the Bishop of all Iceland who was 'observed to be somewhat affected by the potations of the evening'. Small wonder that on being informed that some church wafers had been brought over in the 'Elbe' for religious services the Bishop's response was that 'the Icelandic church could have relished some wine too!'

A further opportunity to learn something of local customs was provided by an Icelandic wedding—the bride dressed in the traditional Icelandic costume and the groom in the coarse blue cloth and seal skin shoes usually worn by fishermen.

Physical discomfort—coping with the elements

Projected excursions were often prevented by the severity of the weather although they did make a further trip to Vidoe. The strong northerly wind prevented them taking a boat and instead they walked three or four miles along the coast finally crossing to the island by a narrow strait which separated it from the mainland. On their arrival they set out with their hammers and bags to take samples of the amygdaloidal rock, the volcanic tuff and the irregular columns of greenstone.

In their domestic arrangements the lack of fuel caused them considerable discomfort. Water that had been kept overnight in the kitchen was covered by a ¼-inch layer of ice and the temperature reached only 34°F. Finally, on Monday 21st May, they were able to set out on their first excursion into the interior of Iceland. Their purpose was to survey the Guldbringe Syssel by way of the South coast of the peninsula; the return journey was to take the northerly side.

The journey to Guldbringe Syssel

The party consisted of Sir George Mackenzie, Richard Bright, Henry Holland, Looptson, and another guide, Jonson, who though unacquainted with the English language was, having been trained for the priesthood, able to converse fluently in Latin. They took with them five horses laden with their tents and other necessities and commenced their travels with the 'independence and freedom which pedestrians always enjoy'.

The approach to Hafnarfjordur took them across lava fields ringed on the edges with high rugged masses which concealed the tiny bay and the 15 or 20 houses around it. Here they were entertained at the home of Mr Severtsen whose son they were pleased to discover, spoke fluent English. They slept in beds of eiderdown, washed in

Windsor soap and enjoyed luxuries which they had 'no previous conception could be possessed by travellers in Iceland'.

During the first excursion into the interior they visited the church and school at Bessasted, the caves beside the river Kalda and the Helgafell mountain. They spent their first night under canvas which was apparently extremely uncomfortable as a result of the cold, against which their clothing was inadequate. The morning also brought rain as an additional trial. They certainly lacked all the basic aids and equipment so essential to the 20th century explorer which makes their adventure all the more amazing.

They set out in the direction of Kryseviig and in doing so discovered something of the difficulties of travel on an Icelandic 'road'—a narrow track only wide enough to accommodate one horse and which was generally filled either with water or fragments of stone.

During this journey they came upon a human skeleton still wearing some fragments of female clothing. Their guide informed them that this was probably the remains of a traveller lost some 18 months previously. In more pleasant contrast they found, nestling among the rocks, gentian plants in full bloom.

First sight of the hot springs

They came upon a hot spring: 'A circular 9 or 10 feet diameter basin' was filled to the brim with a thick bluish coloured fluid through which a gush of steam rushed upwards 'producing the utmost agitation and disturbance'. The vapour which was also forcing its way through ground crevices had a strong sulphurous smell. The fluid in the basin was certainly water holding a suspension of blue clay—but they were unable to determine the source of the blue pigment.

They pitched tent below the village of Kryseviik and from the camp set out to collect specimens from the sulphur springs, 'the most interesting natural object' which had so far engaged their attention in Iceland. The yellow-tinged clouds of steam and vapour were visible from a distance of many miles. The surface surrounding the springs was hazardous as it was too soft to bear the pressure of a foot—indeed Richard Bright suffered an accident when one of his legs was plunged into the hot clay as he tried to escape a scalding from the exploding jets of steam issuing from the spring. Before commencing the return journey to Reykjavik they spent a couple of days at Kieblevig, noted as one of the best fishing areas in Iceland.

The 'Doctor' loses his coat

The trek back to Reykjavik proved difficult for owing to some misunderstanding about the luggage the party got split up. Holland waited for the horses whilst Sir George Mackenzie amd Richard Bright went on ahead. The 24 miles across the countryside was desolate and barren and the lava fields full of deep chasms, some partly obscured by moss. Sir George Mackenzie records how:

'Mr Bright and I walked slowly on. We were bewildered by the
number of tracks and at length lost them altogether. After four
hours walking we began to feel the painful sensation of thirst.
By good luck we found a puddle of rain water near which we sat
down and refreshed ourselves.'[2]

They trekked on over the lava fields until:

'The soles of Mr Bright's shoes having been torn by the lava, he
sat down to cut away the loose pieces which were troublesome.
On rising he neglected to take up his greatcoat which he had laid
down beside him.'[2]

After a couple of minutes he apparently realised the loss but was
quite unable to find the coat though he could not have been more
than 200 yards from the spot where he had sat down.

When they reached Reykjavik the 'Elbe' was still at anchor in the
Bay. They were no doubt glad to resume residence in the relative
comfort of the Governor's house.

After a couple of days rest they made another visit to Vidoe. This
time they went by boat and discovered that this was the height of
the breeding season for the Eider-duck. They were sitting on their
nests: 'so completely deprived of their usual habits of wildness and
shyness as to allow themslves to be stroked and even lifted from
the nests without apprehension or resentment'.[1]

The second expedition—the ascent of Snaefellsjokul
On Friday 1st June they set off on their second journey, this time
through the southern parts of Borgar-Fiord Syssel to Snaefellsjokul.
They intended to return by the northern part of Borgarfiord and
by Thingvalla-Vatn and so to Reykjavik. This time they took a total
of some 10 horses, some for riding. Looptson and two other guides
also accompanied them.

To cheers from the 'Elbe' as they passed under her stern they
crossed the bay in the boat belonging to the galliot 'Bildudald' but
they were almost completely drenched by the time they reached the
other shore as a violent storm had sprung up. Wet and uncomfortable
they had to wait two hours for the arrival of the horses which had
taken the inland route of some 15 to 16 miles.

Throughout their second journey they availed themselves wherever
possible of local churches in which they could set-up their bedsteads
for the night. Richard Bright's sketch of the church at Saurbar which
they next visited gives an impression of their accommodation. Their
further needs were generally provided for by the residents of
adjoining farmhouses. From Saurbar they took the road down the
western side of the Hval Fiord to Indreholm, the residence of
Atastrood Steffensen whom they had promised to visit some time

CHURCH OF SAURBAR.

The church at Saurbar (from a sketch by Dr Richard Bright).

before. Here they were received with some ceremony, being ushered into the best room of the house where they were offered coffee, wine, biscuits and English cheese as a prelude to a more sumptuous feast of 'salmon, mutton and potatoes, sago jelly and cream with very good port wine and London porter'.

They were entertained to music of 'no mean excellence'. The performers were the Atastrood's eldest son and daughter playing upon the Langspeil which was an instrument previously unknown to Sir George Mackenzie's party. Holland commented in a less favourable manner about the young ladies of the household whose cleanliness he found could not 'consistently with truth be praised very highly. The habit of frequent spitting was less disturbing to our sight than a certain complaint upon the hands for which the aid of sulphur might advantageously be called in'.

Whilst in the neighbourhood of Indrehdin they made an ascent of the Akrafiall mountain—which was an 'arduous and difficult' undertaking. It was mineralogically very interesting and having erected a pile of stones on the summit—'a monument of vanity which the next storm would doubtless overwhelm' they made an even more difficult descent of the mountain laden as they were with a variety of specimens.

Objects of curiosity
In his journal Henry Holland remarks on the interest wherever they went that both their persons and pursuits aroused—they were 'curiously and minutely examined by the Icelanders'. This was

particularly evident in Bunderstad. Their excursion in the lava equipped with hammers and specimen bags was attended by several groups of women and children who were clearly puzzled that the explorers should be collecting fragments of what to them was worthless dross:

> 'This astonishment was further increased as was evident on their countenances, when following our steps into the house, they saw us wrapping up the specimens of lava in paper—whether they considered us very wise or very foolish we had no means of determining.'[1]

No doubt a proposed ascent of Snaefellsjokul would for the Icelanders have fallen into the latter rather than the former category! But for Henry Holland and the young Richard Bright the ascent of the snow-clad Snaefellsjokul which always appeared tantalisingly on their horizon was the most pressing ambition of the entire expedition.

It was their intention to attempt the ascent of Snaefellsjokul on Sunday July 1st but the weather was against them and instead they spent the day surveying the shoreline around Stappen which Sir George Mackenzie described as 'remarkable:— presenting, for the extent of about two miles, striking and beautiful columnar appearances both in the cliffs which form the shore and in the numerous insulated rocks which appear at different distances from the land.' On the second day they took a boat to examine the columnar cliffs and caves which could be seen to greater advantage from offshore. As foggy conditions continued to prevent their original plan of ascending Snaefellsjokul from the Stappen side they set out for Olafsvik on the northern coast of Snaefell Syssel. Here they stayed at the house of Mr Clausen, a trader engaged in the export of fish oil, tallow, fox skins and locally-made woollen garments, who treated them with great hospitality.

The next morning promising clear, settled weather, Richard Bright, Looptson, one of the guides who had accompanied them from Reykjavik and a man from Olafsvik who claimed the title 'guide' but could in fact only officiate as such to the foot of the mountain, his spirit of adventure never having carried him beyond this point, declined to participate in the mountaineering expedition. In his book *Travels in the Island of Iceland* Sir George Mackenzie includes Richard Bright's account of the attempted ascent. He describes how they provided themselves with an 'Icelandic walking-staff, furnished with a long spike at the end; and in case of need [they] carried some pairs of large coarse worsted stockings of the country manufacture. [They] likewise had [their] hammers and bags for specimens, a compass and a thermometer, a bottle of brandy, with some rye-bread and cheese.'[2]

The first hour of their ascent was not too arduous with the snow soft enough to make walking relatively easy. Gradually, however, the acclivity became steeper, the snow harder and fissured. The fissures were at least 30 or 40 feet in depth and about two to three feet wide. These had to be negotiated or avoided by taking a sometimes lengthy route around them. Richard Bright describes them as 'a very beautiful spectacle' as they 'admitted light enough to display the brilliancy of their white and rugged sides'.

He was further enchanted when 'From time to time the clouds, partially separating, formed most picturesque arches, through which we descried the distant sea, and still farther off, the mountains on the opposite side of the Breide-Fiord, stretching northwards towards the most remote extremity of the island.'[2]

Their steady progress towards the summit however nearly came to a complete halt when they were faced by a chasm some 40 foot deep and six foot wide:

> 'the opposite side presented a face like a wall, being elevated several feet above the level of the surface on which we stood, beside which, from the falling in of the snow in the interior of the chasm, all the part on which we were standing was undermined so that we were afraid to approach too near the brink lest it should give way.'[2]

A dangerous undertaking

They were determined not to relinquish their attempt on the summit and so followed the path of the chasm until they came upon a possible crossing point where the opposite bank was only about four feet high and a pile of snow formed a very insecure bridge. Using their long staffs they cut steps in the bank and stepped with great care to the other side, but here another danger faced them. 'The snow on the opposite side became immediately so excessively steep that it required our utmost efforts to prevent our sliding back to the edge of the precipice, in which case we should inevitably have been plunged into the chasm.'

This dangerous stage of their journey having passed they were able to move on towards their goal. They soon found themselves on one of the three peaks of the mountain, but sadly they were to be denied the attainment of the summit of Snaefellsjokull by

> 'a fissure greatly more formidable in width and depth than any we had passed and which, indeed, offered an insuperable object to our further progress. The highest peak of the Jokul was still a hundred feet above us; and after looking at it some time with the mortification of disappointment, and making some fruitless attempts to reach, at least a bare exposed rock which stood in the middle of the fissure, were were obliged to give up all hope of advancing further.'[2]

They had reached a height of 4460 feet above sea level and hoped for a glimpse of a mountainous range in Greenland, but were again disappointed for huge masses of cloud obscured the view.

The clouds rapidly accumulated and they were anxious to retrace their steps whilst some visibility remained. However, there were certain tasks to complete before they could begin their descent. They checked on the steadiness and consequent reliability of the 'magnetic needle' and then on the thermometer which they were surprised to find no lower than freezing point. Then 'after an application to the brandy bottle' they began with great care to 'retrace the footsteps' of their ascent.

The recrossing of the snow bridge nearly proved fatal for Henry Holland who was the second to pass over the bridge. 'His foot actually broke through the bridge of snow, and it was with difficulty he rescued himself from falling into the chasm below.' In Henry Holland's own words this was not accomplished 'without much fear and trembling whilst thus hazardously engaged!'[1]

To the great surprise of everyone they reached Olafsvik by about a quarter past six for they were not expected until the following morning such was 'the reverential awe inspired by the Jokul'.

Bright writes how 'none of [their] party seemed more gratified with the exploit than [their] guide who had always been accustomed to look upon the Jokul as some invincible giant, greatly exulted in this view over him: but [they] afterwards learned that he faced considerable difficulty in making his friends credit the narrative of the ascent!'

The summit of Snaefellsjokul (from a sketch by Dr Richard Bright).

The next day they remained at Olafsvik regaining their strength after the previous day's expedition. Mr Clausen brought several patients for medical advice from Henry Holland, the nearest practioner being some forty miles away. The weather was so warm that Sir George Mackenzie and Richard Bright enjoyed a morning bathe in the sea.

Bizarre customs and disagreeable habits

On July 6th they resumed their journey along the nothern side of the Breyde Fiord, planning eventually to return to Reykjavik by the lake of Thingvalla. In the course of their return journey they discovered more bizarre and disturbing Icelandic customs. In the church at Narfeyre Looptson pointed to a strange substance lying on an old painted chest. He told them that it was a mass of fat taken from the human body and destined for medical use—the cure of asthma and other pulmonary complaints. Henry Holland writes that this was not an uncommon practice in Iceland:

> 'when a grave is opened and any of this substance found in it (probably produced by the conversion of muscular substance, into a sort of spermasiti) it is eagerly seized upon and laid up for future use'.[2] He concludes: 'was not this a practice among the vulgar in England formerly?'

At Snoksdalur they suffered from the extremity of the weather in a building which afforded little shelter or warmth in temperatures which never rose above 45°F. Their neighbours at the Farmhouse supplied them with an abundance of milk but Henry Holland reports that subsequent discoveries regarding their domestic cleanliness 'greatly diminished' their enjoyment of the beverage:

> 'We were induced to betake ourselves to the utensils in our own kitchen, upon ascertaining that the spoons belonging to the house were cleaned by the simple process of passing them through the mouth, and, afterwards wiping them, upon a dirty wadmal gown. Other anecdotes of the same kind might be given to illustrate the habits of the family; and we soon discovered that it was wise to keep out of the way of discoveries of that nature.'[1]

Perhaps this might have been a contributory factor to the 'slight indisposition' which a couple of days later prevented Richard Bright from accompanying Sir George Mackenzie and Henry Holland on their visit to the hot springs at Reikolt.

We are allowed a further glimpse of the strangeness of the expedition in Holland's comment that '. . . previously to leaving England scarcely could we have conceived it possible that we should sleep on the ground among the mountains of Iceland, with snow not more than 100 ft above us.'

They returned to Reykjavik by boat from Innerholme. After a midnight sail of four hours they landed on the beach there after 'an absence from the metropolis of Iceland of one month and two days—in the course of which time [they] had traversed altogther a distance of about 335 miles.'

They remained in Reykjavik until the 24th July and were fortunate enough to witness the Handel or annual fair. During this time great numbers of people from all over assembled to dispose of their produce and to purchase necessities from other merchants. Most of the transactions amongst the country folk were conducted in a form of barter; fish and wool generally being exchanged for tobacco, spirits, meal, cotton goods etc.

Mount Hecla—the abode of the damned

On Tuesday 24th July the party set out for Thingvalla with its extensive lava beds and fine aspect of Mount Hecla. One of the main objects of their third journey was to visit the celebrated Geyser Springs situated about 16 miles from Skalholt. They were rewarded by witnessing spoutings from the Great Geyser of which the highest column rose to an estimated height of 60-70 ft. The party camped that night some hundred yards from the Great Geyser and took turns to keep watch for any extraordinary happenings. At 4 a.m. Richard Bright noted a column of water thrown up quite close to him. He wakened the rest of the party and they watched as a 'solid massive column of water and steam' rose from the ground 'with immense impetuosity, violence and noise.'

During this third journey Richard Bright and Henry Holland made an ascent of the volcanic Mount Hecla and Sir George Mackenzie was at last rewarded with the discovery of the native Icelandic agate or obsidian which he had been so anxious to locate. Henry Holland recalls:

'Every traveller, . . . who visits Hecla should make a point of proceeding forwards to the bed of Obsidian and Pumice at Reikiadalr. We claim to ourselves the credit of being the first to explore and examine this singular spot.'[1]

Its 'singularity' stemmed from its remoteness and the fact that it was unknown even to the native Icelanders who believed it to be inhabited by a race of men who differed significantly from themselves. Here travel was made extremely difficult by the lack of tracks or roads, the several impassable rivers and perhaps even more importantly the scarcity of pastureland for the horses. During the Middle Ages Hecla was renowned throughout the Catholic world as the abode of the damned.

On their way back to Reykjavik the party visited Odde where they stayed in the house of the former minister and here they bought several books. As Sir George Mackenzie recounts:

'Sundry chests and other receptacles were opened and a variety
of books were released from dust and cobwebs. We made several
purchases, but the most curious and perhaps the most valuable,
was a superb Icelandic Bible which fell to the lot of Mr Bright.'[2]

This Bible can be seen, with notes that Richard Bright wrote at the
time, in the Bodleian Library, Oxford.

At Odde they received news from Mr Fells regarding the arrival
and possible sailing time of the 'Flora', the vessel by which they
hoped to return to England. They hastened back to Reykjavik but
due to delays in the loading of the vessel and stormy weather
conditions their departure was held up for several days.

Their return voyage was made extremely arduous and
uncomfortable by adverse weather conditions—alternate periods of
calm and high gales. During one such gale the Flora's main top
gallant mast split away and six sails were completely destroyed.

The long voyage home
They had left Iceland on August 19th but it was not until the 30th that
they regained sight of land. The whole of the 31st they tacked to and
fro within sight of the shore with the wind dead against them and
another sail was destroyed. Finally they managed to make Hoy sound
on the floodtide and were relieved to cast anchor once more in
Stromness harbour. Their original intention had been to go with the
'Flora' to London but by now the entire party was set on reaching the
mainland of Scotland with all speed. No doubt Richard Bright was a
strong advocate for the latter plan! But their adventures on the high
seas were not yet done for having crossed the Firth in safety they very
nearly capsized as they coasted along the shores of Caithness, finally
being forced to take refuge in Wick Harbour. The last part of the return
journey was made by a variety of overland modes of transport; partly
on foot, partly on horseback, sometimes in small boats, sometimes
in chairs. Finally they took the coach from Inverness to Edinburgh.

In the preface to *Travels in the Island of Iceland* Sir George
Mackenzie wrote in glowing terms of Richard Bright's contribution
to the expedition:

'Mr Bright has made the most of the materials we had time to
collect for an account of the Zoology and Botany of Iceland. To
him we are indebted for the preservation of the plants we gathered,
and indeed for by far the greater part of the collection, and I shall
ever retain a grateful remembrance of the cheerful and the
undeviating good humour with which he submitted to the cross
accidents which sometimes befell us. In the midst of professional
studies he has found time to furnish me with many valuable
remarks and much useful information, which without his
assistance, I could not have procured.'[2]

Sir George Mackenzie clearly valued him highly both for his equable character traits and for his scholarly contributions to the completion of the book.

In 1808 Bright had gone up to Edinburgh from Bristol very much the untested and in many ways unprepossessing youth. His experiences in Iceland had changed him into a man of greater enthusiasm and vigour. He was more aware of the world around him and much more forthcoming in his manner. His parents in particular noticed the change in him. They had great respect for the 'physical endurance and stout spirit' with which he had faced the many adversities and trials encountered in the expedition to Iceland. Perhaps more importantly they now saw in him a 'philosophical equanimity' which, far from being removed by the disciplines and demands of medicine, would be an important factor in sustaining him in the difficult times which lay ahead.

Chapter 5

Guy's and Edinburgh—
From Student to Doctor of Medicine

'No profit grows where is no pleasure ta'en;
In brief, sir, study what you most affect.'
William Shakespeare

Richard Bright remained at Ham Green to celebrate his 21st birthday with his family. In the October of 1810 he journeyed to London eager to recommence his medical studies and to make up for the time lost as a result of the expedition to Iceland. As he entered the city he would no doubt have been astonished by the ribbon of traffic that wound its way towards the metropolis:—

'Horsemen and footmen, carriages of every description and every shape, waggons and carts . . . stage-coaches, long, square and double, coaches, chariots, chaises, gigs, buggies, and phaetons, the sound of their wheels ploughing through the wet gravel . . . continuous and incessant as the roar of the waves on the sea beach.'[1]

Guy's Hospital—the start of a life-long association
Perhaps like other travellers he was kept awake by the cries of the watchman reporting hourly on the state of the weather. And no sooner had he fallen asleep to the clatter of the night coaches than he would have been awakened by the morning carts; the dustman; the porterhouse boy and the milkman. Would he have taken a boat trip down river to London Bridge to that part of the city where, within sight of St Paul's and the Monument and the distant East and West India Docks, he finally entered the courtyard of Guy's Hospital with which he was about to begin a lifelong association?

The United Borough Hospitals—an expedient liaison
At that time Guy's and St Thomas's Hospital were united for teaching purposes and were known as the United Borough Hospitals. Lectures in anatomy and surgery were given at St Thomas's whilst those on medicine, chemistry, botany, physiology and philosophy were held at Guy's. St Bartholomew's and the London Hospital also provided training in medicine not in Medical Schools as we know them today, but by offering opportunities for students to 'walk the wards', to attend lectures, watch operations from beyond the circle

61

of the main protagonists and finally to jostle for a place at a table
in the less than salubrious atmosphere of the dissecting room. The
day began at 7.30 a.m. with a lecture on midwifery, then a hasty
breakfast was followed by chemistry and physiology until 11 a.m.
at which time ward duties commenced. At one o'clock anatomy
lectures began, lasting until 3 p.m. after which the student was free
to take a meal which was followed by instruction in surgery which
lasted until nine or ten o'clock in the evening.[2]

The hospitals were, of course, all charitable institutions maintained
by the generosity of the hospital governors. The wards provided a
wealth of basic teaching material drawn from a broad stratum of
society for within their walls were to be found beggars, cripples and
the mentally handicapped cheek-by-jowl with the genteel but often
impoverished relatives of the governors for whom beds might be
found upon request.

The chances of survival in these hospitals were poor; disease and
premature death were, sadly, the grim harvest of a society where
ignorance, scant alimentation and the appalling lack of sanitation
created a life of harsh deprivation within a social system which cared
little for the poor in their struggle to survive. Why, we might ask,
did Bright choose Guy's for the furthering of his medical studies?
The most likely reason is that the hospital had strong connections
with Edinburgh University, it was well-administered and the quality
of tuition was excellent, particularly in the field of surgery under
the world-famous surgeon Sir Astley Cooper who had himself spent
the best part of a year at Edinburgh University.

The supremacy of the surgeons
Surgery at this time was the preferred branch of medicine for the
work of a physician was considered too unrewarding and theoretical
in content. Bright, however, had always wished to be a physician
and from the start he was determined to raise medicine to the same
status as surgery; a surviving letter written to his father from
Edinburgh in January 1813, suggests that the place of medicine in
the future would depend largely upon the ability of his generation
to 'do better than the last'. On that first day when he entered the
courtyard of Guy's Hospital he could have had no idea of how, in
later years, he and others such as Addison and Hodgkin would be
successful in achieving that goal.

At the 'teaching' hospitals privileged students who could afford
the fee could gain their instruction by being attached either to a
surgeon or a physician. They would act as assistants helping with
the care of the patients and at the same time learn something of
the treatments and hopefully the cures employed by their seniors.
At Guy's a surgeon was traditionally allowed four dressers and one
apprentice whilst physicians were allowed one clerk. The dresser
played an important role in the hospital for he was able to undertake

all minor surgery leaving only the major operations for the surgeon. It was also his job to collect all vessels after operation, to bandage and to take responsibility for the execution of the surgeon's commands often in the presence of a vast number of spectators.[2]

Richard Bright's privileged background allowed him to join the hospital as physician's clerk to Dr William Babington who had worked there for many years and was known to his father. Lodgings were arranged for him in the home of Dr Richard Stocker, the Apothecary.

Dr Babington—a well-loved physician

The clerk's duties involved daily visits to the medical patients, writing reports on the various cases and in general carrying out Dr Babington's instructions. Dr Stocker was the first to see all the new admissions and Richard Bright learned much from him. He gained experience of some practical medicine, learning to cup and to apply poultices, leeches and blistering agents.

Dr Babington was a highly respected physician for whom the welfare of his patients was his major concern, in strong contrast to the often harsh and boorish behaviour of the surgeons whose necessary speed at the operating table was often translated into brusque impatience at the bedside.

Other notable lecturers included Alexander Marcet and William Allen teaching chemistry and natural philosophy; John Haighton on midwifery and physiology; Dr Curry who shared the Practice of Medicine with Dr Babington and Mr Cline who, with Astley Cooper, lectured on anatomy.

Astley Cooper—surgical skill perfected

Astley Cooper is worthy of a special mention. He was a flamboyant character, dandified in appearance, but a most skilful surgeon and a droll and entertaining lecturer. It was from his surgical lectures that Richard Bright developed his interest in morbid anatomy. It is possible that when he visited Mr Cooper's house at St Mary Axe he participated in the dissection of some of the more exotic creatures which, by arrangement, his tutor received from the Tower Menagerie upon their demise.

In his biography, *The Life of Sir Astley Cooper, Bart* his nephew Bransby Blake Cooper gives a most entertaining account of the problems his uncle encountered when he received an elephant carcass for dissection: it was brought on a covered hired cart so that it would attract as little attention as possible: 'In this manner it arrived at St Mary Axe and the cart having been driven into the courtyard before Mr Cooper's house the outer iron gates were closed and they set about attempting to get it into an outhouse, devoted to the purposes of dissection.' Sadly their efforts failed and they had to leave the elephant carcass lying exposed in front of the building.

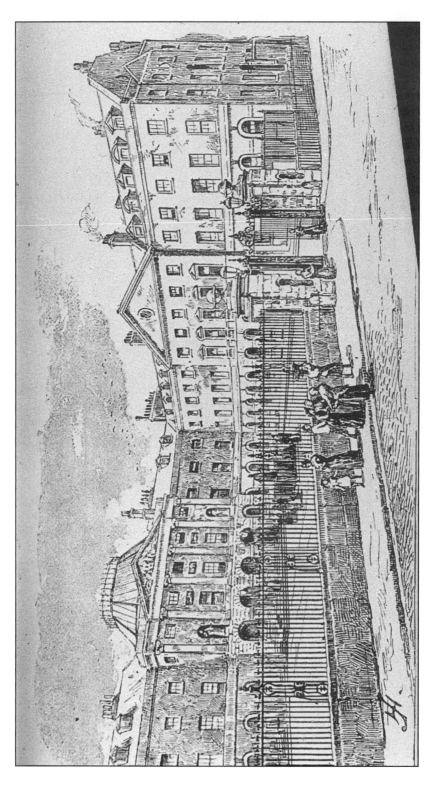

Guy's Hospital

Dr William Babington.

A great crowd had gathered and they were obliged to cover the railings with carpets and to move the body as far from view as possible. 'Mr Cooper was thus compelled to dissect this animal in the open air, and finding himself, from its enormous size, unable to perform the task alone, he invited several students from the Hospital to assist him.' Of course, the procurement of human subjects for anatomy lectures was always something of a problem and Bransby Cooper points out that:

'As well as his professional duties connected with his practice and hospital avocations, my uncle had also to mix himself with a set of persons who were at that time essential to him . . . I allude to the men whose occupation was to procure subjects for dissection, since known by the name of Resurrectionists.'[3]

The importance of morbid anatomy
Richard Bright began to see the importance of morbid anatomy in the understanding of disease. As we have already seen, he was a skilled draughtsman and he now used his talents to record the

appearances of normal and diseased organs. It was in 1811 that he first drew a granular kidney and later wrote to his father the words which in a sense expressed both his professional and personal philosophy: 'For my part I am very fond of seeing'. He was meticulous in the observations that he made noting the tiniest detail in the capillary web of a sectioned organ as he would note the veining in mineralogical specimens or the angle of a shadow when he worked to capture a scene with pencil or water colour.

As he became more familiar with the day-to-day routine at Guy's he gained in confidence and his dedication to work and keeness in observation was noted by more senior members of the hospital staff. Dr Stocker's favourable report on his abilities persuaded Benjamin Harrison the Treasurer, that he was now sufficiently qualified to dispense drugs and other medical preparations.

Elected to Guy's Physical Society
In December 1810 the young student doctor received one of the first honours of his career. He was elected a member of Guy's Physical Society, being proposed by Dr Laird, who from the way he is referred to in Bright's correspondence appears to have been a close family friend; he was seconded by Dr Curry.

Curiously Richard Bright attended so few lectures in the early weeks of his membership that he found himself incurring fines. However, in January 1811 he presented his inaugural paper on blood-letting, a treatment which he believed was often used to excess. He felt that its use should be restricted to certain cases of heart failure and acute lung disease and if possible avoided in cases involving the brain. Despite his determination to become a physician he wisely took some time to gain basic experience in surgery and mastered such procedures as venesection, tooth extraction and the opening of abscesses.

A new outlet for a long established hobby
The somewhat wild and unconventional life of the average medical student was not in accord with Richard Bright's character and temperament. Students who did not have the discipline of the United Borough Hospitals led particularly 'bohemian' lives—wearing attire more suited to artists and poets. Their appalling living conditions drove them to escape to spend their evenings in local hostelries such as 'The George' or 'The Ship and Shovel' where they could discuss their studies, though not always in the most professional manner; the familiarity with the human form gained in the dissecting room seemed to breed a ribald contempt. Richard Bright was as intense in his attention to his studies as he had been in Edinburgh and 'all work and no play' once more began to take its toll. This time it was Dr Babington who tried hard to persuade him to take up some leisure pursuits but he found excuses to avoid the physical outlets suggested

Sir Astley Cooper.

by the good doctor. He did, however, allow himself to participate in 'meetings' of the Geological Society of London which had been founded in 1807 and to which his father had been elected an honorary member.

In February 1811 the Society began with modest informal gatherings which were held in Dr Babington's London house in Aldermanbury where the idea of a 'dining and talking club' was conceived and at a meeting held on November 13th 1807 at the Freemasons' Tavern the Geological Society of London was born. There were thirteen founding members of the Society, of whom four were medical men—Dr William Babington, Dr James Laird, Dr James Franck, and Dr James Parkinson.

The interest in geology which was so prevalent among medical men in the 19th century arose as a result of the introduction to the subject which they received during the course of their study of chemistry which, closely associated with materia medica, was an essential part of their medical training; minerals formed an important constituent in the medications employed in the treatment of disease.[4]

Bright gave to the Society his geological collections made in the Liverpool area and those he had collected in and around Bristol during the many excursions he made with Henry Holland whilst attending Dr Estlin's School. Later in the year he presented them with duplications of the specimens that he had collected during his visit to Iceland. In November 1811 he read his first paper on the geology of his native city. This was based largely on observations he had made even before going up to Edinburgh in 1808 and lacked inspiration; a later paper relating to the Icelandic collection attracted more attention. Meetings of the Geological Society then formed more or less the boundary of Bright's social life apart from keeping in touch with relatives such as the Heywoods who lived in St James Place.

Working for the MD—the return to Edinburgh

The two years of his training spent at the hospital passed rapidly and the October of 1812 found him in Edinburgh once more in the last year of his medical training. As the Morehead's house was shut up Richard Bright had to find other lodgings near to the University. This time he had to fend for himself and learned something of the costs involved in purchasing everyday needs. His studies were again theoretical rather than practical but once more he was fortunate in having some excellent tutors notably Dr Gregory famous amongst other things for his purging powders—as Sir Robert Christison notes in his autobiography: 'Gregorian Physic—free blood-letting, the cold affusion, brisk purging, frequent blisters, the nauseating action of tartar emetic—came to rule medical practice for many years, in all quarters throughout the British Islands and the Colonies.'[5] His measures for the cure of diseases were unwaveringly incisive—he left his students with the belief that they were the masters over nature when it came to confronting acute diseases which must 'of necessity give way before the physician who is early enough and bold enough in encountering them.'

Since Bright had already given a paper at Guy's on the undesirability of excessive blood-letting we might assume that he would have found some of Dr Gregory's methods at odds with his own inclinations. Certainly as far as concerns the practice of blood-letting in fever he warned against its advisability in all classes of epidemic fever. Sir Robert Christison on the other hand found Dr Gregory to have been in advance of his time in his anticipation of certain pathological and therapeutic principles later to be claimed as the discovery of 'young Physic'.

Other lecturers included Sir Walter Scott's uncle, Dr Rutherford, who held his classes in botany in a most pleasant situation at the Botanical Gardens at Leith. Materia Medica was taught by that most popular of lecturers, Dr Home; his class-room was generally so crowded that even a chilly 8 a.m. winter start meant that several students were unable to find seats. Dr John Thomson, blessed with a general professional talent, tutored in pathology and chemistry.

For a second time Bright attended Dr Andrew Duncan's lectures, this time in medical jurisprudence, which had previously been taught on the Continent of Europe but not in Scotland. Duncan had actively campaigned to have Edinburgh University establish a chair in the subject and this was finally accomplished in 1807.

This being the final year of his medical training and with thoughts of the MD thesis still to be completed much on his mind, Bright again found his work all-absorbing. In her biography entitled *Dr Richard Bright* his great-great niece Miss Pamela Bright does, however, assure us that he enjoyed the company of many interesting people.[6] One such was Francis Jeffrey, the advocate and one of the founders of the *Edinburgh Review* for which he had written on politics, travel and verse. He, of course, was a close friend of the Moreheads where, we may assume Bright first made his acquaintance.

As we have already seen, ideas were freely shared between representatives of the Arts and the Sciences and this is borne out by Jeffrey's friendship with both Dr James Gregory and Dr John Thomson—maybe the young doctor was fortunate enough to have taken dinner with them on several occasions and to have enjoyed their eloquent conversation.

Of course he lacked the presence of his friend Henry Holland but he had other interesting contemporaries; Humphry Davy's brother John, Thomas Addison with whom he later worked at Guy's, John Beddoes, son of Dr Thomas Beddoes of Pneumatic Institute fame and of course the talented Robert Knox to whom Robert Christison later attached the epithet 'notorious' which by 1829 he had sadly earned as a result of his involvement with the resurrectionist team of 'Burke and Hare'. 'Dr Knox's classes were universely and deservedly popular and he always guaranteed his [anatomy] students an ample supply of subjects; moreover, he preferred them fresh.'

> 'Down the Close and up the stair,
> But and ben wi' Burke and Hare,
> Burke's the butcher, Hare's the thief,
> Knox the man that buys the beef.'

so said the words of the popular song![7]

Coming 'fresh from Astley Cooper's operating sessions' gave Richard Bright a certain kudos. He was also now known for his contribution to Sir George Mackenzie's book *Travels in the Island of Iceland.* and he was pleased to find that people actively sought his company and appeared to enjoy talking with him.

He was so engrossed in his studies that he rather neglected communications with the family at Ham Green. But fortunately for us there are extant letters and since this is quite rare we have decided to quote quite extensively from them. A letter written to his father in January 1813 begins:

'How far I must go back in order to give you a continued series of my proceedings I do not know, but I too well know that I must look back a great way.' Here he is comfortably seated by the Morehead's fireside where 'Mr Morehead is reading a book' and 'Mrs Morehead sleeps on the sofa.'

Planning for the future

In this letter he is beginning to consider plans for the future after his hoped-for graduation in the coming September. As regards dispensary practice he feels sure that:

'. . . as soon as a man has learnt what he ought to observe it is the best school which he can find and I therefore hope for some time to give myself up to it.'

Female readers, who may be wearying of this exclusively male medical world of the early 19th century, will at this point find some diversion in the fact that Bright narrowly missed consorting with the young James Barry who qualified at Edinburgh in 1812 at the age of only seventeen! She, for after her death her true sex was discovered, presented her MD thesis in Latin, on hernia of the groin, ironically its epigraph, a quotation from the classical dramatist Menander urged the examiners: 'Do not consider my youth but whether I show a man's wisdom.' After graduation Barry proceeded to 'walk the wards' at the United Hospitals of Guy's and St Thomas's as pupil dresser to Sir Astley Cooper.[8] Bright's concerns, however, were bound up with the very real dichotomy which existed between medicine and surgery and not with whether or not an odd female slipped into either branch of the profession which he described to his father as being indivisible:

'it is quite impossible to draw the line between them so much do they run into and depend upon each other. I conceive that the internal and external parts of our frame are regulated by the same laws, and what process on the outside we may see openly, we may infer from analogy to be going on within, and are the surgeon's the only ones to have the advantage of these external manifestations while the physician contents himself with conjecture and hypotheses?'[9]

The pressure of work was such that he felt forced to abandon a treasured dream of a 10-14 day visit to Staffa and to Fingal's cave which he had 'so often gazed at' on paper that it seemed 'quite embodied' with his childhood. He felt that September would be a better month than May in which to take a holiday since his 'mind relieved (he hoped) of a burden would be a much more agreeable companion.'

Within two weeks he was again writing to his father a lengthy and interesting letter setting out in greater detail all the possibilities open to him on successful completion of his MD:

> 'You must suppose that intending to take my degree in September I naturally look about me to discover what step would next follow with advantage and by seeing what other young Physicians of the present day who are to be my competitors are doing I am able to judge what it appears right, necessary or advantageous that I should do. In the first place I lay it down as an axiom that the more practical knowledge I get the better and I assume as an almost undeniable proposition that the more responsibility I have placed on me while I acquire that experience the more impression it will make upon me.'

He notes that since fees are of no immediate consequence he will be free to pursue the most useful and enjoyable course of study and that the more diligently he applies himself during that time the more likely he will be ultimately to acquire fees. The three situations in which he is most interested include Physician's Clerk to the Edinburgh Royal Infirmary, House Surgeon of the Lock Hospital, Westminster and thirdly a post at the Westminster Lying-in Hospital. The first two are in: 'the highest request among young medical men and can only be obtained by offering yourself a year or two before you can hope to obtain them'; his plan is to spend a year in London after graduation either 'with Laird or at Guy's' or three months of the time at the Westminster. He feels that during this time he will have his only chance of getting the Edinburgh clerkship.

One of the advantages of the Physician's Clerk in Edinburgh is that the postholders live 'in very comfortable rooms in the Infirmary, they dine together and have board and lodging found by the house on payment of a sum of about £30.00 per annum.'

The duties of Physician's Clerk included prescribing for patients until seen by the Physician the following day, taking a minutely detailed case history, an 11 a.m. ward round followed by one with the Physician at mid-day when the clerk would be expected to write the prescription as dictated by his superior. Bright had struck up a friendship with Marshall Hall who at that time held the clerkship and it was Hall who strongly recommended him to apply immediately if he wished to get one of the next two vacancies.

His next concern refers to the position at the Lock Hospital:

'You know the nature of the Lock Hospital, and doubtless know how much the complaints to which it is peculiarly and exclusively devoted mix themselves with all the diseases of large towns and what is perhaps of still greater consequence how much the remedy which is so generally used in those complaints lays the foundation for other diseases.'

Here he is referring to the use of mercury in the treatment of syphilis. He again points out how he finds 'the competition for anything in the shape of situations in Medicine so great that it becomes necessary to look sharp and to look a little into futurity'—a situation which still pertains nowadays. A visit to 'see a little of the Paris practice' is also something of a temptation to the young doctor, but not with the state of war still existing between Britain and France when it would be: 'ridiculous to shape any plan upon such a chimera'.

Erysipelas—gathering the evidence
A further important topic in this letter relates to Richard Bright's intention to make contagious erysipelas the subject of his thesis. The subject suggested itself as a result of 'some instances of apparent contagia which occurred under (his) observation at Guy's'. He continues: 'I can only say that I wish I knew more and shall be most obliged to you if you can collect me any facts in a detailed and regular form, pointing out instances of the extension of this disease from one patient to another.' He mentions the reports of cases of the disease in Manchester and York and of course Bristol and stresses the lack of any useful means of preventing the spread of such an infection apart from the well-known but obviously ineffectual use of white-washing, ventilation and fumigation. He is anxious to have his father's opinion and approval for his plans—he also suggests that his father might communicate with Dr Laird to gain his opinion and then:

'if . . . he as well as you would be so kind as to write to me I should like to know all before the end of the month—not that I would be altogether, tho' in part guided by him. If he knows of any situation similar to that of the Edinburgh Infirmary, occurring in London I do not know but I should prefer it, tho' the access to books is very delightful here . . .'

Richard Bright's obsession with these decisions about his future and the need for work on his thesis prompted him to resign his seat in the Speculative Society. However he was engaged to read 'two long papers of other persons compositions' the following night at the Royal Medical Society of which he was President for the year 1812-1813.

His father's reply arrived before the month was out. He had consulted with his old friend and family physician Dr Lovell who was basically in agreement with the projected plans. He had been unsuccessful in his own attempts to obtain the post of Physician's Clerk at the Edinburgh Royal Infirmary and had instead acted as Clerk to the Dispensary Physician which provided him with excellent experience. He also agreed that for the next three years his young friend would be 'far better employed in seeking knowledge than fees and that fees will come faster after a little present self-denial.'

It appears that Dr Laird was basically of the same opinion as Dr Lovell and Richard Bright (senior's) letter to his son concludes with some practical suggestions:

'If upon receipt of this you immediately determine to ask for the Edinburgh Clerkship might not a letter from Mr Evan Baillie and Mr Forbes be useful. I see one of the Mr Thorntons, my friends is one of the Governors of the Lock and another of the Lying-in-Hospital—by this means something may be done towards your successful application—but I shall do nothing without your previous information and concurrence.'

Richard Bright's letters display the anxieties of a young man desperate to make the right decision for his future career. It is interesting that despite his father's original misgivings about his choice of profession it is to him that he turned for advice and indeed practical support in amassing material for his MD thesis. He was perhaps fortunate in that his father had such a deep interest in scientific matters and would readily have understood his needs.

The respect and esteem he felt towards his father was formally but touchingly expressed in the letter he wrote to him at the time of the submission of his thesis:

'Dear Sir,
I feel that I stand in need of your forgiveness when I borrow your name, without permission to adorn my thesis; and I feel this the more when I consider that it is a truly unworthy performance, and calculated to give you nothing in return for the weight and ornament it derives from you. The existence of a Thesis is however so ephemeral, that I conceive myself as offering you a private, rather than a public testimony of my esteem, and as such, originating in the sincerity of my heart I hope you will accept it.'

Richard Bright successfully completed his thesis on contagious erysipelas and with a further 23 young graduands received the degree of Doctor in Medicine on 13th September 1813. At the autumn graduation there were four others who also wrote 'Anglus' after their names: John Conquest, Stevenson Eden, Robert G A Collingwood

and Joseph Dyneley; the total number of doctors graduating from
Edinburgh for that year was 62. On completion of his thesis the
doctor also wrote to Dr Lovell who, it appears, may have had some
influence on his choice of profession:

> '. . . I was first induced to select that path of life which I have
> now begun seriously to pursue and which every day presents me
> with so many new objects of interesting contemplation, that I
> cannot but feel thankful for what I know was unintentional on
> your part.'

Peterhouse disappoints expectations—return to London
His application to the Lock Hospital had been successful but it was
to be a year before the post would become vacant. He had a year
to fill and decided that he would benefit from graduating from
Cambridge as well so in October he accompanied his brother Henry
on his return to Peterhouse. His entry to the college appears in the
admissions register for that year:

> *'Vicesimo tertio die Junii Richardus Bright*
> *ad mensam Pensionariorum admittitur'*

Unfortunately he found the Cambridge library quite inferior to that
at Edinburgh where the 'access to books was delightful'. The
curriculum did not meet with his requirements in terms of furthering
his medical knowledge. It was restrictive and lacking a structured
academic approach. He decided not to return and so, again taking
advice from his friend Dr Laird, in January 1814 he commenced
working at Dr Bateman's Caley Street Dispensary. As with his
correspondence from Edinburgh we are fortunate in having some
surviving letters which provide an excellent insight into his day-
to-day life, his interests apart from medicine and some very
important concerns regarding the organisation of his finance.

In the first letter written to his father on 24th January 1814 it
is snowing outside and he is:

> 'not interrupted by a sound which could surprise' his father in
> his quiet study at Ham Green—'such is the effect, and so far a
> very delightful effect which the snow has produced, partly by
> rendering the streets so inconvenient for carriages as to prevent
> many from coming abroad and partly by covering the stones with
> a soft carpet. About 8 o'clock last night I walked from the Temple
> to St Pauls without seeing a single carriage . . . at low tide the
> view at London Bridge is one entire sheet of ice which however
> breaks away when the water rises, leaving a wide sheet of ice
> about the vessels down the whole course of the river . . . I long
> to see the river at London frozen over. I should enjoy the novelty

and beauty of the sight and never think of the misery and inconvenience which must accompany the cause.'

A matter of great interest both to Richard Bright and his father regarding the purchase of books is also touched upon in this letter. Richard Bright had 'consulted all the catalogues and looked at many of the books in London'. He decided to give his commission 'to Dr Carpenter, telling him to go as far as £16 for certain books'. This would provide him with a collection which 'will be by no means a pocket library. I think about 18 or 20 folio volumes. They are all such books as a Physician absolutely must have in his library, though he as absolutely can not read them all.'—an interesting attention to the trappings necessary to building status! The works included writings by Galen, Hippocrates, Hoffman, Majaori, Bonelius, Paracelsus, Lancisins, Lommins and Sydenham—a variety of weighty tomes that one might be forgiven for wishing to ingest by a process of osmosis rather than in late night readings by expensive candle-light.

He writes that he is very comfortable in his lodgings. There is no servant but he is 'well waited upon by the landlady and her daughters—the only fault I can find is that they will not rise in the morning and as there is no fire I make that a very good excuse for not rising myself.' He adds however that he must make up for this tardiness in rising by sitting up later at night than he would wish for he 'generally thinks the last hour but moderately well spent.'

It appears from this letter that he is not at this time involved in any anatomical study. Henry has offered him the use of his back room for the 'dissection of birds etc.' but he feels that he can presently use his time more profitably in the pursuit of other interests.

A gift for Dr Babington

An amusing episode which he recounts concerns some asparagus which had been sent from Ham Green and which had ultimately fallen into the hands of Dr Babington, but not before brother Robert has been sent 'to the Market to see whether it were sufficiently scarce to make a present and finding that it was very rare indeed neither to be had for love or money it was dispatched to the doctor though a question has since arisen in the Court of Conscience whether we ought not to have considered it in the light of a marketable product of the farm and raised two or three guineas upon it in Covent Garden . . .' The question was apparently 'refuted by the court . . . a gentleman is allowed to sell his oxen, his sheep, his grain, his grass, but his sparrow-Grass let no man sell—his apples but not his pine apples!'

A subsequent paragraph pours scorn on some reports from the Clifton Dispensary which his father has sent on to him. There is also a rather curious comment regarding his sister Phoebe's medical aspirations:

The George Inn, Southwark.

'The paper which you sent us with a report of the Clifton
Dispensary is amusing—I am sure Phoebe no longer hopes to be
a Doctor without learning—She will surely be some time before
she can even read that long catalogue of hard names and when
will she be able to apply them to their appropriate combination
of symptoms? Dispensary doctors have great facility in giving
names, they see a case for two months and give it a name in these
books—see to what absurdities this has lead our friends at
Clifton—out of 22 patients in consumption (which nothing can
cure) they have cured 15—Is this intended as a puff on the air

and water of Clifton—it is singular if they have had two cases of catalepsy in one year—it is a rare disease.'

The remarks referring to Phoebe are hard to understand—did she aspire to some kind of medical 'career'? We do know that she was very involved with charitable works and particularly with the Clifton Dispensary. Did this brotherly response reflect, what was for those times, a customary lack of belief in a female's intellectual ability? As we have already seen in the case of Dr James Barry, medicine, as other professions, was for women a completely closed shop.

At the Dispensary
The day-to-day routine at the Dispensary provided Bright with an insight into the powerful influence of poverty on the health of the nation for we must not lose sight of the fact that if there was a dichotomy in medicine then England was similarly divided—'The two nations' as Disraeli later called it. War with France had done nothing to improve the lot of England's urban poor, indeed throughout Bright's life-time their plight, if anything, grew worse. The appalling lives of the 'flotsam and jetsam' of London's sub-culture is only too well documented in Mayhew's contemporary journalistic accounts and in the words of Charles Dickens: Joe, the crossing-sweeper when asked: 'What do you know my poor fellow?' replied 'I knows how to sweep the crossing.' He certainly knew nothing of the existence of the Public Dispensary; even poverty had its strata.

The severity of the winter of 1814 produced bronchitis and pneumonia in epidemic proportions. Bright, in a vain attempt to alleviate the suffering of patients struggling for every breath must have thought back to the early visits he had made with his father to the Pneumatic Institute for he administered oxygen employing a pig's bladder for the purpose instead of a cylinder.

A growing 'wanderlust'
By mid-February 1814 the genesis of a plan for a visit to the Continent was already forming in Bright's head. On February 11th he wrote to his father tentatively outlining his ideas: 'I wish you to consider what I am going to say rather as a meditation, than as the expression of a wish'—his feeling is that previously everything connected with his education had been in pursuance of his wishes rather than those of his father. He reminds him of the plans for his future that they had made whilst he was still at Edinburgh—his intention to spend sixteen or seventeen months at the Dispensary then in June 1815 go to the Lock Hospital. After that, if all goes according to plan he will succeed Dr Laird at the dispensary and 'never leave London again'. He reminds his father that he had once suggested to him how beneficial it would have been for his student son to visit the 'great Continental schools of medicine.'

Now that circumstances in Europe are easier and 'more aspiring
young men' of his profession are journeying there he is considering
when he can make time to 'extend' himself 'beyond the limits of
our little island'. He sees it as a 'very desirable object to visit the
principal medical schools of the Continent' and to visit on his way,
all those countries can show him:

> 'I cannot hesitate in declaring—I think it desirable on account
> of the real information I shall obtain and still more on account
> of the Ideal Value which others will bestow upon that
> information—I think it greatly desirable as being the only means
> of acquiring the languages of these countries and I think it very
> desirable on account of the general expansion of mind and the
> delightful remembrances which remain our pleasant companions
> through life.'

His reasons for considering such a tour worthwhile reveal several
facets of his character; the keen professional eager to possess valued
information and thus further his career; the linguist already eagerly
studying German, French and Italian; the intellectual seeking to
broaden his horizons and lastly the romantic who, with the eye of
an artist, will gather a fund of delightful lasting impressions and
memories.

He put his case most persuasively pointing out that there would
be no time like the present—he had gained much experience in his
two months at the Dispensary and within two more would feel 'very
little repugnance in taking upon [himself] all the duties of a
Physician at this institution'. With the supreme arrogance of youth
he believes the dispensary already to have yielded up all its secrets
of curative medicine and in any case it is 'a school . . . to be long
within [his] reach' whilst the chance to visit Europe may not occur
again so conveniently.

He had, he said, 'no inclination to make adventures with a
Pacha'—the main purpose of the projected tour was to spend some
time in 'some two schools of medicine' and also to make himself
master of French and German. As far as expenses were concerned
he felt that 'the product of the Icelandic journey'—a sum of money
which his father had set aside for him would 'completely cover the
difference' between a year spent in London and that spent on a
European tour as he had outlined 'provided a man does not come
with servants and equipages and pretensions'.

During the next four weeks Richard Bright concentrated on his
language studies believing that in a short time he would be 'obliged
to rely on the German language entirely for information'. An
opportunity arose through the searchings of his brother Henry for
him to take lodgings in the house of a French emigrant. He wrote
to his father in some detail regarding the costs involved in such a

move. The previous tenant, a friend of Henry's, had paid a guinea and a half for his bed, breakfast and tea: French lessons cost 2s 6d—but Bright felt certain that prices would have risen. He felt that he would now have to pay at least two guineas. He wished to know how far his father 'would think it worthwhile to exceed the price of common lodgings for the society of the French man'.

Balancing the budget

On the very same day he wrote again to his father—and clearly was still very concerned about the additional expenses to be incurred in the move:

> 'The great objection is the greater additional expense—I cannot live and board and receive three lessons a week from the host as a master for two months under 40 guineas—and I have particularly to request that if you think, upon the whole, the advantages are enough you will at once say to me, here are 40 guineas and you must make them do for every expense which you incur within two months from the time you get into your new lodgings; reckoning coal and candles at 8s per week, washing and shoe cleaning 5 pl, less 7s 6d, entrance to lessions £1.1 I make the whole to come to 39.1 guineas and as we all know that, do what you will a pound or two will go in the course of a month I do not suppose it possible to do under 40 guineas.'

This anxiety over financial arrangements may seem surprising to us given that Bright came from an affluent background and yet the sum of £240 guineas a year for living when translated into today's figures, would be quite a considerable amount. It is also worth remembering that thrift was an undoubted virtue in the Dissenter's code of behaviour although Richard Bright obviously found his budgeting something of a trial—he wrote:

> 'I hope you will burn this letter together with all which I have ever written to you with accounts in them—I detest the subject!'

His letter also gives news of family members as he describes visits made to his Aunt Heywood, sister Sarah and his uncle Birch. He writes of other books he wishes to purchase, of his friend from Edinburgh Dr Leech, the young entomologist and of Thomas Coachman whose sister had been in Guy's Hospital. In his opinion she 'will never get perfectly well, as she has in all probability organic disease about the heart'.

From further correspondence dated 1st March we learn that his father concurred with the proposed change of lodging but suggested he consult with Dr Laird who apparently also gave his blessing to the idea since the house was still close by the Dispensary. He included then a draft of his letter to his brother Henry's friend Kenyan in which he accepts the lodging arrangement with a rather charming post scriptum: 'I have not mentioned WINE bcause as I very seldom take any I do not intend to provide myself with any'— a very sober young man!

In this same letter he expressed some concern for his mother's health. Since it was Dr Laird's intention to visit Bristol he wished his father to call upon him with regard to Dr Lovell and his mother; her case he was pleased to note had already been discussed with Dr Babington.

For his father's particular interest he included in his letter a description of a 'peculiar species' of mouse which he had been shown the previous night by Sir Joseph Banks. The creatures looked like 'small rats without tails, large heads, ears hidden in the fur', and had for some time been 'committing the most dreadful depredations on the trees in the King's Forests in Hampshire'. No doubt some of the boxful were added to his collection of anatomical specimens!

Preparing for the European tour
As the time for the commencement of his European tour drew closer his letters to his father reflected his eager anticipation as well as some anxiety regarding the procurement of the many promised letters of introduction:

> 'I am glad on several accounts that you have spoken to Lord Sheffield, it really seems to me that the compliment of asking little favours such as this fully repays the obligation under which they would put you—it may be a reason for his Lordship remembering hereafter that there is such a person as Dr Richard Bright.'

He had also dined with a Mr Wardrop, a friend from Edinburgh days who having himself spent some time in Vienna and Paris was a useful source of information. He promised Bright a letter from a 'relation of Lord Aberdeen's who has been the Ambassador at Vienna'. Such an introduction would be gratefully accepted 'whatever Lord Sheffield may do besides'. Dr Laird introduced him to the clergyman at the German church in London who promised him a letter to his counterpart in Vienna. His father was determined that he should have a passport in order to have 'all possible countenance' and although it was in fact quite unncessary, Francis Horner was to be instrumental in procuring the necessary document.

The days flew by and the young doctor was too busy 'running about after people who tell [him] to come again' to enjoy the visit of a cousin from Liverpool. He did, however, manage to accompany his brothers Bob and Henry to the Exhibition and Panarama but sadly had to forgo a visit to 'the wonderful stage—last night to see Kean.'

He breakfasted with Sir Walter Scott and with Sir Joseph Banks who asked him what he should write in the promised introductory letters:

'I did not know what to say but told him I had devoted my life to Medicine, had made great acquirements in Minerals and had been in Iceland.'

He hoped also for an introduction to Madame de Stael the famous critic, novelist and hostess who to the newspaper reading public of her day was considered the 'apotheosis of the blue-stocking'.

His travel plan was to take him first to Holland and then to Hamburg and on to Berlin or alternatively to Frankfurt, Leipzig or to Ratisban. A final decision would be left to Ham Green and Amsterdam where the 'plans may be brought to perfection'. His final task was to confirm his appointment at the Lock Hospital. Consequently, in company with Dr Laird, he called upon Dr Pearson who felt that the possibility of his spending some time in Vienna before the commencement of his post would have considerable advantages.

Having taken leave of his family he set off on a journey that was to provide him with a plethora of new experiences and knowledge not only in the field of medicine but also in the social sciences, linguistics and the arts. With the keen observant eye of doctor and artist his experiences were captured for posterity, particularly the time spent in his travels through Lower Hungary.

Chapter 6

Beginning to Observe—
Traveller, Author and Artist

'Travel in the younger sort, is a part of education;
in the elder, a part of experience.'
Francis Bacon

In the months prior to Richard Bright's departure for Europe the British Allies including Russia, Austria and Prussia defeated the French at Leipzig, Wellington won a major battle at Toulouse and the British and Allied armies marched on Paris which fell in March of 1814. In the April of 1814 Napoleon gave up the French throne and was exiled to the island of Elba. At the ensuing conference held in Paris it was the intention of the Allied powers to restore the French Monarchy, to re-draw the maps of Europe, to reward themselves and, finally, to punish the French.

In January 1815 the peacemakers left Paris for Vienna to participate in Metternich's Congress which also lured Bright to the city. His travels and the finalisation of his plans began in Amsterdam and from there he went on to Rotterdam. Here he no doubt found much to interest him in the changes and improvements made to the docks which he could compare with similar changes which had been so badly needed to provide Bristol with a floating harbour. The medical faculty at Leiden, distinguished by the reputation of the great Boerhaave, provided him with a fine opportunity for study and for gaining further experience in his professional calling.

Freedom from the iron grasp of Napoleon was a cause for rejoicing for those countries such as Holland, Belgium and Germany through which Bright would pass—Europe's doors were open once more and Frankfurt, Leipzig, and Berlin were the next cities on his planned route.

It seems likely that his choice of intinerary may have been influenced by the writings of an earlier doctor and traveller, Edward Brown, who was born in Norwich in 1644. In 1669 Brown journeyed from Vienna, through Hungary, along the Danube, south to the Balkans and back to Vienna through Bulgaria. In 1673 he published a 144 page book on his travels entitled *A Brief Account of Some Travels in Hungaria*.

In this same tradition Dr John Paget (not to be confused with Sir James Paget) later wrote about the travels he made in Hungary and Transylvania in the years 1835-36. His two-volume work was

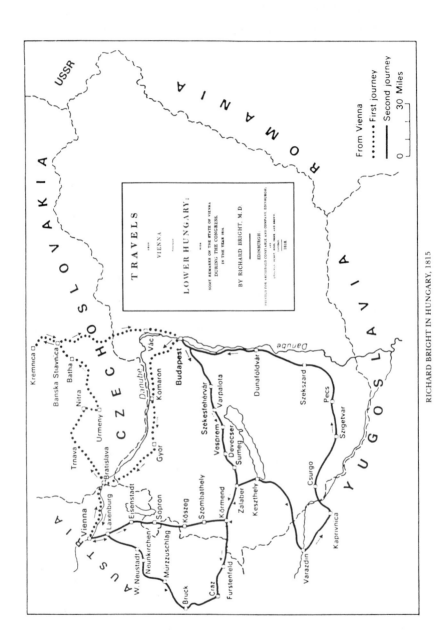

RICHARD BRIGHT IN HUNGARY, 1815

Frontispiece to Travels through Hungary and map of Dr Bright's travels.

published under the title *Hungary and Transylvania; with remarks on the condition, social, political and economical.*[1]

Berlin—'en route' for the Congress
When he at last reached Berlin Richard Bright was delighted to meet with Professor Durnheim who had been recommended as a teacher of Latin by the clergyman of the German church in London. He lodged with the family and as they spoke no English his German quickly improved. Neither was medicine neglected for in Berlin he was able to see something of the neurological practice of Horn and to visit the clinics of Hufeland. He also met Dr Klaproth the famous chemist and discoverer of the elements of uranium, zirconium, titanium, and cerium. When he was younger Bright had made a study of Blumenbach's craniological work; how thrilled he must have been now that he was able to see for himself the famous man's fine collection of skulls.

In the nearby town of Amorbach there was the pleasure of a family reunion for he also met up with his sister Sally who was studying German at a seminary for young ladies. Suddenly, however, news of the imminent dissolution of the Congress reached Berlin and Bright being anxious to 'become a spectator of this most extraordinary assemblage' quickly recommenced his travels. By the time he reached Dresden a second message informed him that the Congress was over; on hearing this he decided to enjoy the charms of this ancient city and he remained there for several weeks.

When he got to Prague, further conflicting reports told that a few more days of the Congress remained so this time he made for Vienna with all speed, arriving there towards the end of November. As it turned out, such speed was unnecessary for, in fact, the Congress sessions continued until June 10th, 1815.

Vienna—'Le Congres danse, mais il n'avance pas'
Richard Bright decided to spend the winter in the capital and the account of his sojourn there and his subsequent travels in Hungary provide the fascinating text of his book *Travels from Vienna through lower Hungary with some remarks on the state of Vienna during the Congress in the year 1814.* The book, illustrated with some delightful sketches made by Bright during his travels and with chapter heading vignettes by Craig and one by Austen, was published in a 600 page quarto volume by Constable in Edinburgh and by Longmans in London. The opening chapters provide an excellent picture of life in the capital during the colourful months of the Congress when monarchs, princes, foreign ministers and proud aristocrats were to be seen 'two a penny'.

His first lodgings were in 'a busy dirty inn in the commercial part of the city', which put him 'more in mind of London' than anything he had so far seen in Germany. His 'large and desolate' apartment was representative of the 'miserable accommodation in most of the inns in Vienna'. That first day provided him with kaleidoscopic images of the life of this vibrant city. It began with a continental breakfast 'a jug of hot scalded milk and another of coffee'. Next he was further aroused by a 'succession of visitors, one presented himself as a chiropodist another was a barber; a woman came to supply me with tooth-brushes and trinkets; a turbanned figure had beautiful amber mouth pieces for tobacco-pipes; and another excellent meerschaum tobacco-pipe heads.'[2]

Mingling with the crowd

It was Sunday, a day of contrasts, of festivity and devotion—shops were closed and masses celebrated hourly but the theatres were open and the streets were thronged with a lively crowd. He found these narrow streets on a level with the carriageways somewhat hazardous, 'the foot passenger has no safety but in the judgement of the charioteer, who frequently risks an encounter with your feet, rather than with the wheels of a passing carriage.'

Later in the day he was persuaded by a 'gentleman of Vienna' a chance acquaintance, to visit a place of public amusement called the Redoute. He was told that here he would have the opportunity to see 'many of the distinguished persons then collected at the Congress'. In the brilliantly lit salon which formed part of the Bourg or Imperial Palace the entertainment was in full swing but:

'Never was an assembly less ceremonious. Everyone wore his hat; many, till the room became heated, their great-coats, and no-one pretended to appear in evening dress, except a few Englishmen, who, from the habits of our country, and some little vanity, generally attempt to distinguish themselves by an attention to outward appearances.'

—a perceptive comment from a young man of twenty-five years of age and one certainly displaying an awareness of human nature!

Amongst the 'moving multitude many of whom were in masks, or in dominos were many important personages: My companion squeezed my arm as we passed a thin figure with sallow shrunken features, of mild expression with a neck stiff, bending forwards and walking badly. "That is our Emperor". I shook my head and smiled. He was alone, and dressed like the rest. "Pray allow me to doubt a little until I have some further proof"—"There, do you see that little man with white hair, a pale face and aquiline nose? He was almost pushed down as he passed the corner, that is the King of Denmark." Again I shook my head in disbelief."

The procession of Kings, Emperors, Crown Princes, Grand Dukes and other nobles continued so that:

'In this way, for two or three hours, did we continue meeting and pushing amongst hundreds of men, each of whom, had he but made his appearance singly at a fashionable rout in London, would have furnished a paragraph to our news papers, prints to our shops, titles to our bazaars, distinctive appellations to every article of our dress , and themes, if not ideas, to our poets.'

This was his first introduction to some of the members of the Congress. He succeeded in finding himself a private lodging and continued to increase his 'acquaintance with the town and its inhabitants'. He confessed that he was 'somewhat disappointed in the magnificence which [he] had anticipated, as attendant upon so important an assemblage from all the powers of Europe. In fact, the splendour was entirely that of the Austrian Court, which had given to its visitors a most imperial reception.' He found many of the outdoor scenes very attractive and with his customary keenly developed powers of observation brings them to life for his reader. Again the foibles of human nature are not lost upon him; for at the Carousel he saw the magnificent tournaments 'contrived to dissipate the ennui of royalty' by the nobility. The idea was that the horseman should ride full tilt at a row of dummy Turk's heads in an attempt to sweep them off one by one with mighty strokes of the sabre. He writes that the sumptuous uniforms of the participants 'bore the appearance of being the substantial fruits rather than the honourable testimonials of victorious arms.'

A different way of life . . .
At times the tone of society in Vienna apppeared too frivolous for Richard Bright's restrained nature but paradoxically he found the freedom from formality or the impositions of etiquette extremely attractive. In a sense his life seemed to reflect that same kind of ambivalent attitude—on the one hand the dedication to duty, the restraint of the professional man and on the other the artist, the linguist—fascinated by the gypsy travellers but who as a student could neither effect the dress of the bohemians nor join in their wild carousings in the taverns close to Guy's.

Certain aspects of Viennese dinner parties Richard Bright found to be of 'peculiar excellence'. Such parties often included a drive, a visit to the theatre or to other places of amusement and when they at last sat to dinner the table would be 'round or oval, so that each guest has means of intercourse with the whole party' and the conversation would be 'general and lively and beyond a doubt, much more interesting that that which is heard on similar occasions and in similar society in England'. Whilst in Vienna he visited the theatre and he also attended a musical occasion at the Redoute when he heard Beethoven's 'grand piece of music' entitled 'Battle of Vitoria.'

He was delighted, as an artist, with the many fine art collections of the city—for here were Rembrandts, Vandykes, Rubens, Titians, Murillos and Velasquezs to say nothing of the 159 drawings and engravings of Durer—displaying 'delicacy and minuteness, combined with perfect freedom'; Richard Bright himself had a fine collection of Durer's work. The general state of education and science in Vienna the doctor found to be far from flourishing—difficulties and obstacles abounded and the narrow-minded censorship of the press and foreign publications severely hampered growth. The government also discountenanced 'all assemblies and societies of men, whether their purpose be friendship, scientific or political'.

Medicine—the Vienna School
There was only one small medical society and even that was stifled by the constantly superintending censorship of all publications. There remained a relatively small number of scientific men to uphold the traditions of 'The Vienna School' which had for decades been the most celebrated stronghold of Boerhaave's doctrines of clinical observation. The Vienna School of Medicine had, through the writing and teaching of Boerhaave's disciples Van Swieten and De Haen, come into contact with British medicine:

'That sober empiricism, resting on the accumulation of detailed observations, which was characteristic of English Medicine in the eighteenth century, and which it has never lost, became the guiding star of the Vienna Medical School also. Its independent and unprejudiced spirit, combined with great powers of observation made it the example of the true clinical method.'[3]

This, of course was the tradition in which Richard Bright had received his medical training in Edinburgh where the influence of Boerhaave, as we have already seen, was also prominent in the early teachings of Alexander Munro and John Rutherford.

A link between Vienna and London also existed in the work of Robert Willan who in his celebrated work *Description and Treatment of Cutaneous Diseases* (London 1798-1808) developed the ideas of J J Plenck which based the classification of skin diseases solely on their external clinical signs. Willan's pupil and friend Thomas Bateman of the Public Dispensary where Bright worked completed the treatise under the title: *Practical Synopsis of cutaneous disease, according to the arrangement of Dr Willan.* This edition, published in 1815, had the widest circulation and the greatest possible recognition throughout Europe.

A visit to Johann Peter Frank
Of these former Viennese medical giants Johann Peter Frank was the sole survivor. He had been the first physician to emphasise the

importance of diseases of the spinal cord and to have demonstrated the importance of public hygiene. Now in his seventies we are given a picture of a kindly old gentleman, gracious in the hospitality he extends to the unknown young English doctor:

'He is a man of the most instructive and pleasing conversation, with great knowledge both of books and men, and is most universally respected. He is now above seventy years of age, is perfectly firm and upright, and, in all his faculties and dispositions, possess the force and energy of youth, tempered by the mildness of advancing years.'

Besides Dr Peter Frank other notable medical figures which Bright met included Hildenbrand, renowned for his early work on typhoid fever, Beer, the opthalmologist, Vincenz van Kern, the surgeon, who revived the idea of cold water bandages as a treatment for wounds, Dr De Carro the pioneer of Jennerian vaccination and Professor Prochaska, the anatomist.

Bright was, of course, most interested in all the Charitable Institutions of the city which were 'for the most part, monuments of the kindness of government towards its distressed subjects, or of dying devotees towards the salvation of their own souls . . .' His attention was, however, 'naturally drawn in a peculiar manner, to the magnificent General Hospital, where the medical lectures of the Hildenbrand, the instruction of Beer, and the surgical practices of Rust and Kern, afford great attractions to those who are interested in such pursuits.' The hospital was designed to receive 2000 patients but owing to funding problems at the time of Richard Bright's visit there were not more than 800—a situation that has, for us, a distinctly contemporary ring about it! The wards were 'high and well-proportioned, heated by stoves, and, as fuel is dear, the windows, which are small, but numerous, and provided with double glass, are never opened during winter.'

Patients were divided into four separate classes, the first three comprised of those who were not entirely destitute and thus able to contribute something to the 'restablishment of their health.' The patients' diets were 'daily tasted by some of the attending physicians, both in the kitchen and in the ward'. Bright found the clinical wards to be greatly superior to the others—they were situated in a separate building in one of the squares of the hospital where Professor Hildenbrand also had his residence. Bright was full of praise for the doctor:

'This very able physician is the worthy successor of the celebrated Stoll and Frank: he devotes himself very assiduously to the improvement of the students, whose education, in the practical parts of medicine he superintends. He visits the patients, in company with the pupils, as early as seven o'clock in the morning, and afterwards delivers a very excellent course of medical lectures in Latin, Professor Beer likewise lectures in this hospital . . .'

Also of great interest to the doctor was the considerable collection of anatomical preparations found both at the hospital and the University—these were used in the medical education of the students. Particularly impressive were the anatomical wax casts that had been made by the skilful Florentine artists 'representing in the minutest detail, all the parts of the human body, with their anatomical structure fully displayed.' In later years Bright was to utilise the skills of Joseph Towne for a similar purpose for, as we shall see, his artistry provided some compensation for the general lack of teaching materials with fine examples of his work even now on display in the impressive Gordon Museum at Guy's Hospital.

Dr Prochaska's treasures
Particularly 'worthy of attention' was the museum of Professor Prochaska which contained 'the most minute injections of the vessels of the human body in existence'. The professor was apparently in possession of a certain art of injecting which, on condition of secrecy, he had learned from Barth and 'in defiance of all the rules of philisophic liberality, these two enlightened men deny to the world the valuable means they have discovered of increasing our knowledge of the human frame.'

Apparently this art of 'subtle injection' was the same as that employed earlier by Lieberkuhn. Bright felt that it would be a 'blot upon the scientific spirit of the University of Vienna if such a discovery should be suffered to perish.'

The Narrenturm or Asylum for the Insane won less approval from the Doctor. The large four storey building contained '300 patients, whose condition is far from being as comfortable as in many of the establishments for the insane which I have visited.' This was one of the show places of Old Vienna and on payment of a small fee the public were able to view the insane who paced up and down or were confined like animals in a menagerie. He also visited the Lying-in Hospital, the Hospital of Foundlings and the Institutes for the education of the Deaf and Dumb and the Blind. These he found to be 'conducted with much spirit and success, on plans similar to those of Paris and Berlin.'

The castle of Shonbrunn also claimed his attention for there he saw Napoleon's young son, the Prince of Rome. He found the child quite delightful: 'His appearance was so engaging I longed to take him in my arms.' This fondness for children was later fulfilled in his own family of seven.

During his stay he found time to discuss the general attitude to the political arrangements which would be the likely outcome of the

Congress. 'The grand subjects in discussion were the future condition of Poland, Saxony, and the Italian States—in fact, all those points in which political expediency appeared to be in opposition to justice.'

Beneath the carnival facade he encountered feelings of anxiety, discontent and apprehension. There was also a degree of distrust towards the English for it was generally believed that the decisions that had been taken were largely brought about by their influence:

'. . . it was ever the anxious enquiry whether England was the steady champion of justice?—whether she boldly asserted and strenuously maintained that character which the boasted freedom of her principles led Europe to expect . . .'

Across the border—the first journey into Hungary
In March of 1815 Richard Bright, now well-provided with letters of introduction to Hungarian nobles, set out on the first of his journeys into Hungary. At the frontiers he was questioned regarding possible contraband. He apparently earned 'the admiration of the officers' when he told them that he 'neither smoked nor took snuff—a phenomenon which' he believed had 'very seldom come within their observation'. He crossed the Danube at Pozsony known also as Pressburg and travelled northeast to the Carpathian Mountains. He arrived at the estate of Count Hunyadi and although the Master was away from home he was received with all possible hospitality. Here he stayed for some days before moving on to visit the silver mines at Schemnitz, then on to Pest-Buda finally returning by a westwards route to Vienna via Gyor (Raab). Bright's original plan had been to visit Venice and Milan and to return home to England through Paris, but arriving back in Vienna after his first trip to Hungary he was met with the news that Napoleon had escaped from the island of Elba, had landed in Antibes and was even then marching with an army to Paris. In view of this he decided to make a second journey into Hungary, this time going south from Vienna to Lake Balaton, along the borders of Croatia to Pecs (Funfkirchen), then north to Pest-Buda finally returning eastward through Styria.

The history of the people of Hungary is essentially one of trial and hardship. For a period during the reign of Matthias Corvinus the country experienced a period of stability and progress but with his death at the end of the fifteenth century Hungary was prey once more to invasion by the Turkish armies. Bright visited the famous fortress town Szigetvar and saw for himself the bravery and determination which drove Count Nicolas Zrinii to defend his town with only 2,500 men against 164,000 Turks; the battle claimed the Count's life.

The Hungarians—resolute in the face of adversity
The Hungarians displayed great fortitude in the way they managed to survive centuries of destruction and misery—such fortitude

persisted even into the twentieth century for as an Hungarian friend remarked recently 'If we could survive two centuries of Turkish dominion then forty years of another repressive regime was a mere drop in the ocean!' Hungary had experienced years of splendour as well as centuries of devastation and oppression. She had somehow managed to escape the ravages of Napoleon's war machine and at the time of Bright's visit she remained firmly in the grip of feudalism. In his book he endeavours to bring his reader to an understanding of the virtually medieval status of the Hungarian peasant at the beginning of the nineteenth century. He found this to be:

'Not only in appearance, but in reality, oppressive. The appearance of oppression constantly imposing on the sufferer a consciousness of his humiliation, is of itself an evil hard to bear.'

This great divide between nobles and peasants made Richard Bright

'certain that the whole system is bad . . . let a cold east wind blow for one night—let a hail storm descend—or let a river overflow its banks—and the peasant, who has nothing but his field, starves or becomes a burthen to his lord.'

The Doctor is certainly forthright in his comments but rather in the same spirit as his 'short sketch' of the history of Vienna it is not his intention to 'ingraft a political discussion' but rather to allow 'the reader to form correct ideas' of the condition of the peoples of Hungary.

'It is the humble duty of the Traveller to collect, under all the varieties of circumstance, such materials as may supply a ground work for connected history, and for general deduction. Correct observation and faithful statement are the cardinal virtues on which his character must depend . . .'

Such principles, of course, informed much of his work in the field of medicine.

His observations regarding the peasants themselves again displayed an insight beyond his years:

'They were cheerful—but it was the cheerfulness of boys under the eye of their master—and there was something disagreeable in that appearance of timorous yet rebellious, subordination, which seemed to say—"This is hard—but it must be so . . " No-one can remain long in Hungary, without seeing that all who are in stations superior to the peasant look on him with contempt, mingled with suspicion and dread.'

It would have been interesting to have had some record of Bright's opinion with regard to that chasm of class division, the 'two nations' which existed in Britain throughout his lifetime and was the source of so much misery, injustice, poverty and disease.

Prisons—a reminder of home

Prisons in Hungary and the survival of the ancient Jus Gladii which gave the feudal lord the right to inflict capital punishment or imprisonment upon his serfs also provoked a critical response:

> 'The traveller seldom approaches the house of a Hungarian noble, who possesses the Jus Gladii without being shocked by the clanking of chains and the exhibition of these objects of misery loaded with irons. The prison itself is never concealed from the curiosity of strangers; I should almost say that it is considered a boast—a kind of badge of the power which the lord possesses; (it is scarcely credible that men of the noblest and most refined minds, should persist in the barbarous custom of placing in the very gateway of their hospitable mansions—in the only path by which their offspring can approach the domestic hearth—the miserable victims of a most sacred, but, at the same time, most painful and revolting duty.')

He described in some detail one prison that he saw in Keszthely reflecting that some of its wretched inmates had already spent the long nights of seven years or more lying on the bare dungeon floor chained all together at the ankles. This barbarous behaviour, however, he sees as a universal human failing rather than an inhumanity unique to his hosts:

> 'In speaking thus freely of the prisons of the Hungarian Chieftains, I mingle with my feelings as little inclination to censure them as possible, I consider them as affording a remarkable example of one of the most common of all incidents, the aptness of the human mind to view with indifference objects that are constantly presented to it. In conversation with foreigners how many things do we hear respecting our own customs of which, at first, we are almost inclined to question the existence; and how unconsciously may the eye of an Hungarian nobleman be closed, with respect to many important circumstances in the situation of the great mass of the inhabitants of his country, from whom, under a change of system, that country might derive additional security and happiness and the proprietor an enormous increase of power and wealth.'

Yet this humanitarianism which considers how a change in 'system' i.e. greater freedom for the peasants might ultimately result in

improved output in terms of labour and thus improved power and
wealth for the 'proprietor' bears something of the mark of the realist,
perhaps even the tradition of mercantile endeavour, which had
formed such a strong part of his youth. He goes on to quote examples
of some of the abuses against prisoners perpetrated in his own
country—these he takes from the publications of a 'Society for
diffusing information on the subject of capital punishment and prison
discipline'.

Amongst these descriptions is one of 'a pit . . . in constant use,
in the gaol of the opulent commercial city of Bristol. Their dungeon,
the pit, down eighteen steps, is about eighteen feet by seventeen,
and nine high. Barrack bedsteads; no bedding, nor straw. It is close
and offensive; only a small window.' Some years later when his
brother Henry was elected as a Member of Parliament he persuaded
him to champion the cause of prison reform. Bright's stay at Count
Hunyadi's castle provided him with an opportunity to learn and see
something of the management of the estate, the breeding of horses
and other livestock. The estate books showed details of both crop
and livestock yields.

He visited peasant homes which surprised him by their
'appearance of comfort and good order'. They were well provisioned
with 'bags of grain', bladders of tallow, sausages and other articles
of provision, which would astonish us to find in an English cottage'.
Bright, having grown up with the horticultural splendour of Ham
Green, was disappointed by the lack of gardens and flowers which
he sadly missed. In contrast he saw that the peasants of Martonvasar
did take a pride in their gardens: 'It was truly gratifying to find
the peasant taking pleasure in the cultivation of his flower garden,
which is perhaps one of the most certain marks and best promises
of rural civilization.'

An "unseemly disease"
The difference in appearance between the Slovak and the Hungarian
peasants was not lost on the artist's perceptive eye. Of the Slovaks
he was somewhat dismissive for:

> 'When you have seen one you have seen them all. From the same
> little head covered with oil, falls the same matted long black hair,
> negligently plaited or tied in knots; and over the same dirty jackets
> and trousers, is wrapped on each a cloak of coarse woollen cloth,
> or sheep-skin still retaining its wool.'

Apparently they were also afflicted with:

> 'that unseemly disease known by the name of Plica Polonica in
> which the hair grows so matted that it is impossible to disentangle
> it, and becomes actually felted into balls, which, from an

unfounded apprehension of bad consequences, the peasants are very unwilling to have removed.'

He was however pleased to report that the real Hungarians:

'showed far greater attention to personal neatness and like the gypsies were often dressed in hussar jackets, blue pantaloons, boots and broad-brimmed hats which gave them the appearance of banditti.'

Gypsies—a life of freedom
Richard Bright found the gypsies particularly fascinating. He noted that both their appearance and their language was similar to that of the gypsies at home. He made an extensive list of their vocabulary and when he returned to England he sought out a group of travellers living at Norwood who he was delighted to find understood many of the words. He was attracted by the apparent independence and freedom of the open air life:

'I leave it to those who have been accustomed to visit the habitations of the poor in the metropolis, in great cities, in country towns, or in any but those Arcardian cottages which exist only in the fancy of the poet, to draw a comparison between the activity, the free condition, and the pure air enjoyed by the gypsy, and the idleness, the debauchery, and the filth in which a large part of the poorer classes are enveloped.'

He was, of course, well acquainted with the condition of England's urban poor through his work at the Public Dispensary.

A chance to puruse his hobby
On his first journey into Hungary, Bright visited the gold and silver mines at Schemnitz and Kremnitz and with his interest in geology he took the opportunity to descend some 72 fathoms below ground where in the cold and wet a miner worked an eight hour shift. His book describes in detail the working of the mine with its water-driven machinery, through the raising of the ore right to its final destination in the Royal Mint.

Travelling has its drawbacks!
His travel through Hungary was certainly lacking in comfort for the roads were pitted and deep in mud, little better indeed than those he had encountered in Iceland. He often found it difficult to obtain transport and his conveyance was usually a peasant's wagon —but undaunted by such setbacks and no doubt benefitting from experiences gained during his student expedition he managed to visit all the places he intended. The cleanliness of the wayside inns was

View of Buda and part of Pest (sketch by Dr Richard Bright).

often doubtful for at one place he was told 'very few persons had slept in the bed'. Despite his professed lack of interest in wine he did taste those he encountered in Hungary including the famous Tokay.

Pest-Buda afforded much to capture his attention—theatres, a museum, the warm public baths, some dating back to the Turkish occupation, the many fine buildings of the city and naturally, that which was of particular interest to him—the University Hospital of Pest. The student body of the University of Pest, now the Semmelweiss University of Budapest, was comprised mainly of Hungarians and Transylvanians. Lectures were delivered in Latin and it is interesting to note that whilst in England medical lectures were, by the mid-18th century, given in English it was not until the mid 19th century in Austria and Hungary that German was used.

Medical studies similar to those in Britain

The medical course at the Faculty at Pest extended over five years. This same course structure formed an almost identical curriculum for the first three years of medical study in both England and Scotland until the 1960s.[4]

First year: Anatomy, chemistry, botany, natural history, general pathology and surgery.

Second year: Physiology, more minute anatomy, the theory of operations, surgical instruments, midwifery.

Third year: Pathology, materia medica and diseases of the eye.

Fourth year: Therapia of acute and chronic diseases, clinical lectures in medicine and surgery; and lastly the veterinary art which however may be postponed until the fifth year or till the course is completed, but must be pursued before a diploma can be obtained.

Fifth year: Particular therapia and clinical lectures continued, to which were added medical jurisprudence and medical police

Bright was impressed by the small University Hospital at Pest despite the fact that there were, at the time, no medical men of any real consequence with the exception of Professor Kitaibel, the botanist, who showed him through the hospital. This was divided into six wards; medical, surgical, gynaecology, diseases of the eye, one for lying-in women and one special ward for syphilis which appears to have been a disease prevalent at that time: each ward contained six beds. The fourth and fifth year students attending the patients were required to report on the cases in Latin. They also had to keep a 'thermometrical and barometrical register' which was checked regularly by the Professor of Astronomy.

A visit to the baths
A visit to the warm baths in Buda made a lasting impression on
our young traveller:

> 'Amongst the objects of curiosity, which attracted my attention
> at Buda, the public warm-baths are too singular to be forgotten
> . . . . On entering from the open air, the room filled with steam,
> was so insufferably hot, as almost to oblige us to retire.'

A descent into the circular basin revealed:

> 'ten or twenty persons of each sex, partially covered with linen
> drawers and the long tresses which fell loosely from their heads,
> amusing themselves by splashing in the hot sulphurous water.
> Disgusting as this was, it formed the least disagreeable part of
> the scene . . . in different corners were groups of naked families,
> enjoying their mid-day meal, sour crout and sausages, amidst all
> the luxury of a profuse perspiration. To complete the scene, there
> was a row of half-naked figures like those in the bath, on whom
> a poor miserable surgeon was practising the operations of cupping
> and scarification, studiously inflicting as many wounds, and
> making as much show of blood as possible, in order to satisfy the
> immoderate appetite of the Hungarian peasant for this species
> of medical treatment. With such a mixture of disgusting objects,
> it never before happened to me to meet and almost faint with heat,
> I was glad to make my escape, yet my curiousity led me to several
> others . . .'

At least the baths at Buda elicited a rather more animated response
than the 'tedium' engendered by the numerous visits he made as
a child to the Hotwells in Bristol. Then, as we recall, feelings of 'pity'
had been the predominant emotion.

The theatres of Buda-Pest gave Bright a chance to hear an overture
by Beethoven and also the playing of some unusual musical
instruments. One of these resembled the Langspiel which he had
seen in Iceland, another was the 'Dudelsack' or Hungarian bagpipe
and the third was the cymbalom or Glockenspiel.

Lake Balaton
On his second journey into Hungary he visited Lake Balaton where
he spent his time mainly in the observation of the flora and fauna
of the lake and with excursions to study the extinct volcanoes such
as Csobanc, Szentgyorgyhegy, Szigliget and Badacsony. At Keszthely
he stayed at the castle of the Count Festetics. At the main entrance
of the castle a plaque, unveiled in 1962, commemorates the visit
of Dr Richard Bright in 1815. The event was reported in *Guy's
Hospital Gazette:*[5]

Balaton Lake seen from Keszthely (sketch by Dr Richard Bright) and the commemorative plaque at Keszthely.

'There was a simple but pleasing ceremony at Keszthely, 'Capital' of Lake Balaton in Hungary, on 18th August of this year (1962) ... On a day when the temperature was 100°F in the shade, it was a pleasure to sit in the cloistered and shaded entrance, to listen to some excellent music beautifully played by the Budapest Chamber Orchestra and to hear the short but appropriate speeches by the Assistant Mayor of Keszthely ...

In the handsome columned entrance to Keszthely Castle a tablet was unveiled to the memory of Richard Bright, famous English doctor who travelled extensively in Hungary in the early part of the nineteenth century and wrote a book, *Travels from Vienna through lower Hungary* published in 1818. The inscription read:

Richard Bright
1789-1858

To the memory of the English physician, scientist and traveller who was one of the pioneers in the accurate description of Lake Balaton. He sojourned in this building in 1815.

In the late 1960s a copy of the doctor's book was discovered in the famous Helikon Library at Keszthely. The dedication inside read: 'To His Excellency, Graf George Festetics with the respectful compts of his much obliged and obed' servant the Author.'

Taking Stock
A summing-up of what he had learned from his travel with regard to national character traits is revealed in the following comments:

'I am strongly inclined to believe that the blazing hearth and the comfortable carpet do more to form the domestic character of the English nation, than any original disposition of physical temperament; and that the crowded theatres and tea-gardens of the Continent give evidence of the want of comfort at home rather than of the gaiety of the heart.'

One of the Continental habits, that of members of the male sex greeting each other with salutations 'on both cheeks' was as strange and distasteful to him in Hungary as it had been when first encountered in Iceland!

Waterloo
Within a few days' distance from Brussels on his return journey to England, Richard Bright learned of the Duke of Wellington's great victory against Napoleon. *The Times* official Bulletin dated London, June 22nd, 1815 reported his triumph:

London, June 22nd 1815
Downing Street.
'The Duke of Wellington's Dispatch dated, Waterloo, the 19th June, states, that on the preceding day Bvonaparte attacked with his whole force the British line supported by a corps of Prussians, which attack after a long and sanguinary conflict, terminated in the complete overthrow of the Enemy's Army . . . Such is the great and glorious result of those masterly movements by which the Hero of Britain met and frustrated the audacious attempt of the Rebel Chief . . .'[6]

Everyone went to Waterloo to sightsee, to seek information about wounded kinfolk, some merely as refugees. Brussels was overjoyed at the victory and threw itself into celebrations in an attempt to suppress the sorrow at the hundreds that had died in the achievement of the 'great and glorious result'. The diarist Miss Mary Berry wrote how in London: 'All the world was out of doors during the best part of the night, asking news of their neighbours.'

Richard Bright was much moved by the suffering he witnessed— here were no well-run field hospitals or organised medical corps—a doctor, a dresser, a couple of orderlies and a mule to carry medical supplies was the only medical care afforded a regiment. He quickly picked up the threads of medicine again as he became involved in caring for the wounded. Here he found old friends from Edinburgh days, John Davy, Robert Knox, and Dr Thompson. Astley Cooper sent out a team from Guy's including Aston Key, Henry Cooper and Henry Wakefield; they were popular with the men for their kindness of manner. Sir Charles Bell of Bell's Palsy was also tending the wounded and as surgeon at the Middlesex Hospital was an authority on gunshot wounds.

The young doctor concerned himself with the problems of dysentery, pneumonia and tetanus but at other times he acted as a dresser assisting at the surgical operations. He found much to interest him professionally and stayed in Brussels beyond the time he was expected at the Lock Hospital. The 22-page review in the *Edinburgh Review* of 1818[7] described *Travels through Lower Hungary* as:

'evidently the work of a very amiable and intelligent man, who has observed with the utmost diligence, everything remarkable that came within the sphere of his observations, and set down in his book, perhaps with too much minuteness, everything that he had so observed.'

For the future those 'astonishing powers of observation' would be directed almost exclusively to his work in medicine—there would be other visits to Europe, other opportunities to indulge his love of painting, but sadly his emergent talent for writing of this kind was given no further space in which to develop. Some might consider his rather prosaic style more suited to the subjects under discussion in the *Reports of Medical Cases* for which he is certainly better remembered.

Chapter 7

Physician and Family Man—
A Brief Moment of Happiness

'. . . An age of anxiety from the crown to the hovel,
from the cradle to the coffin; all is an anxious
straining to maintain life, or appearances—to rise
as the only condition of not falling.'
Samuel Taylor Coleridge

England in 1815 was in the midst of far-reaching social transformations; she was entering an era of prosperity and greatness as yet unrivalled in her entire history. Sadly, hand-in-hand with such progress came a period of remarkable social distress and unrest, economic crisis and political change. Unfortunately this new-found wealth and world supremacy were built upon foundations of harsh sweated labour, appalling slum conditions in urban areas and a resulting human misery of immense proportions. The struggle to establish the ideals of political democracy was always dogged by the realities of distress and oppression. This was the country to which the survivors of the 30,000 British men who fought at the Battle of Waterloo returned.

Richard Bright too returned from his travels to a London which had to a large extent escaped both the crippling pauperization which had a stranglehold on the greater part of agricultural England and also the catastrophic fall in wages which occurred in so many places. The transition from war to peace had, however, brought to the metropolis much unemployment and deep social problems.

In contrast, Regency London's wealthy strutted their fashions through the city for this was the age of Beau Brummell, the dandies and the dandizettes, and the popularity of Brighton was at its height. Charles Lamb in a letter to the Wordsworths, declining an offer to join them in Cumberland, writes of the London with which he had formed

'as many intense local attachments as any of your mountaineers can have done with dead nature. The lighted shops of the Strand and Fleet Street, the innumerable trades, tradesmen and customers, coaches, waggons, playhouses, all the bustle and wickedness round about Covent Garden, the very women of the Town, the watchmen, drunken scenes, rattles-life awake if you awake, at all hours of the night, the impossibility of being dull

in Fleet Street, the crowds, the very dirt and mud, the sun shining
upon houses and pavements, the print shops, the old book stalls,
parsons cheap'ning books, coffee houses, steams of soup from
kitchens, the pantomimes, London itself a pantomime and a
masquerade . . .'[1]

The Lock Hospital
In this city of contrasts almost as vivid as those he had encountered
in Vienna, Richard Bright returned to his work in medicine, first
for a short time at the Dispensary where the ailing Dr Bateman
was, of course, eager to keep him, then on to take up his post at
the Lock Hospital under the guidance of Dr John Pearson. The Lock
Hospital was dedicated to caring for those suffering from that most
dreaded of all venereal diseases—syphilis: *Post voluptatem
misericordia* was the dire warning on the sundial of the hospital
at Kingsland. The name 'Lock' was originally used in mediaeval
times for a leper hospital where patients were literally locked in
or excluded from the rest of society.

Both the symptoms and the mercury employed in the treatment
made the patients depressed and temperamental and, as a
consequence, the study of the disease extremely difficult. This was
exacerbated by the rule that since the cause of death was already
known, autopsy was not permitted. Bright found this frustrating
since he believed that the viscera as well as the brain could be
affected, but unfortunately he was unable to check his theories.

The second of the great triumvirate arrives in London
At this time Thomas Addison came down from Edinburgh, he shared
many of Bright's views on medicine, particuarly those relating to
the value of *post-mortem* investigation. A friendship developed
between the two men which was later to take firmer root in the
professional relationship which so benefited Guy's Hospital.

Bright met up with other old friends and acquaintances, John
Leech, the entomologist whom he had so admired in Edinburgh,
Humphry Davy now engaged on developing a miner's lamp, Michael
Faraday and at last, Henry Holland who had also just returned from
his travels. Unfortunately their lives in medicine were to follow very
different directions. Henry Holland was determined to distance
himself from the disagreeable side of doctoring which would have
brought him into contact with all the worst diseases of poverty—
instead he chose to follow his professional calling amongst the
wealthy members of society who could afford to live away from
London in the summer months, so leaving him free to pursue his
other interests.

Bright also had the pleasure of spending some time with his sister
Phoebe who was staying in London and also his favourite brother,

Benjamin. He was delighted when Dr Babington invited him to lecture on the volcanic areas of Hungary at the next meeting of the Geological Society and also to give an account of his experiences in the Continental hospitals to the Medico-Chirurgical Society, later to be known as the Royal Society of Medicine. In some measure, this society managed to forge some very necessary links between the unfortunate professional dichotomy that existed between the physicians and the surgeons.

The Willan Fever Hospital
In February 1817, on account of Dr Bateman's ill-health, Dr Laird found himself hard-pressed with work both at the Public Dispensary and the Willan Fever Hospital and he asked for further assistance. Both he and Dr Bateman recommended Dr Richard Bright as an able physician who had already a year's experience of work at the Dispensary. John Pearson strongly supported the recommendation, finding the young doctor sound in his professional knowledge and displaying integrity of character and great benevolence. In his paper 'At the Public Dispensary with Willan and Bateman' MacCormac writes of the young doctor's acceptance of the post:

> 'The Paragon is elected and writes in April 1817 from 22 Spring Gardens, entreating the Secretary to communicate to the Committee the importance he attaches to the duties and his hope that he shall prove himself worthy of their good opinion.'[2]

The Willan Fever Hospital, which was set up in 1801, provided for the needs of isolation cases as part of the work of the dispensaries which were burdened by a succession of epidemics and usually fatal diseases such as dysentery, consumption and typhus. A compact example of Georgian architecture it stood on the site of today's Kings Cross Station.
There were several important rules laid down for the running of the institution including:

1. There should be a 'constant admission of fresh air into the room and especially about the patient's bed.'
2. 'An attention to cleanliness is indispensable. The linen of the patient should be often changed and the floor of the room cleansed every day with a mop.'
3. 'Nurses and attendants should endeavour to avoid the patients' breath and the vapour from the discharges or when that cannot be done they should hold their breath for a short time.'
4. 'Visitors should not come near to the sick, nor remain with them longer than is absolutely necessary.'
5. 'No dependence should be placed on vinegar, camphor, or other supposed preventatives which without attention to cleanliness and admission of fresh air, are useless.'[3]

There was a special carrying chair for the transport of patients to the hospital where they were consigned to 'separate apartments' according to the differing stages of their fevers.

The staff consisted of a matron to superintend the domestic concerns, a porter and as many ordinary nurses as required, the number to be augmented if it were deemed necessary by the Committee. The Committee, consisting of 32 members, met each month at the Freemasons' Tavern and throughout his life the doctor always endeavoured to attend these meetings.

Bright saw the terrible effects of poverty at close hand; the overcrowding, inadequate facilites to maintain any standard of cleanliness and of course the ever-present problem of poor nutrition. Preventing the spread of disease was a task quite beyond the medical profession—curing its worst ravages taxed their knowledge and resources to the limits. The young doctor's respite from the day's work was to undertake more work, this time the writing of his book on Hungary. He also went to Guy's Hospital whenever possible to watch Astley Cooper operating, as there was always something new to see and to learn.

An invitation to the Freemasons' Tavern.

Typhus—the doctor succumbs

The winter of 1817 brought a minor typhus epidemic and the hospital was as overcrowded as the houses from which the sick had been brought. The doctor worked unstintingly and ignored signs within himself indicating the onset of illness. Eventually he succumbed to the disease, so prostrate with fever that he was unable to rise from his bed.

His father consulted with Dr Babington and Dr Laird. He then sent for Dr John Estlin, the family physician and also Dr James Cowles Prichard, Consultant Physician to the Bristol Royal Infirmary, who in contrast to his patient was a keen advocate of blood letting and cupping:

> 'Dr Prichard do appear
> With his attendance and care
> He fills his patient full of sorrow
> You must be bled today and cupped tomorrow'[4]

When Bright was sufficiently recovered, he convalesced in Malvern and at Ham Green, where, still too weak to work, he passed the time chatting to tenants on the estate and renewing his acquaintance with the bustling Bristol quaysides.

As soon as he was fit enough, and despite his mother's protests he returned to London and to his work at what she termed that 'abominable Fever Hospital'.

Dr Laird insisted that he undertake only a light work load. This was doubly fortuitous as he was pressed to complete his book on Hungary. He sought advice and encouragement from the family, sending chapters to his father to read whilst his brother Benjamin edited his work and advised him on the choice of sketches. Benjamin, now a recognised book collector, acted as a liaison between Constable the publisher and his brother. There were data and information to check and often a delay in receiving letters from Hungary containing important details.

Travels in Hungary is published

At last, however, the book was completed and Richard Bright was pleased with the news from Constable that sales were going well. As we already know, the *Edinburgh Review* gave it a favourable write-up, as did a number of other journals and periodicals. Apparently Longmans in London paid him £500 for the first edition.[5]

Apart from all the praise there was some criticism, generally regarding the rather over ambitious range of topics which he covered; politics, agriculture, religion, local customs, and economics. Perhaps it was fortunate that he did not also include the material he had amassed on Hungarian literature.

Family affairs also claimed his attention at this time for his father was involved in what would turn out to be a protracted inheritance dispute relating to the estate of his cousin Richard William Meyler who died intestate. Richard Bright (senior), through his mother Sarah Meyler, inherited all the landed properties both in Wales and in Jamaica. The Welsh branch of the Meyler family who had inherited all their relative's personal wealth, were unsatisfied and laid claim to the properties as well. The law suits continued until 1829 and legal costs swallowed £20,000 of Richard Bright (senior's) personal finances.

A death in the family
A further blow for the young doctor came in July of this year with the news that his Uncle Lowbridge was dying. Perhaps all these things contributed to his continuing lack of vigour and pallor of complexion which prompted Dr Laird to suggest a further sojourn abroad. The idea was certainly appealing for it would afford an opportunity for Richard Bright to pursue his developing obsession with the value of autopsy in providing links between the physical signs of disease manifest in bedside examination and the eventual causes of death. In Paris, Laennec had already blazoned the trail with his close scrutiny of all organs of the body. Now Bright was becoming increasingly interested in the many cases of dropsy which he encountered in the course of his work. He was beginning to conceive of a possible connection between that disease and the function of the kidney but as yet both his knowledge and the facilities available for testing out his theories were too limited. He was, however, hopeful that perhaps Europe could provide some of the information which he lacked.

Further journeyings in Europe
He again visited Leiden then moved on to Gottingen, Frankfurt, Munich, Innsbruck and Freiburg. On the Continent it was the accepted practice to examine every corpse and so the hospitals and *post mortem* rooms yielded an abundance of material for him to study. His particular interest was the kidney, in contrast to the usual pre-occupation with the morbid state of the liver, from time immemorial considered to be the seat of all ill-humours, not to mention disease! Unfortunately, this time we do not have the advantage of Brights's own account of his experiences but apparently he was well received wherever he went and enjoyed hospitality from other members of the medical profession.[7]

In the autumn of 1818 be set aside his studies in order to spend some time in Aix-la-Chapelle with his sister Sally and the Randolphs. They all spent Christmas together at Amorbach and then in the spring of 1819 he set off on his travels once more. He had apparently written to resign his post at the Fever Hospital as he felt his absence from England would be protracted due to ill health; his place was taken by Thomas Addison.

The doctor's journey next took him into Italy via the Simplon Pass. On his return he took another route, visiting the Great Saint Bernard convent and the slopes of Mont Blanc. This time he sought out the alpine flowers rather than geological specimens and employed his artist's palette to capture de Saussure's hut which had been used in the early study of glaciation.[5]

Finally he made his way to Paris and there he met with Laennec, renowned for his work on diseases of the chest; at last he had fulfilled the ambition of his student days to 'see a little practice in Paris'.

He returned to England with his head buzzing with all that he had seen and learned. He was anxious now for better opportunities to develop his interest in pathology. He was also keen to teach, particularly since he felt that he could contribute something to the education of medical students which at that time was still woefully inadequate. There was much work at the dispensary as a result of Dr Bateman's retirement. Family affairs also demanded his attention for Elizabeth Heywood, his sister-in-law, was in very delicate health and Bright did all he could to help out and to support his anxious brother Benjamin: sadly Elizabeth died in the May of 1819.

The winter of 1819-1820 was again severe with the floating harbour at Bristol a sheet of ice. It afforded an excellent opportunity for the skaters to demonstrate their skills, Bright's sister Elizabeth cutting a fine figure as she flew across the frozen surface. At this time there was welcome and cheering family news for Henry Bright who had been put up as a likely Parliamentary candidate, was duly elected. Richard Bright persuaded his brother to take up the cause of both prisoners and seamen in Bristol; he also wished to see a rise in the status of medical students. It is interesting to note that his birthplace, 29 Queen Square, is now a sailors' home.

A move to Bloomsbury Square

It was time to make a change in his domestic arrangements so he took out a lease on Number 14 Bloomsbury Square. The house where he lived is one of the four original houses of that period remaining in the square. It has a much more elegant facade than the house in Savile Row which he later purchased. The frontage is also much more spacious with an open aspect to the central gardens.

A lack of family letters relating to this period means that details about his personal life are scarce. We do, however, know that in March 1820 he was nominated for membership of the Royal Society, but who sponsored him and on what basis he was elected remains a mystery. Sir Humphry Davy had succeeded Sir Joseph Banks as President and he drew in a variety of literary men and artists to broaden the horizons of this hitherto exclusive world of science—

Bloomsbury Square (reproduced with permission of the Royal Pharmaceutical Society).

a move which would clearly have proved attractive to Richard Bright.

Assistant Physician to Guy's Hospital

A most pleasing piece of news came to Bright from Dr Laird who told him that despite the fact that there were no vacancies on the medical staff at Guy's Hospital, he was to be appointed Assistant Physician. There is similarly some confusion surrounding this appointment. Was a new post created especially for him? We do know that his father had written many letters to influential persons and also to the Governors of Guy's Hospital in support of his son's application for a medical appointment. However, as it came about he certainly re-paid several times over the trust placed in him. He resigned his post at the Dispensary but chose to remain on the Committee of the Fever Hospital.

There had been some changes for the better made at Guy's under the Treasurer, Mr Benjamin Harrison. There was better organisation, a higher standard of cleanliness, and notably tougher discipline:

> 'If any patient that is able, neglect or refuse to assist their fellow patients that are weak, or confined to their beds, or to assist when called on by the Sister, Nurse or watch in cleaning the ward, helping down with their stools, fetching coals, or any other necessary business relating to their ward or shall absent themselves at the time they know such business must be done, they shall, for the first offence, forfeit their next day's diet, and for the second offence, and persisting therein, they shall be discharged by the steward'.
>
> Benjamin Harrison.
> Treasurer of Guy's Hospital[7]

In his reforms, and in the extensive additions be made to Guy's, Benjamin Harrison was accused of high-handed arbitrariness but the Minutes of the Court of Commitees do not support the charge—although he was said to be an autocrat Committee Minutes reveal that he always sought the approval of the rest of the committee before making changes.

When Bright returned as Assistant Physican Guy's was still in partnership with St Thomas's to form the United Borough Hospitals; it was 1825 before it was to have its own medical school. The Guy's physicians of this period included Dr James Cholmeley who was said to be a quarrelsome man, hard to work with and above all, jealous of Astley Cooper the surgeon. Of Dr William Bank little was known apart from the fact that he kept a pet canary and drove around in an open carriage; he lived to a ripe old age and was a colleague to Richard Bright for more than twenty years.[8] Dr James Laird who seems to have been such an influential figure in the young doctor's life was also a Guy's physician but as has already been shown he remains, in personal terms, something of a mystery.

The duties of Assistant Physician were not substantially different from those of physician's clerk though now, of course, the young doctor undertook treatment on his own authority. He had particular responsibility for those patients belonging to Dr Laird—this worked well as they were both still much involved with the Public Dispensary and were able to develop a good understanding of the patients' needs. Bright as always 'very fond of seeing' spent much time with the patients observing and recording every detail of the diseases from which they suffered. In the *post-mortem* room he tried to identify and understand the reasons for death; the struggle against disease was completely absorbing to him. He was disappointed that his seniors were little interested in morbid anatomy but, undeterred, he worked alone in 'the dead room' before ward rounds. With his characteristic attention to detail he drew and carefully described each specimen.

Once again he was fixed firmly on the treadmill of his work—such relaxation as he took appears to have been in Dr Babington's home and it was here that he was to meet and fall in love with Martha, the doctor's daughter.

Marriage to Martha
There is no real record of the progress of his relationship with Martha nor when exactly he asked for her hand in marriage. In his own family love seemed to be much in the air—his brother Robert announced his engagement to Caroline Tyndall, his brother Benjamin was to marry for the second time and his parents were celebrating their thirty-ninth wedding anniversary. At last he must have summoned up the courage to propose—Martha accepted and Richard Bright was overwhelmed with joy. Little is known about the wedding or his honeymoon nor indeed about the preparations that were made. We do, however, know from a letter be wrote to his father that Bright made a pre-nuptial visit to Brighton where be enjoyed warm sea baths and found it 'scarcely credible how much good three days' had done both to his 'feelings' and his 'looks'. He was clearly eager to have everything settled, writing that he naturally grew 'every day more impatient' adding that people often congratulated him, believing him to be already married! Dr Babington was a very popular figure in the City of London and the marriage of his daughter drew a large crowd of well-wishers. The wedding took place at St Mary's, Aldermanbury on the 14th August 1822.

With Martha, Bright found 'such happiness as falls to the lot of few men on earth'; sadly this joy was short-lived for Martha died a year later, five days after the birth of their son William.

As a doctor's daughter Martha clearly had a good understanding of the demands made upon her husband by his work at the hospital. She would have had more patience than many with his long absences, late hours and pre-occupation with the diseases that threatened the lives of his patients. As we have seen, prior to his marriage, work filled Richard Bright's life but now he had domestic responsibilities, companionship and the warmth of a close physical relationship. Martha was popular with everyone, especially the Bright family and Richard Bright was similarly much favoured by Dr Babington. Once the student, now the equal who could discuss difficult cases with him, his father-in-law came to depend on him more and more. The two also had shared interests at the meetings of the Geological and Medico-Chirurgical Societies.

The scurge of mercury
Throughout the winter of 1822 Bright was kept extremely busy. There were many interesting cases to hold his attention, in particular one involving mercury poisoning. Whilst working at the Lock hospital he had seen the devasting effect of the use of mercury as a cure for syphilis now he saw the danger it brought to those working with it who absorbed its poisons through the skin. The couple Bright attended made their living by extracting every last globule of mercury from the leather pouches in which it had been imported:[9]
'They were sallow, emaciated, and enfeebled; their gums were ulcerated, and their teeth loose from a long-continued slight degree of salivation; they were unable to stand steadily and could scarcely speak intelligently . . .' reminiscent of the 'Mad Hatters' upon which Lewis Carroll modelled his famous character. They lived in appalling conditions in one filthy room where the whole atmosphere was polluted with quicksilver:
'. . . all the implements, the tables, and the man's hands were discoloured by the particles of the metallic oxide and the air of the room was close and unwholesome. Of course no remedies could be of any avail while they persisted in breathing this polluted atmosphere.'
They were of course too poor to pay the fees for hospitalisation and as a result the wife did not survive. The doctor himself apparently paid the fee for the husband who was nursed back to good health and subsequently went to work as an agricultural labourer.
Of course these rather hazardous means of earning a livelihood were not at all unusual in late Georgian or even Victorian England, as is only too readily revealed by a dip into Mayhew's chronicles. One that seemed particularly unpleasant and likely to be injurious

Boy crossing-sweepers.

to health was that of the 'pure' collectors who gathered dog excrement for use in the tanning trade.

This was indeed a world where all was 'an anxious straining to maintain life' from the rat-catchers to the crossing sweepers, costermen, chimney sweeps and the tiny girl who sold water cress in Farringdon market. We can only imagine how such scenes of hardship and misery must have touched the heart of the young doctor and filled him with a sense of impotence but at the same time a determination to alleviate the suffering as best he could.

A year of personal tragedy

It was a year of sad losses for Richard Bright—he learned of the death in Yorkshire of his tutor and friend Dr Bateman and his old chemistry teacher Alexander Marcet, who had been suffering from angina, died the same week. In happy contrast the young couple discovered that Martha was pregnant. They looked forward eagerly to the birth of their first child, planning that a boy would be named William Richard after his two grandfathers. On 30th December, 1823 their son William Richard was born—five days later Richard Bright's beloved Martha was dead. She was buried in the crypt of St Mary's Church where 16 months previously she had been the happy bride.

A vital part of Bright's world was shattered, his year of joy turned to no more than a collection of vivid memories that haunted him night and day; it was only in the incessant demands of his professional life that he was able to find some measure of forgetfulness.

Chapter 8

Dr Richard Bright of Guy's—Physicians Challenge Surgeons' Supremacy

> There Physic fills the space and far around,
> Pile above pile her learned works abound;
> Glorious their aim—to ease the labouring heart;
> To ward with death, and stop his flying dart.
>
> *George Crabbe*

In the changing world of the post Napoleonic wars came a growth of new ideas in religion, agriculture, industry and education. Training for the professions and adequate qualifications became more important and highly valued. Sadly, however, the Royal College of Physicians and the Royal College of Surgeons continued to live in the past.

The Royal College of Physicians, born of the English Renaissance recruited its members almost entirely from Oxford and Cambridge and did precious little for medical education. By as late as 1834 there were only 113 fellows and 274 licentiates of the College. The Royal College of Surgeons founded in 1800 had by the same year 200 fellows and 8,000 licentiates most of these apothecaries who had taken the college examinations.

The Colleges were not ignorant of the causes of disease, i.e. poverty, overcrowding and poor sanitation but they felt that addressing these issues was very much the duty of the dispensaries and the apothecaries; they appeared to see themselves as above involvement in socio-political issues and to be content to carry out their professional duties as if untouched by time and progress.[1]

Some twenty years earlier Thomas Beddoes had already recognised the social nature of disease and its place as an indicator of pathological trends in the body politic. As his biographer, Roy Porter suggests, Beddoes considered disease to be:

'Wealth-specific, class-specific, gender-specific, mores-specific. Its incidence was an index of certain social realities; it spoke about absolute and relative distribution of plenty and poverty, of power and oppression, of education and ignorance, succour and neglect.'

It therefore followed that medical techniques and, indeed, medical men, would have the power to further 'the causes of popular rights and citizenship, of liberty, equality and fraternity'.[2]

In contrast to the conservatism of the older generation, young men of the Edinburgh School such as Bright, Addison, Davy, Roget and Bostock, whilst they were not necessarily motivated by socio-political considerations, were eager to make changes and improvements. They realised that scientific thoughts and methods were the weapons which must be employed if man was to control disease or, indeed, come to understand it. These were the challenges which would help Bright to overcome the desperate sense of loss he experienced after Martha's death. A death which family and friends feared would cause him to founder and lose direction became instead the spur which urged him on to even greater success in his professional life. His domestic arrangements were eased by the arrival of his sister Sally, newly returned from Germany. She stayed long periods at Bloomsbury Square helping to care for young William.

The launch of *The Lancet* exposes medical malpractice
Naturally Bright also spent much time with his father-in-law for Dr Babington's grief was no less acute than his own. He also became a member of the newly formed Athenaeum club—'brainchild' of the historian John Wilson Croker. It provided a meeting place for artists and literary men and to be accepted as one of its forty strong membership afforded one a certain kudos. Richard Bright was proposed by Humphry Davy and seconded by the founder.

Support for a more scientific approach to the new wave ideas in medicine came indirectly with the publication of the new journal *The Lancet*. Thomas Wakley the editor, used its first number to criticise in abusive terms the current malpractices of the medical profession. For his part, Bright thought the academic content of medical education to be of a suitably high standard. If there was a problem it lay in the lack of practical experience gained by the students, and on the irregularity in the standard required by examiners.

Bright recognised this need for students to have greater practical experience. Only too often they were 'short changed' by their tutors who were cavalier in their behaviour, uncommunicative about their patients and the prescribed treatment, and certainly unreliable in undertaking their professional duties—patients awaiting the surgeon's knife were often abandoned because of the overpowering stench emanating from their bodies!

Full Physician to Guy's
A further fortuitous event in terms of career progress came for Bright when, on Dr Lairds's retirement due to ill health, he was appointed Full Physician to Guy's Hospital. At a subsequent after-dinner anniversary speech Bright expressed his feelings on the appointment:

'To hold the situation of Physician to Guy's Hospital is to be placed at the pinnacle of the profession'.[3]

Bust of Richard Bright, by Behnes.

Now an opportunity presented itself for the young doctor to undertake the teaching of practical medicine. Dr Babington resigned his lectureship at about the same time as Dr Laird and Dr Cholmeley suggested to Bright that he take Dr Babington's place and go into partnership with him as joint morning lecturer.

Dr Cholmeley offered the partnership for the fee of £700.00-£500.00 more than he had paid Dr Curry when he himself had purchased the lectureship. The selling of lectureships was disapproved of by Mr Harrison, The Treasurer, who considered Dr Cholmeley to be making 'an unwarrantable and unjustifiable demand' but at length he reluctantly conceded on condition that 'Dr Bright should take all the risk of loss upon himself and stipulate not again to dispose of the lectures'.

Mr Harrison also had to advance the sum of £300.00 to allow Dr Addison to purchase from Dr Bank, Dr Curry's evening share of lectures which he had been offered. Dr Bank was 'availing himself

of a right which he now considered established' he was unwilling
to provide Dr Addison with the lecturer's notes until he received
the £300.00. Mr Harrison then put a stop to this trade in lectureships
and in future lecturers were nominated and appointed by him.[4]

Innovative ideas in diagnosis of disease

Richard Bright lectured on Mondays, Wednesdays and Fridays. He
broke with the old tradition for he involved his students in all practical
aspects of the profession—they were to see and to do, rather than
to trail dutifully along behind whilst the physician strode majestically
past the beds of the unfortunate and certainly anxious patients.

The undressing of patients and the attempt by palpation to discover
the exact location of an organ, a gland or severe pain—these things
were strange and previously unheard of, but Bright employed these
innovative techniques. He used percussion, he also used a
stethoscope, the new 'toy' which Dr Cholmeley had referred to as
a 'capital bouquet holder'. He also encouraged his students to take
specimens from the patients—these were to be carefully studied,
analysed and described. We know, of course, that it was Bright who
so carefully examined all urine samples for albumen, employing only
a single candle and spoon for his investigation:

> 'One of the most ready means of detecting albumen is the
> application of heat by taking a small quantity of urine on a spoon
> and holding it over a candle.'[5]

His views on blood letting were similarly enlightened. He believed
in a judicious and limited recourse to such treatment. For example
in the case of continued fever:

> 'If it occurs early and in young persons of good constitution a
> moderate bloodletting may occasionally be beneficial; but if
> general bloodletting to any considerable extent be an ambiguous
> remedy, even in idiopathic bronchitis, it is a practice which
> requires much more scrupulous caution in fever'.[6]

His day-to-day work in the hospital sadly provided him with access
to the 'largest repository of disease in the metropolis', a plethora
of material for his detailed study of disease; he observed minutely,
he made copious notes on all that he saw, he drew with exactitude
examples of *post mortem* specimens. These long hours of tireless work
were to form the basis of his *magnum opus* the *Reports of Medical
cases selected with a view of illustrating the symptoms and cure of
diseases with a reference to Morbid Anatomy.*

The dissolution of the Borough Hospitals

In the year after his appointment as Full Physician at Guy's certain
events that occurred hastened the dissolution of the partnership of

Guy's and St Thomas's as the United Borough Hospitals. It was the surprising refusal of St Thomas's to agree to Sir Astley Cooper's wishes regarding the appointment of his successor in the anatomical lectureship which acted as a catalyst in the affair.

In January 1825, deciding that the time had come for him to retire, Sir Astley Cooper confidently proposed that his young nephew Bransby Cooper should lecture in his place. The Treasurer of St Thomas's refused and appointed John Flint instead. Sir Astley tried to withdraw his resignation but this too was refused and so he agreed to Mr Harrison's suggestion that a separate Medical School should be founded at Guy's. Unfortunately there was also a negative response to Sir Astley Cooper's request to remove one half of the vast museum collection of specimens which he had personally provided:

> 'Thus on 13th April 1825 The Court of Committees at Guy's resolved:
> 'that an Anatomical Theatre, Museum, Dissecting Room and other requisite offices be built on the vacant freehold ground in Maze Pond belonging to this hospital under the direction and at the direction of the Treasurer and that he be authorized to borrow such a sum of money as may be requisite beyond that which this hospital can conveniently supply'.[4]

Guy's was determined that teaching at the hospital should not be halted for lack of accommodation and the building went on apace so that by October 1825, only six months after the plans of the new school had been conceived, it was available for use. Miraculously too, the shelves of the museum were filled with specimens—Sir Astley Cooper and his assistants worked hard to augment the small existing collection until it rivalled that which had been retained at St Thomas's.

The great triumvirate: Bright, Addison and Hodgkin

The hospital was entering a new era although the idea that it should be a centre for research was not entirely innovative for in 1754 Joseph Warner, Surgeon to Guy's had written:

> 'A hospital is not only an instrument of relief to the distressed who are immediately helped there, but also a means of helping others, by furnishing such principles and practice as may improve the art of Surgery, and thus render the benefit more general."

However, it is from the time of that great triumvirate of Bright, Addison and Hodgkin that we have the concept of the Medical School as being not only a place of education for students but also a centre for research. And in those early days of Guy's Medical School we would probably agree with H C Cameron that:

'If Bright and Addison put their whole souls into their task of teaching and research, they looked on their reward not in terms of money but of the honour and reputation thereby brought to the school'.[4]

Thomas Addison (1793-1860) who as we have already seen had, like Bright, studied in Edinburgh was elected Assistant Physician to Guy's in 1824, four years after Bright. Outwardly, a less charismatic figure than his colleague, Addison was a sensitive, solitary man. He recorded a diseased condition of the suprarenal capsules and we are led to believe that real recognition of his work, similarly to that of Richard Bright, first came from the French with Trousseau according the eponym *Maladie d'Addison*. He also described pernicious anaemia.

Addison's needs were modest and were easily satisfied with his income from the Medical School. He immersed himself in research work, teaching and the general concerns of the hospital and medical school. If he won little recognition or acclaim in his life time he at least shared with Astley Cooper the honour of receiving from the General Court a tribute of gratitude when in 1860, due to his ill-health the Hospital was sadly 'deprived of [his] valuable services'; he was at this time appointed Consulting Physician to the Hospital. This should not be confused with our modern use of the term 'Consultant Physician' which would be equivalent to a Full Physician in the mid 1800s.

It is interesting to note that Thomas Wakley in the general tone of invective levelled at Guy's descibed Addison as 'a bundle of loquacity' and Bright as 'a heavy, conceited person' and seemingly it was only after his death that Wakley conceded the latter's outstanding contribution to medical science.

The third member of the great triumvirate was Thomas Hodgkin (1778-1866) who sadly never achieved a place on the Guy's Medical Staff. Again, like Richard Bright and Addison he had studied in Edinburgh; he had also spent a considerable amount of time on the Continent where he learned to speak both French and Italian.

One of the works at Guy's for which Hodgkin will be particularly remembered will be that undertaken in his capacity as Curator of the Museum and Demonstrator of Morbid Anatomy. He made a fine catalogue of the early specimens located in the museum. The 'Green Inspection Books' in his handwriting record *post mortem* examinations and he also introduced a systematic plan for the arrangement of the museum to illustrate the occurrence of disease in different organs and tissues of the body. His original contributions to the Medico-Chirurgical Society included that relating to 'a peculiar enlargement of the lymphatic glands and spleen' which although this was many years later, won him, on the proposal of Sir Samuel Wilks, eponymous recognition.

It was probably Hodgkin's radical and progressive views which earned him the label 'unreliable' and as a consequence caused his failure as candidate for the Assistant Physicianship at the time of Cholmeley's death and Addison's promotion to Full Physician. Rumour had it that the ventures in which he was involved did not win the approval of that influential figure, Mr Benjamin Harrison. Whatever the reasons Hodgkin was rejected and the affable, popular Benjamin Babington appointed in his place. It is sad that the promise of his early work did not blossom more fully—for a short time he transferred to St Thomas's where he lectured on pathology, but this connection was similarly unsuccessful. This lack of advancement in his professional life seems to have been brought about through a combination of factors—certain character traits and also a perverse inability to accept success; an example of this is shown in the difficulty he experienced in asking an adequate fee for his services, which led to financial difficulties. In later life Hodgkin was to travel extensively in the East; he died at Jaffa in 1866.

Thomas Wakley attacks nepotism

As we have already noted the school suffered in its early days from abusive and ill-informed attacks by *The Lancet* under the editorship of Thomas Wakley. One practice which came in for particular criticism was the method by which the staff of the London Teaching Hospitals were appointed. Wakley found nepotism to be rife and he believed that incompetent persons were appointed merely on the basis of their relationship to current incumbents of the posts. One of the main targets for his invective was Astley Cooper the attack being made directly on his nephew Bransby Cooper. Wakley witnessed a lithotomy operation performed by him in which he appeared to be totally incompetent and bungling. The unfortunate patient was bound down for 50 minutes whilst the stone was gouged from the bladder; sadly he perished some 29 hours later.[4]

Although Bransby Cooper brought a successful libel case against *The Lancet* supported fully by his friends, his reputation was permanently damaged. For a long time after the trial the journal attacked Guy's whenever possible and advised prospective students to attend St Thomas's instead, where the teachers were far superior.

Marriage to Elizabeth Follett

With the opening of the new Medical School Richard Bright's name was entered for the first time in the prospective as a full lecturer in the theory and practice of medicine. He was set firmly on course for the major part of his working life in medicine, for his association with Guy's continued until his retirement from the hospital in 1844. During the years 1825-1827 whilst he worked on the research and writing up of cases for the first volume of *The Medical Reports* he

Elizabeth Follett—second wife to Dr Richard Bright.

found some relaxation and a developing romance with a childhood friend, Elizabeth Follett, whom he married in 1826.

Elizabeth was one of eight children, her father Benjamin Follett, a retired army captain was in business as a ship's chandler and timber merchant, her mother Ann Webb was of Irish descent. The family home was at Topsham in Devon and it seems likely that it was on a visit here that Richard Bright proposed to Elizabeth and she accepted. In her biography of her great-great uncle, Miss Pamela Bright provides a glimpse of a romantic side to the doctor's character as he and Elizabeth explore the channel of the Exe, negotiating the narrow water-side path known as the 'Goat's walk':

'Exploring with him was a wonderful experience. He was always stopping to pick up a flower, to identify the sound coming from a bush or to scoop up the clay where the river Clyst met the solid wall of the old Bridge Inn'[7]

The wedding took place in the old church of St Marguerite at Topsham in July 1826. As with his marriage to Martha we have no surviving details of the ceremony nor the honeymoon.

Eventually they returned to the house at Bloomsbury Square and Eliza was tactful in her attempts to maintain all the many associations that preserved for Richard Bright the precious months of his life with Martha. Eliza had some difficulties to overcome; the servants were at first unwelcoming and uncooperative, particularly Jones, the valet who, since Martha's death, had assumed many of her duties.

Fortunately, Eliza was quick to form a warm, loving relationship with young William. One can imagine how hard it must have been for Bright's sister Sally to give up the role of surrogate mother which she had undertaken since Martha's death; her brother's second marriage certainly brought changes requiring tact and diplomacy on all sides. Bright was a considerate husband and father and Eliza a loving, companionable wife though, not coming from a medical family, she lacked Martha's understanding of the demands made upon her husband's time.

Life in London was quite a contrast to the quiet peace of Topsham and links with home in the form of visits from her brothers Spencer and Robert were eagerly anticipated. Eliza's favourite brother was Webb Follett later appointed Attorney-General under Peel's second administration. Webb was never physically strong and this gave Eliza much cause for anxiety throughout a large part of her married life, and up until his death in 1845. One certain advantage that Richard Bright found in marriage was that the old maxim 'two can live as cheaply as one' seemed to have some truth in it for having anticipated an increase in expenditure he was delighted to find that living, in fact, cost less with Eliza managing household matters. This must have been a great relief because, as we know, he abhorred anything to do with accounts!

On September 15th 1826, however, he wrote to his father with details of his financial situation which, as a result of certain heavy expenditure over the past year was not yet as healthy as he could have wished:

'My dear Father,
I have made what as far as I can understand is the correct statement of my affairs. I am very sorry to think that it is less prosperous than on former occasions however considering the varied and great expenses of the past year I trust a very few

William Webb Follett—brother to Elizabeth Follett.

months will put it all back into its wholesome train—two or three of the items of outgoing have been peculiarly heavy in the last year—it is within that period that I have paid for the carriage £240 . . .'[8]

The death of Sarah Bright
Unfortunately the happiness of the first year of their marriage was marred by the increasing ill-health of Sarah, Bright's mother. In December of 1825 Richard Bright (senior) wrote telling his son of his mother's continuing decline:

'My dear Richard,
'I was much pleased when I found by a letter from Sally to your mother that you had determined to spend your Christmas day with us—I think you suggested to Estlin the possible advantage that might arise from a consultation of Carnock and Pritchard on your mother's case—will it not be a good opportunity during your short visit with us. Without your being present with them it would by no means be satisfactory to me, or pleasant to your mother—but I think it ought to take place and not be deferred later. She has been very indifferent all this week past—she says herself she grows much weaker and I think is more out of spirits.'[8]

By March of the following year Richard Bright was to join his brothers in the unhappy task of carrying his mother to her last resting place in the family vault in Brunswick Square, Bristol.

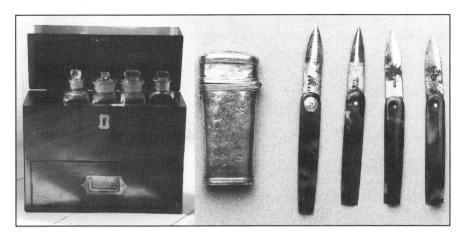

Bright's medicine box and silver instrument case containing lancets.

A further sadness lay in store for in May the doctor and Eliza lost their first child. Ultimately, though, their marriage was to be blessed with seven children, six surviving to adulthood: Anna (1828-1832), Follett (1831-1851), Revd James Franck (1832-1920), Emily (1835-1896), Clara (1837-1913), Henry Eustace (1838-1875), George Charles (1840-1922).

These were formative years in Bright's career and the hospital absorbed much of his time, a fact which Eliza often found hard to bear. Of necessity she would go alone with the children to visit her family in Topsham or the relatives at Ham Green or even on visits to seaside resorts. She wrote sometimes twice daily to her husband, speaking of her reliance on him, her needs, her supposed ill-health:

'My dearest Husband,
'I think I get a little better; I do not sleep so well at night as is my custom, I am very restless, I do not stay awake long at a time but do not feel refreshed in the morning . . .'

She gave him endless commissions to be fulfilled—lists of items to be purchased which were burdensome since they often took him far out of his way—yet at the same time she worried about his health and the demands that his profession laid upon him such as having to rise from his sick bed to attend the Brunels, father and son who had suffered internal injuries whilst working on the construction of the Thames tunnel.

We might ask ourselves whether Eliza provided Richard Bright with the kind of support in his work that he surely at heart desired? Certainly the rather fussy demands, the constant pleas to have him always by her side would appear less than supportive and yet we are led to believe that the marriage was successful. Eliza tried, at times unsuccessfully, to enter his world. She questioned him about his work yet the gulf must inevitably have been wide—and we must remember that the expectations of that time would have applauded a woman competent in the running of a successful household rather than one who sought to involve herself in a man's world. Again it is sad that we have no record in the form of personal diaries recording Bright's feelings or reflections regarding his day-to-day routine and it is only through the many surviving letters written by Eliza that a picture emerges of a busy life in medicine as he battled not only to understand the processes of disease but also to cope with a domestic life that was equally demanding.

The house in Bloomsbury Square was soon outgrown and in 1831 the family moved to Number 11 Savile Row where Richard Bright was to live for the rest of his life. He was hard at work on the second volume of his book *Reports of Medical Cases*—recognition both national and international was soon to reward his efforts.

Chapter 9

The Medical Writings—
A Legacy of his Life's Work

'What a piece of work is man! How noble in reason!
How infinite in faculty! In form, in moving, how express
and admirable . . . The paragon of animals!'
William Shakespeare

On medical matters Richard Bright was an accomplished and prolific writer; his most productive years, measured in literary output alone, corresponded to his time while on the staff of Guy's Hospital, from 1825, five years after his appointment as an Associate Physician, until 1843 when he retired from hospital practice and clinical research. Therefore his most important and memorable clinical writings spanned a period of only 18 years and during this time he produced what must be regarded as his *magnum opus*: the two volumes of *Reports on Medical Cases selected with a view of illustrating Disease with a reference to Morbid Anatomy* published in 1827 and 1831 and hereafter known as *The Medical Reports*.[1,2] The year 1827, when the first of his writings on kidney disease appeared in Volume 1 of *The Medical Reports*, became, in retrospect, his *annus mirabilis* as this brought him international acclaim and within 10 years the eponymous recognition of Bright's Disease. The zenith of his professional writing career, however, probably came a little later, from 1835 onwards when he became a regular and voluminous contributor to the medical journals, transactions and proceedings of the day and, of course, from 1836 to the *Guy's Hospital Reports*. His subject material touched on all the major and often incomprehensible clinical problems of these disease-ridden times. As Sir Robert Christison, the great Scottish physician and friend of Richard Bright said, 'The causes of most chronic diseases of the great viscera are enveloped in obscurity.'[3] Few systems escaped his attention but the main thrust of his work was directed towards the triad of dropsy and coagulable urine, indicating the presence of albumen or protein, associated with disease of the kidney at *post mortem*. He wrote one volume of a medical textbook in 1839 with Dr Thomas Addison as co-author but the second volume did not appear. Quantitively perhaps he was not in the same class as Dr Thomas Beddoes, whose wide ranging and often philosophical interests led to a vast literary output on all of the burning issues of the time, because, apart from his travelogues, Bright confined

REPORTS

OF

MEDICAL CASES,

SELECTED

WITH A VIEW OF ILLUSTRATING

THE SYMPTOMS AND CURE OF DISEASES

BY A REFERENCE TO

MORBID ANATOMY.

BY RICHARD BRIGHT, M.D. F.R.S. &c.

LECTURER ON THE PRACTICE OF MEDICINE,

AND ONE OF THE PHYSICIANS TO

GUY'S HOSPITAL.

LONDON:

PRINTED BY RICHARD TAYLOR, RED LION COURT, FLEET STREET.

PUBLISHED BY LONGMAN, REES, ORME, BROWN, AND GREEN.

1827.

Frontispiece of Medical Reports, *Volume 1.*

his writing almost entirely to medical topics. Nevertheless, writing did appear to come easily to him; as we know in addition to his book on *Travels in Hungary* he had written the biological sections in Sir George Mackenzie's *Travels in Iceland* in 1811 while still a medical student and also his MD thesis two years later in 1813. It is said that, 'He wrote as no man had written before and as all who followed him were to attempt to write.'[4] Fine prose it may well have been but to the modern day scholar the archaic Victorian style can make for heavy reading with its tautological excesses and the semantic differences inherent to another century.

He proceeded to his MD on 13 September, 1813; interestingly the thesis for his doctorate was composed in Latin and entitled *De Erisipilate Contagiosa* and was dedicated to Dr Robert Lovell, Physician to the Bristol Royal Infirmary and the Brights' family doctor, with the inscription from Horace *'Foenum habet in cornu longe fuge'* on the title page.[5] Dr Thayer in the Bright Oration mentions this as a 'happily chosen motto' without translating or enlarging upon it; he assumed that in 1927 the average physician would be well-versed in the Classics and would have little trouble in understanding the significance of the words.[6] In the intervening years, however, the use of Latin in medical studies has declined, so, with apologies to the more erudite of our readers, one interpretation of the message is: 'Avoid the animal with hay on its hoof' and from this loose translation we assume the advice to be 'Erysipelas is contagious so the wise physician will avoid placing his patient in a bed next to one already infected.'

Bright frequently deferred to his father and often depended on him to some extent, for advice on scientific matters, even those of a more medical nature. Earlier he had written to ask permission to dedicate his doctoral thesis to his father and was keen to enlist his help in collecting accounts of patients with erysipelas possibly from doctor friends in Bristol and Bath. In the thesis he compares erysipelas with puerperal fever and recommendations are made about cleanliness in the wards and washing of hands. So Bright was clearly aware of the measures designed to reduce the spread of contagious diseases several years before the famous work of Semmelweiss on puerperal fever, which was transmitted from fatal cases in the *post mortem* room to healthy patients in the ward by the unwashed hands of medical students, sadly ignorant of the silent danger of bacterial spread. Bacteriology, as a subject did not become established properly until the time of Louis Pasteur in the 1860s.

During that autumn graduation at Edinburgh University in 1813, Richard Bright was one of four Englishmen among twenty-three candidates defending their theses for the Degree of Doctor of Medicine and who wrote 'Anglus' on the frontispiece. The young Englishmen seemed to have integrated well into the student life of Edinburgh without encountering much anti-Sassenach prejudice. This is surprising and might not have been expected as memories are long and, following Bonnie Prince Charlie's uprising in 1745, many of the staff of the Royal College of Physicians of Edinburgh, including the President, had been imprisoned for their Jacobite sympathies. Of the other three 'Angli' only John Conquest received any future recognition; as one of the early man-midwives he wrote

Outlines of Midwifery and a handbook for nursing mothers; later, in 1825, he was appointed Lecturer in Obstetrics at St Bartholomew's Hospital. It was exactly at this time, twelve years after they had been students together, that Richard Bright was embarking on what was to become his epoch making work on the kidney, in the hospital which provided the atmosphere to nurture his undeniable talent.

Over 160 years later today's modern visitors who walk past the statue of the founder of Guy's in the hospital forecourt and on through the cloisters to the Gordon Museum must surely be imbued with something of the spirit of scientific discovery which dominated that heroic period of Victorian medicine. Here, in the awesome silence of a room which sets before us so many reminders of man's mortality, the solemn, impressive portraits of Guy's most famous triumvirate, Bright, Addison and Hodgkin guard the tiered rows of specimens which they were so instrumental in gathering. This sense of the past, of industry and selfless dedication, is further accentuated as one pauses to gaze at the bookshelves of the Wills' Library lined with leather-bound volumes of Guy's Hospital Reports in which Bright and his colleagues recorded so much of their original work. Had he visited the hospital today the Doctor might not have approved of the Tower Block, nor the frenetic commercial activities of this 1990s flagship of the National Health Service reforms. On the other hand, he could not help but be impressed by the care that has been taken to preserve the hospital's great heritage: Keats' House, the museum and library and the various paintings, statues, plaques and busts which commemorate the deeds and lives of the famous 'Guy's Men' of his era, dominated, as it was then, by the omnipresence of that indomitable surgeon, Sir Astley Cooper.

In the 19th century, an age of burgeoning scientific advances, and within a galaxy of talented medical contemporaries, how did Bright take his place as one of the foremost physicians of that time and from the results of his painstaking research, become known as the 'Father of Renal Medicine' and earn the honour of an eponymous title for the disease he described? One need not look too far for the answers to these questions: the time was ripe for discovery, the air was redolent with a feeling of anticipation that medical knowledge was on the brink of rapid progress and Richard Bright, truly a 'man of his time' was uniquely placed not only with his clinical skills but with his oratory and literary ability to grasp the opportunity to communicate to the 'brave new world' of science, the results of his remarkable work.

Medicine, at this time, was emerging from a dark period of ignorance, when a 'snap diagnosis' from the end of the bed was considered not only laudable but the accepted norm, into an ordered and disciplined art of careful history-taking complemented by a full and thorough examination. Some 40 years earlier Dr

Thomas Beddoes had already advocated this approach and Sir William Blizard, Surgeon to the London Hospital was the first to encourage students to 'walk the wards' and visit the patients.

The strong ties between Leiden and Edinburgh had further encouraged this essentially clinico-pathological approach engendered by the great Dutch physician, Herman Boerhaave, known as the 'Teacher of all Europe' and the 'Dutch Hippocrates'. As a medical student at Edinburgh University, Bright would have been exposed to this school of thought.

The family motto *Post Tenebras Lucem*—out of darkness into light—would seem fairly appropriate as it has been said that Bright emerged from the Cumaean Darkness. However, it is unlikely that 'working the oracle' or divine intervention played any part in his philosophy of dedicated fact-finding: it would have been totally alien to his nature. Indeed he arrived on a scene where medical enlightenment was already dawning, largely as a result of the bloodless revolution brought about by better clinical practice in the wards and a more aggressive policy of obtaining *post mortem* material for examination. He became a tenacious exponent of the pursuit of necropsy material when, in the absence of refrigeration, *post mortem* examination had to be conducted expeditiously before putrefaction set in. It would perhaps be apposite to apply to the situation that well-worn cliche, 'the right man, in the right place, at the right time'. His qualifications to undertake the task that lay before him were unimpeachable: he had inherited the Brights' business-like approach to life plus a strong work ethic instilled in him by a father whose own interest had a highly developed scientific bent and also by his various tutors at school, university and hospital. No doubt the Scottish trait for hard work had been impressed on him by most of his Edinburgh faculty professors and medical lecturers: as Louis Pasteur said 'Chance favours the prepared mind.'

He was known, like most artists, to have a great eye for detail and by his own admission in a letter to his father, already mentioned, he wrote, 'The physician contents himself with hypothesis and conjecture. For my own part, I am very fond of seeing'. He obviously felt that many physicians of the time, like the Greeks, did too much thinking and not enough actual work. His biographer in the Munk Rolls of the Royal College of Physicians recorded that 'Upon each and all of the varied subjects treated in his work, Dr Bright showed the most sagacious observation, untiring industry and wonderful powers of investigating truth, the end and aim of all his work'.[7] He was said to have naturally clear judgement, a gift of great industry and a vigorous intellect: in Dr Thayer's 'Bright Memorial Oration' mention is made of 'steadfastness of purpose' and 'conscientiousness' —these characteristics added to his skill with the pen, paintbrush and scalpel made him the ideal candidate for the key position of 'the right man'. Even by Victorian standards he seems to have been a bit of a 'workaholic'.

Dr Thomas Hodgkin. (Courtesy of Guy's Hospital.)

Frequent mention is made of the 'six hours' that Richard Bright spent at Guy's each day which does not, by present day standards, seem excessive but one must remember that this represented only his clinical input and one suspects that he modelled his day very much on that of his old and much admired friend, Sir Astley Cooper, who set a very daunting pace with an extremely exacting time-table. We are told that

> 'He rose at six, dissected until eight, light breakfasted on two hot rolls and tea, saw poor patients until nine, attended to his regular consulting practice until one when he would drive rapidly to Guy's Hospital to visit the wards. At two he lectured in anatomy at St Thomas's Hospital, after which he went through the dissecting

rooms with students and visited or operated on private patients until seven. He would then bolt his dinner, snatch forty winks of sleep and start out again for a possible clinical lecture with another round of visits until midnight, dictating whatever he wrote while in his carriage'.[8]

The physician's life may have been a little less arduous, surgeons today certainly like to think so!

Professor Robert Kark in a Richard Bright memorial lecture delivered in Bristol in 1981 on the subject of 'Richard Bright and Richard Bright the Lesser'[9] suggested in his introduction that if it were possible to go back in time most of the audience would like to spend a day accompanying the Doctor on his rounds; one suspects that few of us would have stood the pace! Selwyn Taylor, in his book on the life of Robert Graves published in this present Eponymists Series was tempted to draw an analogy between the great Irish physician and Richard Bright but rather unfairly suggested that the latter, by spending so much time on his work, might also have neglected his family in pursuit of self-agrandissement: on the contrary, and unlike Graves, as his letters to his wife and children have shown, he was a caring husband and a devoted father who tried desperately to strike a balance between the conflicting demands of professional and domestic life.[10]

It was at Guy's Hospital that another of Bright's attributes was nurtured. His ability to work closely with his consultant peers meant that in response to this rapport they were only too willing to refer to him most of their dropsical patients.

In addition he gained the admiration, loyalty and support of his students, young friends and junior colleagues; he engendered in his team an 'esprit de corp' and was probably the first Guy's consultant to attract bright young men around him with whom he freely collaborated in his research. This was a policy that was to be followed some years later in Paris by the famous French renal physician, Dr Pierre Rayer.

The best known of Bright's team of assistants were Drs Bostock,[11] Barlow,[12] Rees[13] Toynbee,[14] and the long-suffering medical student Mr Tweedie and they were joined later by the young Dr Benjamin Babington[15] and Dr George Robinson.[16] Dr George Johnson although not a member of the team was very much a follower of the Bright School.[17] He was unstinting in praise for his staff, often mentioning them in the introductions or prefaces to his publications. He continued to encourage them after his retirement as they, in turn, added to the research initiated by him and he watched their progress with great enthusiasm. His delight and pride were undisguised as in turn most of them became distinguished members of the profession which was so dear to him.

There is no doubt then, that the general mores of Guy's provided the ideal media for Richard Bright, surrounded as he was by like-minded

Dr John Bostock. (Courtesy of Surgeon General's Library, Washington. Engraving from portrait by J Partridge.)

investigators of the calibre of Addison and Hodgkin—the 'right place' then, was the hospital that was, in those days, known as 'the largest repository of disease in the Metropolis'. Furthermore in 1820 when Richard Bright was appointed to the hospital as an Assistant Physician one could also say 'the time was right' as the idea of correlating clinical features with *post mortem* findings was already well-established. The two most outstanding protagonists of the principle were Giovanni Morgagni from Padua and Matthew Baillie, nephew of the famous anatomist and surgeon, William Hunter. Morgagni's book *De Sedibus et Causis Moriborum* had been translated into English in 1769 and contained early reports of, amongst other things, acute yellow atrophy of the liver and

Dr Matthew Baillie. (Portrait by Mr Hoffner, RA.[10])

heart-block (Stokes-Adams disease), both of which were later described by Bright.[18]

Baillie's *Morbid Anatomy* was published in 1793 and was in its third edition by 1808 when young Richard Bright was a medical student in Edinburgh—the work included many original descriptions and outlined the difference between renal cysts and hydatids, but interestingly the small contracted kidney of chronic nephritis was only rarely reported.[19] Many clinico-pathological connections vaguely suggested and hinted at by previous workers were waiting to be confirmed as definitive diseases including that of Bright's. Sir Charles Sherrington in his work on Jean Fernel said that 'Essential to a great discoverer in any field of nature would seem to be an intuitive flair for raising the right question' but continued with the caveat that 'To ask something which the time is not yet ripe to answer is of small avail.'[20]

Bright seemed to have possessed the flair, posed the right questions and had impeccable timing as indeed nephritis, which became his disease, was ripe for discovery. Successively down the years, the bricks had been built into the wall of research and finally all that remained to be added were the keystones. This applied particularly to the kidney which, potentially, as an organ for investigation was 'coming of age' and the latter half of the 18th century and the first half of the 19th century saw a period of intense interest in its structure and function both in health and disease. It was as if the kidneys had remained hidden from view lurking, but often unnoticed, in the shadowy confines or recesses of the retroperitoneal space, largely ignored at *post mortem*. Then quite suddenly medical investigators became aware of and orientated towards the kidney; research in that field accelerated and attracted many of the brightest doctors to the ranks, including some who later became better known in other medical spheres e.g. Robert Graves and William Gull who described thyrotoxicosis and myxoedema respectively and Sir William Bowman who, after earning the title of 'Father of the Kidney' for his work on the structure of the glomerulus, became one of the founders of modern ophthalmology.[21]

Indeed, the fact that Richard Bright is remembered for his seminal work on renal disease may be incidental as the vast proportion of his work on other medical subjects testifies.[22] Few systems escaped his attention and one cannot be other than impressed that his master plan was to correlate the signs and symptoms of a given disease to the underlying pathology seen at *post mortem* examination. In his own words:

> 'The work which I now commence will not, in theory at least, be thoroughly completed until every disease which influences the natural structure or originates in its derangement has been connected with the corresponding organic lesion.'

Sir Robert Platt's axiom 'Truly the study of the kidney is not a narrow specialty' partly explains Bright's wide ranging interest in so many systems of the body. Furthermore, one can follow the logic of his researches and explain the pattern and natural progression of his work as it moved from the kidney to one topic after another. The main thrust was directed towards the enigma of dropsy, hitherto thought of as either the result of heart or liver disease or even idiopathic—as a spontaneous occurrence. We shall see that these beliefs were already being questioned by, amongst others, the inspiring works on the kidney by William Wells[23] and John Blackall[24] who both had noticed coagulable urine in some dropsied patients.

Gross distension of the abdomen with ascitic fluid is a common finding in dropsy whether it be the result of cardiac, hepatic or renal disorders, but conversely any enlargement of the abdomen from intra-abdominal pathology could simulate dropsy. Therefore it is not surprising that Bright should have become involved in the care of these gastro-enterological patients referred to him by his colleagues with a mistaken diagnosis of dropsy and then, as a result, write extensively on abdominal tumours.

Similarly a large number of his renal patients died of cerebral haemorrhage or apoplexy from, the, as yet undiscovered complication of renal hypertension and also, following uraemic convulsions, lapsed into coma; this would explain his other great interest, that of diseases of the central nervous system. He was very much a general physician but in modern parlance would have been accredited with special interests in nephrology, neurology and gastroenterology!

Although his *magnum opus* will always remain the two volumes of *Medical Reports* it was his renal work which became a classic in the medical literature and was sufficiently well-regarded to win him the equivalent of a Nobel Prize in Medicine, i.e. the Monthyon Medal and led to the honour of an eponymous title. Therefore it is fitting that we look first at the work on the kidney that collectively led to the adoption of the eponym 'Bright's Disease' and gave its author international acclaim.

The eponym: Bright's Disease

A propos of Bright's disease, Sir James Paget once said to Dr Milner Fothergill who had dedicated his book on renal diseases to Richard Bright, 'So long as a disease carries a man's name it shows we know little about it'[25]. As far as nephritis is concerned this maxim has a ring of truth. Sir James had several diseases named after him, including those of the bone and nipple so he had some entitlement to this view.

A great deal has been written about the use of eponyms and not all of it complimentary—some have viewed them as a complete anathema, and often totally inappropriately applied. At best their use was considered woefully imprecise but Lord Byron, on the other hand, clearly felt that they were commendable when he said 'But these are deeds which should not pass away and names that must not wither.' When used in medicine they are often considered an abomination by purists, largely because they feel them to be not only imprecise but also inaccurate. Wright, in an amusing and logical article gives excellent reasons for retaining them and certainly medical history would be the poorer for their demise.[26] Eponyms may disguise the distressing aspects and stigmata of a disease: obviously one would rather have Hansen's disease than be a 'leper'! It is just possible that as dropsy carried such a poor prognosis in the 1800s that Bright's disease was similarly employed as a euphemism in this context.

In addition, to credit originality of description and highlight original work seems an attractive way of immortalising the memory of the discoverers. This may, however, lead to an invidious situation provoking vituperous argument regarding precedence particularly of a chauvinistic nature, a game of which medical historians never seem to tire. Of course, ideas have legs and no doubt professional jealousy and plagarism existed very much as it does today. Many examples testify to this problem of 'who was first?' Thomas Hodgkin wrote about aortic insufficiency in 1829, five years before the classical paper by the Irish physician, Dr Dominic Corrigan: Bright himself had noted what was later to be known as Hodgkin's disease and Addison's disease and also antedated Hughlings Jackson's discovery when he described localised fits which were later referred to as Jacksonian epilepsy. One must, of course, remember that the exchange of ideas both on a national and international level was, of necessity, limited by poor communication and the lack of learned journals available in the eighteenth and nineteenth centuries which may explain some of the erroneous claims to originality of description and what some may see as a rather unfair awarding of eponymous recognition. In Sir Thomas Browne's *Hydriotaphia* one is asked to consider '. . . whether the best of men be known or whether there be no more remarkable persons forgot than any that stand remembered in the known account of time'. In the end and in defence of eponyms it is, perhaps, their impreciseness that appeals and certainly this factor applied to the situation where the eponym had to encompass the multiple types of nephritis that Richard Bright described.

Finally, if eponyms were no longer in use medical examiners would be at a loss for questions to pose prospective MB candidates and as a result would be denied the more outrageous answers and therefore useful material for their after dinner speeches. A fine example of this is the story of Professor Gregory's 'Stomach Powder': at a viva-voce examination on materia medica a student was asked about the contents of the medicine and having answered correctly he was then asked by the examiner 'And who was Gregory?' to which he replied, 'A Saint, Sir!'[27] Perhaps Jessie Dobson got it right when she said: 'The eponym tends to serve as a mnemonic, since it arouses the interest of the student in the historical side of his studies'.[28]

Within 10 years of the publication in 1827 of his original work on the kidney the eponym was in common usage as *Morbus Brightii*, Bright's Disease or in France as *Maladie de Bright*. Although the introduction of the eponym is attributed to Dr Pierre Rayer in Paris, he himself, without in any way detracting from Richard Bright's contribution—in fact he very much revered his English colleague—preferred a more 'significant pathological term' for the renal condition and suggested 'albuminous nephritis'. Dr T J Pettigrew in his Medical Portrait Gallery suggests that *Morbus Brightii* was first used in 1837 by Drs Bresslar and Jacobsen from Berlin about the same time that Drs Forget and Rayer were corresponding about *Maladie de Bright*.[29,30] Drs Bright, Addison and Hodgkin, all English born, but Edinburgh and Guy's trained were to have their names immortalised through the diseases they so ably described yet sadly the term 'Bright's disease' is rarely used, Addisons's disease is just holding on and Hodgkin's disease has the doubtful distinction of having a variant, non-Hodgkin's disease, in common usage!

The evolution of kidney research before Richard Bright
Bright's discovery that some cases of dropsy were not related to diseases of the heart or liver, but to that of the kidney, was not an entirely new concept as several references had been made in the past to such an association: perhaps he was fortunate in having this knowledge on which to base his original research. As Claude Bernard remarked 'We stand upon the intellectual shoulders of those medical giants of bygone days and because of the help they afford us we are able to see a little more clearly than they would be able to do.'

To justify our belief in Bright's exalted place in the history of renal medicine and particularly nephritis it is necessary to know something of the work that had already been undertaken on the subject and the state of knowledge pertaining to that time; work to which he had access. As his research unfolded from the study of dropsy, coagulable urine and diseased kidneys at *post mortem* it extended and explored the realms of cardiac enlargement, cerebral vascular accidents, both secondary to the 'hard pulse' or what became known as hypertension and further into the biochemical changes associated with nephritis, e.g. uraemia.

Down the years several of these areas had been touched upon, often independently, and disjointed facts concerning coagulable urine, diseased kidneys, high blood pressure and even rudimentary biochemistry had been reported but had not been brought together to give a cohesive account or an explanation which would correlate the many disparate clinical features and pathological findings.

How much was known then about these different, yet apparently loosely related subjects in the early 1800s when Bright commenced his research? The history and the story of nephritis is a very long saga; suffice it to say that one could be forgiven for having an overwhelming belief that on any medical topic including that of the kidney, if Hippocrates[31] did not mention it Galen certainly did.[32] In fact it seems likely that dropsy, urine abnormalities such as glycosuria and albuminuria and the role of the kidney in removing impurities from the blood was recognised in Hindu medicine as early as 2000 BC.[33] However confusion did exist as Galen said: 'all patients who suffer from painful urination and retention of urine are called nephritics or kidney patients'.[34] Certainly even in Richard Bright's time the distinction between pyelonephritic infections from bacteria and glomerulonephritis inflammation from unknown non-bacterial influences was very hazy indeed.

Ralph H Major, the American medical historian and author of *The Classic Descriptions of Disease* has written extensively on the history of nephritis and this has been most elegantly supplemented by a scholarly history of the nephrotic syndrome, the purest form of renal dropsy, written appropriately by Professor Stewart Cameron, Head of the Department of Renal Medicine at Guy's.[34-36] Although it may seem an incongruous source it is to Richard Bright's French contemporary, Dr Pierre Rayer, that we must look for, by far and away, the most comprehensive account of kidney research before and during the Bright era.[37]

Littré, who probably gave the first account of polycystic kidneys refers in his translation of Hippocrates, to the fact that the great man mentions urine no less than 188 times and that when bubbles settle on the surface of urine they indicate disease of its kidneys: 'frothy urine' is still a valid sign of albuminuria today.

Galen was said, in a moment of exasperation with the medical heresies of Aesculapius to have written that many eminent physicians including Hippocrates might know that the kidneys are organs for secreting urine but so did most lowly butchers as a result of slaughtering animals and seeing the connection between kidneys and bladder via the ureter. It is believed that Homer Smith, the quintessential American renal physiologist, novelist, essayist, and philospher who devoted most of his life to studying the function of the kidney was heard to say after many years of hard labour that one thing he did know about the kidney was that it made urine!

It is to Frederick Dekkers, a Dutch physician from Leyden that one of the earliest accounts of albumen in the urine is attributed: in 1695 he reported a milky appearance when he boiled urine from tuberculous patients. This was followed by the account of Domenico Cotugno, Professor of Anatomy in Naples in the mid 1700s; he described a 25-year old soldier with dropsy and what appeared to be acute nephritis whose urine when evaporated over a fire left a whole mass, loosely coagulated like egg albumen. In fact Cotugno was still alive during the period of Richard Bright's earlier work on the kidney as he only died in 1822 at the age of 87.

The association between damaged kidneys, usually described as hard, and dropsy was known from the earliest times: Rufus of Ephesus 100 AD, Aetius of Armida 501-575 AD, Paul of Aegina 625-690 AD and the Arabian physician Rhazes 860-923 AD were amongst the earliest to make the connection. Also Aurelius Celsus, the early Christian encyclopaedist precised most of the knowledge up until this time in *De Re Medicina* including facts about dropsy, anasarca and ascites. With quite remarkable foresight he writes of diuretics and the importance of measuring fluid intake and urine output suggesting that if the latter is in excess of the former the prognosis will be good—a lesson which could have helped Richard Bright in his treatment regimens and something which nephrologists often re-learn in the 20th century. At the time of the first century Avicenna (980–1037) AD 'The Prince of Physicians' had noted hardening of the kidneys, dropsy, scanty urine output, and the lack of pain in some patients; the latter symptom probably differentiating infected pyelonephritic kidneys, distended with pus, from true nephritis or glomerulonephritis. Major states that by 1000 AD several of the physicians referred to above, had described exactly the same clinico-pathological features in very similar language and suggests that it might all have originated from the work of Rufus. William of Saliceto, Professor of Medicine in Bologna between 1269 and 1274, knew about renal atrophy with copious urine, but more importantly makes reference to hard kidneys associated with oliguria and ascites in his book 'Durities in renibus', the classical presentation in some of the patients of Richard Bright's early studies.

One of the most illuminating accounts of the history of the contracted kidney in more recent times starts with the story of the illness and later death of the 47-year old Count Furstenberg as told by the grandsons of the great seventeenth century physician and scientist, Dr Johann Jacob Wepfer and published in 1727, 33 years after their grandfather's death.[38] Apparently the Count had not been in good health for many months; he had lost weight and complained of vomiting, double vision and polyuria. He travelled to Strasbourg to witness the triumphant entry of Louis XIV with his army of occupation but sadly fell down the stairs, struck his head, became unconscious and died within twenty hours. Dr Wepfer performed an autopsy and found that in addition to a cerebral haemorrhage the kidneys were remarkably small and thin, about the size one would expect to find in a nine-year old child. The dilemma of Johann Jacob Wepfer was why had these small, contracted kidneys produced so much dilute urine? It seems likely that these kidneys were not the result of chronic Bright's disease but were atrophic from bilateral obstruction, as Wepfer states 'Certainly the pelves and ureter were extremely wide . . . .'. Nevertheless, clinically the end result of high urea in the blood and high blood pressure would have been the same and it is significant that the Count succumbed, as Richard Bright might have predicted, from apoplexy. This seems to be the first account of the association between contracted kidneys and apoplexy until Richard Bright noted the connection.

The Middle Ages provided few new discoveries and will be remembered largely for the emergence of uroscopy, the ability to make a diagnosis from 'urine gazing' much as an astrologer might look at the stars, and was really no more than quackery in most instances. It was eventually exposed and debunked by the more discerning physicians such as Dr Thomas Brian who in 1637 published his lectures castigating 'pissie-mongers' stating that 'there is nothing but fallacies in giving judgement of diseases by the Urine alone.'[39]

Dr Latham once remarked that with the arrival of Dr Richard Bright chemistry was placed in the realms of clinical medicine, so perhaps it is worth looking at the development of clinical pathology and the state of the art at that time in relation to renal disease. By the late sixteenth century interest was being shown in chemical rather than physical examination of the urine including the comparison of the weight of blood and urine, the forerunner of specific gravity and osmolarity measurements. In Foster's history of clinical pathology he recounts that the specialty grew from the naked eye examination of urine, faeces and sputum, and as such, was as old as medicine itself.[40] Then in the 17th century, the birth of scientific chemistry, the development of the microscope and the idea that disease might produce chemical changes in the blood, brought further advances in clinical pathology.

Apparently this latter idea occurred to John Locke, the philosopher and physician who implanted it in the mind of Robert Boyle, who in 1684 performed chemical analysis using distillation and weighing and found salt in the blood; he suggested that urine might be examined in the same way.

This was all happening about the same time that the Dutch physician Frederik Dekkers demonstrated albumen in the urine. In 1735 Dr Browne Langrish, a country physician, hoped that 'the proportion of several principles of the blood and urine, both in a sound and diseased state, will be highly useful in investigating the cause of the phenomena of disease and the most expeditious way of relieving them.' He undertook chemical analysis of blood in patients with febrile disease and recognised that the appearance of the blood shed at phlebotomy could be diagnostically helpful; he even invented an instrument to measure the toughness or degree of cohesion of the blood clot. He reported also that the colour, sediment and smell of the urine: 'furnishes us with signs as well diagnostic as prognostic'.

Almost one hundred years later physicians interested in kidney disease began, at an early stage, to recognise the importance of what was to become known as animal chemisty and then biochemistry.[41] Richard Bright soon enlisted the services of John Bostock to analyse the blood and urine of his patients and Gabriel Andral, who with Pierre Rayer and Claude Bernard founded the Paris School of Renal Medicine, was similarly employed on chemical examination of blood; he confirmed Bostock's finding of low levels of serum albumen in patients with protein loss in the urine and will be remembered for

THE
PISSE-PROPHET
OR
CERTAINE PISSE POT
LECTURES.

Wherein are newly difcovered the old
fallacies, deceit, and jugling of the Piffe-pot
Science, ufed by all thofe (whether Quacks and
Empiricks, or other methodicall Phyficians)
who pretend knowledge of Difeafes, by
the Urine, in giving judgement
of the fame.

By T H O. B R I A N, M. P. lately in the Citie
of *London*, and now in *Colchester*
in E s s e x.

Never heretofore publifhed by any man
in the *Englifh* Tongue.

Si populus vult decipi, decipiatur.

LONDON,

Printed by *E. P.* for *R. Thrale*, and are to be
fold at his fhop at the figne of the Croffe-
Keyes, at *Pauls* gate
1 6 3 7

Frontispiece of Dr Thomas Brian's book.

his stand against excessive blood letting and for editing the works
of Laennec.

We now turn to the period at the end of the eighteenth century
and the beginning of the nineteenth and to the story of the two
men, Drs Wells and Blackall who, by their endeavours most
closely challenged Richard Bright's right to the eponym. In fact

Professor Cameron has pointed out several other important milestones in the intriguing story of nephritis. Dr Cruikshank, Apothecary to the Army Hospital at Woolwich, had noted albuminuria in diabetic patients in 1798 and Dr Brande in 1807 divided dropsy into those with coagulable urine and those without. Dr Rayer recounts that Matthew Baillie sent two urines to the latter; one from a renal patient and the other suffering from liver disease: Dr Brande found albuminuria and decreased urinary urea in the first and no abnormalities in the second, representing one of the earliest reports of diminished urea in the urine of dropsical patients.[37] Scarlatina or scarlet fever and the relationship to renal disease was very well-known and described; but quite extra-ordinarily a German, Dr Johann Reil had differentiated the acute onset of dropsy in the acute nephritic syndrome from that of the more insidious nephrotic syndrome, something about which Richard Bright was at times curiously reticent.[42]

In 1811, just about the time that Bright was beginning to think seriously about kidney disease, Dr William Charles Wells, who was born in South Carolina, had returned to England with his parents because of their affiliation to the British cause during the American War of Independence. He presented a paper to the Society for the Improvement of Medicine and Chirurgical Knowledge; in it he reported finding 78 patients with coagulable urine out of a total of 130 dropsical patients.[23] In this study, undertaken at St Thomas's Hospital, the now well-established high ratio of male to female patients with nephritis was first recorded.

Although Wells undertook very few *post mortems* he did describe both hard contracted kidneys and large soft kidneys in one or two patients, corresponding to two of the three types in Bright's classification. Interestingly, a year earlier he published a paper on the cardiac complications of rheumatism, a subject later touched upon by Richard Bright; doctors in those days were very much versatile general physicians.

Dr John Blackall, Exeter Grammar School, Balliol College Oxford, St Bartholomew's Hospital and latterly the Devon and Exeter Hospital, published in 1813, the first edition of his book *Observations on the Nature and Cure of Dropsies*.[24] Blackall was more conservative in his management of his dropsical patients than Richard Bright and was extremely chary of the use of mercury which he saw, correctly, as a cause of coagulable urine and renal damage. That, and the fact that his patients came from a younger group and suffered mainly from post scarlet fever nephritis accounted for the better prognosis in his study—as we shall see, the majority of Richard Bright's original 24 patients with nephritis succumbed.

He remained on the staff of the Devon and Exeter Hospital for 40 years until his retirement in 1847. Many tributes were paid

OBSERVATIONS

ON

THE NATURE AND CURE OF

DROPSIES,

AND PARTICULARLY ON

THE PRESENCE OF THE COAGULABLE PART OF THE BLOOD IN DROPSICAL URINE;

TO WHICH IS ADDED,

AN APPENDIX,

CONTAINING

SEVERAL CASES OF ANGINA PECTORIS,

WITH DISSECTIONS, &c.

BY

JOHN BLACKALL, M.D.

PHYSICIAN TO THE DEVON AND EXETER HOSPITAL, AND TO THE LUNATIC ASYLUM, NEAR EXETER.

THE FOURTH EDITION,

LONDON:

PRINTED FOR

LONGMAN, HURST, REES, ORME, BROWN, AND GREEN, PATERNOSTER-ROW.

1824.

Frontispiece of Dr Blackall's book.

Dr John Blackall.
(Courtesy of Royal Devon and Exeter Hospital.)

to him, including that of Bright, who based his own work on that of the Exeter physician. He was said to have 'a sagacious mind' and with regard to his studies on dropsy 'discovered the importance of hitherto unappreciated facts' but was also a bit of a character and several quaint anecdotes have survived.

He had enormous faith in the value of baths and one pompous, well-to-do patient with a classical bent, after receiving his treatment said, 'Thank you most heartily. I hope the treatment may be successful, and having had the calidarium, the frigidarium and the tepidarium, allow me to present you the honorarium!'[43] The book gives a good insight into contemporary thoughts on the kidney and a historical account of the discovery of coagulable urine; curiously it has an appendix recording several cases of angina pectoris.

It was at this stage then that Richard Bright arrived on the scene. Why he should have had a foremost interest in the kidney on his mind is not at all certain but we do know that he had drawn a contracted kidney at a *post mortem* as early as 1815 or even 1811 and in Edinburgh Drs Gregory and Alison were pursuing research into renal disease.

Chapter 10

The Renal Portfolio—Bright's Disease

'The organs of the human body were created to perform
ten functions, among which is the function of the kidney
to furnish the human being with thought'
                    Leviticus Rabba 3. Talmud Berochoth 61b.

It could be said that Richard Bright was 'looking through a glass
darkly' when viewing the problem of kidney disease; he had an
awesome task before him. The story of his renal researches begins
with the triad of dropsy, coagulable urine and the finding of diseased
kidneys at autopsy; obviously if a dropsied patient survived, the state
of the kidneys whether large or small, hard or soft, or indeed red
or white would never be known. Initially, this gave a very narrow
view of nephritis as before renal biopsies became available in the
1950s *post mortem* findings were the only arbiters. Kidney disorders
secondary to tuberculosis, other bacterial infections and hydatid
disease were rife in the 19th century; they could all cause coagulable
urine and must have obscured the search for pure nephritis or
glomerulonephritis. Furthermore a simple case of cystitis could cause
albumen in the urine without any kidney involvement, at least
transiently: the fact that 'persistent proteinuria' is the *sine qua non*
of nephritis was, at that time, unknown.
   We now also know that, depending on the type, degree of severity
and duration of the disease, nephritis can present in several different
ways and not always with obvious dropsy. Firstly, simple
proteinuria, which if severe enough to deplete albumen stores in
the blood can lead to one form of renal dropsy, i.e. the nephrotic
syndrome characterised by swelling of the legs and abdomen with
fluid—oedema and ascites respectively. Secondly, the acute onset
of renal failure causes fluid retention not unlike the first group but
is more often associated with a low output of urine, a combination
known as the acute nephritic syndrome. In Bright's time this would
have been caused by acute nephritis following scarlet fever and
represents another form of renal dropsy. Finally, chronic renal
failure produced by the scarred end-stage of any nephritic process,
a stage when the kidneys can no longer handle either the waste
products of metabolism like urea, or salt and water, results in
generalised oedema of the body, fluid retention or over hydration,
whatever you wish to call it. This illustrates the last form of dropsy
but in addition these latter patients suffer both from high levels of
urea in the blood, i.e. uraemia or the uraemic syndrome, and often

the ravages of high blood pressure. So unbeknown to Richard Bright, if renal dropsy did exist, it could present in three different ways. Incidentally some patients with renal damage secondary to high blood pressure, as yet poorly defined, did not have coagulable urine; this was to cause a good deal of *angst* amongst Bright's contemporaries writing on renal disease in later years. How much of this highly convoluted and complicated story did Bright unravel? The panegyrists would say almost all of it and one might concede that they were almost right.

Quite remarkably he recognised three basic types of pathological changes in the kidney at autopsy, namely, the large white kidney often associated with the nephrotic syndrome, the large red kidney presenting as acute glomerulonephritis, acute renal failure or the acute nephritic syndrome and the small, shrunken schirrous kidney of chronic glomerulonephritis, chronic renal failure or chronic uraemia. This, alone, was a quantum leap which would carry renal research into the next century. However, his initial study was essentially pathological and even during the intervening years his description of the accompanying clinical syndromes remained a little ill-defined and vague. It is easy to be critical when one is in full possession of the facts but certainly, although Richard Bright felt quite correctly that he was seeing a spectrum or continuum of a disease process the edges between the different clinical features sometimes remained a touch blurred. He has been criticised for this and adjudged merely a recorder of medical data, the intellectual interpretation of which he left to others. We know he could be diffident, was not aggressively dogmatic and was said to be unable to theorize; that he could see the map but could not fully understand the topography. One suspects that, as he himself said, his work was often 'misunderstood' and 'misrepresented'. This could be explained by the fact that some of the views and theories which he did have, tended to be lost in his rather prosaic style of writing, but probably like many of us he preferred to leave his options open until he had absolute proof to confirm his work.

The original papers
We are fortunate that in 1937 Dr A Arnold Osman, from the nephritis clinic at Guy's Hospital, edited a book entitled *The Original Papers of Richard Bright on Renal Disease*, containing the four most important seminal works relating to the kidney; the first section in Volume I of the *Medical Reports*; the second Goulstonian lecture delivered by Richard Bright in 1833 and the first two papers in the inaugural edition of the *Guy's Hospital Reports* in 1836 entitled 'Cases and observations, Illustrative of Renal Disease accompanied with the secretion of albuminous urine' and 'Tabular views of the morbid appearances in 100 cases connected with albuminous urine, with observations'.[1] The book contains beautiful reproductions of

the coloured plates from the *Medical Reports* and Dr Osman has added a section describing the histological appearance of Bright's original three kidney specimens taken from the collection in the Gordon Museum at Guy's. These kidneys have been examined recently using more modern staining and microscopic techniques and we shall return to these findings later in the chapter. What is not included in Dr Osman's collection are two contributions recording some of Richard Bright's later thoughts on renal disorders, engendered by a feeling that he had been misjudged by some of his contemporaries. The first of these, and his last major work on the kidney as a sole author, was in the familiar mode of his first article 'Cases and Observations, Illustrative of Renal Disease etc'—'Memoir the Second' in which he seeks to set the record right and vindicate his earlier views: this was published in 1840 in the *Guy's Hospital Reports*.[2] The other omission from Dr Osman's book is found in volume II of *The Medical Reports* published in 1831 and entitled 'Observations on the Deranged Action of the Kidney as it affects the Cerebral function.'[3] Properly one should mention the last of Richard Bright's contributions to kidney disease, the letter in the *London Medical Gazette* in 1840 recounting the development of his collaborative work on the microscopic appearances of nephritis with Dr Toynbee and this has been included for completeness at the end of the chapter.[4]

Turning back now to the classic work in *The Medical Reports*, Volume I, describing the original 24 patients—25 records were actually included because William Roderick, Case 15, went into remission for about one year. Case 24, William Elsely, a patient of Dr Hodgkin, was included at the last minute as the book was going to press because he exhibited the largest amount of protein that had ever been seen in the collected series. Unlike some of his later studies all these patients had dropsy as he was testing the hypothesis that not all dropsies were of cardiac or of hepatic origin. The fact that only five survived accounted for the gloomy prognosis for which in later years Richard Bright was openly criticised by his contemporaries.

These patients were collected during an intense period of research between October 1825 and April 1827 and it is assumed that William Brooks who was said to have been admitted to Guy's on 25 October 1862 represents a misprint for 1826. By August 1827 Richard Bright had written the preface from Bloomsbury Square and the book was published, a remarkable achievement and an example of the author's enormous energy, dedication and industry which hallmarked all his work. It is in Volume I of the *Medical Reports* that many of the most well-known quotations appear, some directing the reader's attention to the importance of renal dropsy, hitherto suspected but unproven. Having pointed out that dropsy could be caused by heart and liver disease and by local disease of the peritoneum, usually secondary to tuberculosis or 'morbid growth', he goes on to say 'There are other appearances to which I think too little attention has hitherto been paid. They are those evidences of organic change which occasionally present themselves in the structure of the Kidney; and which, whether they are to be considered the cause of the dropsy effusion or as a consequence of some other disease cannot be unimportant. Where those conditions of the Kidney to which I allude have occurred I have often found the dropsy connected with secretion of albuminous urine more or less coagulable on the application of heat.' and importantly he adds 'I have in general found that the liver has not in these cases portrayed any considerable mark of disease either during life or on examination after death' and, finally, the essentially important corollary 'On the other hand I have found that where the dropsy has depended on organic change in the liver, even in the most aggravated state of such change, no disease has generally been discovered in the kidneys and the urine has not coagulated by heat. Finally I have never yet examined the body of a patient dying with dropsy attended with coagulable urine, in whom some obvious derangement was not discovered in the kidneys.'

It is upon these above remarks that the whole basis of Richard Bright's work is built. Here in this preface to Volume I is the first reference to heating the urine in a spoon over a candle to detect the presence of albumen in the urine and of the findings of blood in the urine in these patients with what was to become known as nephritis; he does try slightly unsuccessfully to differentiate the pathological appearances in the kidney in patients with very recent onset of their illness from those with a more insidious onset.

The preface includes a generous tribute to Dr Blackall's 'valuable treaties' and mentions how it is nearly 12 years since he had noticed altered structures of the kidney in a patient who had died of dropsy and of how he had made a 'slight drawing' of it at that time, which would have been about 1815. So obviously the seed had been sewn with regard to the kidney and dropsy many years before, probably in Edinburgh as a medical student when the Boerhaavian teaching had been adopted and where the kidneys were known to be organs which when obstructed could lead to dropsy and where research into renal disease was blossoming. Dr Cruikshank had suggested that dropsy could be divided into two main categories according to whether the urine was coagulable or non-coagulable but by the time Dr Alison, Clinical Professor at Edinburgh and a pioneering nephrophile, had delivered his lectures on renal disease in 1823 Bright had returned south to Guy's.

He then goes on to discuss the famous 24 patients and it is worth just looking at a few of the more interesting case histories. Richard Bright's first report was on a certain John King who has become perhaps the most famous renal patient in the world and who has been immortalised in many texts; he was a 34-year old ex-sailor, now cutler, who liked to drink, and here one is struck by the

Dr William Cruikshank.

fact that Richard Bright was almost looking for patients who might have alcoholic hepatic disease maybe to harden the case in favour of his theory about renal dropsy. However we know that physicians of that time were slightly obsessed with the intemperate life, inclement weather, dampness and inadequate or wet clothing plus membership of the lower classes as a cause of disease and in the case of kidney trouble a 'blow to the loins'.

As with much research, luck, chance, serendipity, however one expresses it, played a part in Bright's work, as after studying only a handful of patients he was able to describe the three major types of pathology in nephritis which, with a few reservations, stands scrutiny even today. It is a remarkable feat of observation that in the morass of multiple pathologies he was able to pick out these three types and so accurately describe and illustrate them.

John King showed all the signs and symptoms of chronic uraemia; he was oedematous, anaemic, with herpes labialis, pericarditis, bloody stools and most important of all, scanty urine coagulable with heat and containing blood. The pericarditis is an interesting finding—'by assistance of the stethoscope,' Richard Bright states, 'I thought the sound of the heartbeat was as if performing through fluid'—what an excellent description. In spite or because of an impressive application of polypharmacy the patient succumbed within fourteen days.

Mr Stocker, the long suffering apothecary, and a sort of guardian to the medical students was in attendance mainly during the night for the administration of cupping, bleeding and other remedies. The *post mortem* or sectio cadaveris illustrated the small granular contracted kidneys of end-stage renal failure which would be associated with chronic uraemia and appear as Plate I in the *Medical Reports*, Vol I.

Fortuitously, his next patient, Elizabeth Brewer, illustrated a totally different sort of renal disease and was admitted in a terminal stage with gross generalised dropsy. She died in three days and this time the kidneys were very large as they were in Mary Sallaway, the third case, whose kidneys provided Plate 2. Although Bright thought that the kidneys at *post mortem* were unremarkable it is fairly obvious that they showed what became known as the large white kidney. Although this patient was later found to have amyloid infiltration of the kidney secondary to advanced pulmonary tuberculosis, her kidney, plus that of the previous patient, provided Richard Bright with his second type of renal disease. This latter variation might be considered to be the truest form of renal dropsy, usually with massive albumen loss in the urine, resulting in what became known as sub-acute nephritis, in the early part of the 20th century, and the nephrotic syndrome today. We now know it can be produced by a variety of microscopic changes in the glomeruli as seen on renal biopsy.

Elizabeth Stewart, Case 7, was a 40-year old woman 'exposed to the difficulties and temptations of the lower classes'. Again Richard Bright was convinced originally that renal disease was very much a prerogative of those from a lower social plane and in the spirit of the age the result of alcoholic debauchery and licentiousness of all types; and here he again mentions that continual soakings and wet clothes did not help.

She had been ill for eight years and in Plate 3 the kidneys are similar to those of John King, small and contracted as compared with the large white kidneys of the two other patients. Now if we move forward to Henry Izod who provided Case 11, we find a 25-year old man who was a Smithfield drover; he had spent a great

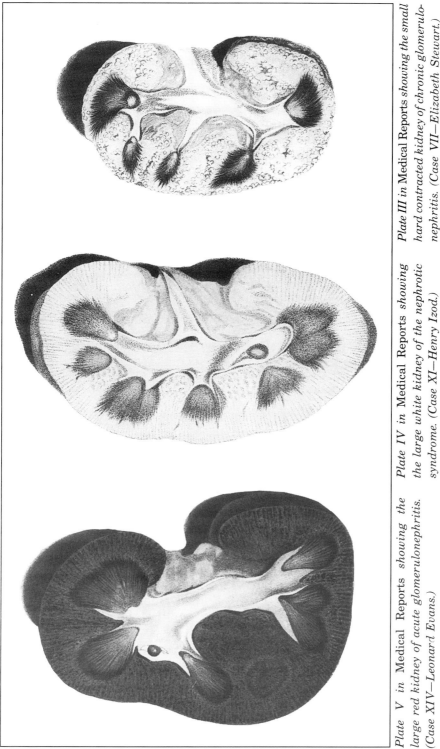

Plate V in Medical Reports showing the large red kidney of acute glomerulonephritis. (Case XIV—Leonard Evans.)

Plate IV in Medical Reports showing the large white kidney of the nephrotic syndrome. (Case XI—Henry Izod.)

Plate III in Medical Reports showing the small hard contracted kidney of chronic glomerulo-nephritis. (Case VII—Elizabeth Stewart.)

deal of his time in public houses intoxicated on porter. Richard Bright was convinced that he had chronic hepatic dropsy and when he died 'my zealous friend Dr Hodgkin' undertook a *post mortem* and found again large white kidneys. Unfortunately the patient had escaped having his urine tested; it is gratifying to know that just occasionally even Richard Bright and his team forgot to test the urine. Henry Izods kidneys provided Plate 4 of the book.

The last of the more interesting patients, because it demonstrated Bright's third type of nephritis, was a man called Leonard Evans, Case 14, and illustrated in Plate 5. He was a remarkably stout Welshman and the strongest man out of over a 1,000 in Deptford dockyard. Unlike the other patients, he had shown a rapid onset of his dropsy and he had died quite suddenly and rather unexpectedly; the cause of death was found to be occlusion of the larynx from oedema. At *post mortem* the kidneys were swollen, large and engorged with blood, typical of underlying acute haemorrhagic nephritis presenting with an acute nephritic syndrome. It was, in the case of this unfortunate man, that Richard Bright received what in research might be called 'a break'. This patient may well have survived his disease and the opportunity to have examined his kidneys would have been lost but fortunately he was able to describe them, the third classical pathological appearance of nephritis and with it came the realisation that possibly he was seeing three clinical syndromes that accompanied the pathological entities albeit ill-defined.

In his 'Some general remarks on the foregoing cases' he says that 'From the observations which I have made I have been led to believe that there may be several forms of disease to which the kidney becomes liable in the progress of dropsical affection: I have even thought that the organic derangements which have already presented themselves to my notice, will authorise the establishment of three varieties, if not of three completely separate forms of disease structure, generally attended by a decidedly albuminous character of the urine.' Although he attempts to describe the three pathological types he admits to uncertainty and vagueness and believed that he was observing a continuum of disease processes, one blending into another. It is easy for the present day reader and physician with the benefit of hindsight to see quite clearly the three distinct pathologies with the three clinical syndromes, namely the chronic end-stage renal disease, the acute nephritic syndrome and the nephrotic syndrome. It has been said that he would not theorise and that the weakness in his work, if it exists, lies in the fact that, compared with his brilliant pathological descriptions the clinical features are imprecise. This may be a fair criticism but we do know he was not a forceful man by nature, his work had a pathological bias and he was exploring a completely new concept.

As regards treatment Bright says 'I wish that I were now able to add anything completely satisfactory to myself with regard to the mode of treating these diseases of the kidney. It will be very obvious from a view of the cases I have cited that they sometimes present difficulties so formidable as to defy the ordinary means of cure; indeed I am inclined to doubt whether it be possible after the decided organic changes takes a firm hold on the kidney, to affect a cure or even to give such relief as may enable a patient to pursue for a few years the occupations of life. Where however, the mischief is less rooted we may undoubtedly do much.' These sentiments could very well be repeated in the 1990s. At the end of this section of Volume I of the *Medical Reports* on renal cases, Dr John Bostock's 'Observations on the chemical properties of the urine in the foregoing cases' provides the foundation of clinical biochemistry in renal medicine and in it he recognises the changes in the specific gravity of the urine, and the quantity of albumen and urea in both blood and urine. These are remarkable studies and one can not sufficiently emphasise the importance of his contribution to Richard Bright's clinico-pathological studies. Bostock was able to show that one could have urine with a low urea content and blood with a high urea content as a result of renal damage, and consequent failure, and perhaps an even more important finding, that as a result of the protein loss in the urine the albumen level in the blood dropped; here we have an early clue to the mechanisms of oedema in renal patients, in particular those with the large white kidney or nephrotic syndrome.

It may be said that the other papers Richard Bright wrote on the kidney did not have the same enormous impact that this initial study provided, though they represent a consolidation and modification of his first impressions. Even if he had never written anything other than this section of Volume I he would have been accredited with the title of the discoverer of what we now know as nephritis, and which has been referred to as the 'concept of the century'.[5] It has been said that multiple publications reiterating the same views lay undue emphasis on any findings or data.[6] Richard Bright, with certain modifications, tended to write again and again about 'the message' to the profession regarding his triad and one feels that had he not been so single-minded this research like many other contributions would have been lost with the diuresis of time; one can only be thankful for his persistence! The final word came from the *Lancet* who gave a favourable review of Volume 1. 'Dr Bright thinks that too little attention has been paid to diseases of the kidney. To this point we call the attention of our readers and hope those physicians who are morbid anatomists will never open the body of a person who has died of dropsy without a careful examination of the internal structures of the kidney.'[7]

In 1833 Richard Bright delivered the Goulstonian lectures published later that year in *The London Medical Gazette* and entitled 'The Functions of the Abdomen, and some Diagnostic Marks of its

Disease.'[8] In the second lecture, changes in the urine as a means
of recognising renal disease are discussed. There is nothing very new
in this work, but he enlarges on his 'favourite topic'. He recommends
Dr Prout's work on urinary secretion as the latter had been helping
with the measurement of the blood or serum urea. He acknowledges
'The Great assistance from the intelligent and zealous co-operation
of three of my young friends and pupils, Mr Barlow, Mr Tweedie
and Mr Rees.' Mr Owen Rees was later to replace the ageing Dr
Bostock as biochemist to the team. In addition to the technique of
heating urine in a spoon over the flame of a lamp or candle, nitric
acid is used to detect albumen. There is an early report of screening
healthy patients for the presence of coagulable urine, this
undertaken by his three students.

The difficulty of interpreting the significance of the specific gravity
of urine is discussed and preliminary attempts to quantitate urea
levels in the blood introduces the idea of 'the great office of the
kidney', that of 'depuration of the blood'. The concept of albuminous
urine in the absence of dropsy was recognised, but perhaps more
disquietening as far as Richard Bright's *credo* was concerned were
the odd reports of contracted kidneys without albuminuria. Both
Dr George Burrow of St Bartholomew's Hospital and Dr Watson of
the Middlesex Hospital had shown him damaged kidneys in patients
with anasarca who had not exhibited coagulable urine during life.
As these two puzzling cases had enlarged hearts Richard Bright
suggested that they might well have represented a group of patients
with a derangement of the heart and which were later identified
by Dr F A Mahomed at Guy's as patients with Bright's Disease but
without coagulable urine, i.e. hypertensive nephrosclerosis—the
subject of the latter's remarkable MD thesis in 1881.[9]

In recording the patient under the care of the Guy's surgeon Mr
Morgan he recognises that the mode of death from chronic urinary
tract obstruction is identical to that of his chronic nephritic patients,
i.e. advanced uraemia. He cautions against elective surgery in
patients with albuminous urine and suggests that wound healing
might be impaired; also that a high incidence of secondary infection
occurs in patients with longstanding dropsy such as peritonitis which
we now know was caused from loss of immunoglobulin in the urine.
He finishes his lecture by listing other diseases of the kidney that
he could have talked about but felt that although he was on his
favourite subject he may have spoken 'too much at length'. He
probably spoke for a little over 45 minutes which would have been
a relatively short lecture by Victorian standards!

Turning now to the other works on the kidney; in the first of his
two papers entitled 'Cases and Observations, Illustrative of Renal
Disease Accompanied with the Secretion of Albuminous Urine'
published in the first edition of *Guy's Hospital Reports* in 1836 more
emphasis is placed on the clinical features and biochemical changes

rather than pathological descriptions.[10] The terms 'mottling', 'white degeneration' and 'contraction' or 'granulation' are now being used corresponding to the large red, large white and small contracted kidneys respectively. We see in this paper evidence of Bright's interest in epidemiology when he states that he thought 500 patients with his disease died each year in London and that there could be 20 or even double that number of cases in each of the large London hospitals at any one time. He regretted that so little had been done in the ten years since his first description to help alleviate the sufferings of patients with renal disease. It is in this first paper that one finds the best description of acute nephritis or glomerulonephritis and what we would now describe as the acute nephritic syndrome.

'A child or adult is affected with scarlatina . . . he finds the secretion of his urine is greatly increased . . . tinged with blood . . . he awakes in the morning with his face swollen or his ankles puffy . . . his urine contains a notable quantity of albumen; his pulse is full and hard, his skin dry, he has often headache and sometimes a sense of weight or pain across the loins . . . the calls to micturition disturb the nights repose . . . the urine is carefully tested; the quantity of urea is gradually diminishing . . . blood is drawn; and nice analysis will frequently detect a great deficiency of albumen and sometimes manifest indications of the presence of urea . . . the swelling increases, the urine becomes scanty . . . the lungs become oedematous . . . seized with an acute attack of pericarditis . . . he is suddenly seized with a convulsive fit and becomes blind—overwhelmed by coma, the painful history of his disease is closed.'

Following this classic description he relates some of his experiences in the intervening 10 years since his original observations. Posing the question to himself

'Do we always find such lesion of the kidney as to bear us out in the belief, that the peculiar condition of the urine, to which I have already referred, shows that the disease, call it what we may is connected necessarily and essentially with the derangement of that organ? After ten years attentive—though, perhaps, I must not say completely impartial observation—I am ready to answer this question in the affirmative; and yet I confess that I have occasionally met with anomalies which have been somewhat difficult to explain.'

It makes the point but is rather long-winded.

He then goes on to say a little about the fact that the albumen in the urine can wax and wane, that patients may go into remission and that the prognosis may not be quite as bad as first thought. With remarkable perspicacity he points out that the length of time during which the nephritic process has been present prior to the patient becoming known to the doctor was of prime importance, what we would now call the lead time—that this alone would explain many of the inconsistencies in some of the data which had been collected. This paper adds yet a further complication to the saga of patients dying of renal disease as it includes 11 case reports, eight of whom die of apoplexy, or a cerebrovascular accidents of some sort, and two from peritonitis; most of the patients had enlarged hearts. The paper concludes with some very interesting reports of preliminary studies, the first of which records perhaps one of the first examples of a screening programme undertaken in the winter of 1828-29.

Urine from 130 patients is taken randomly or 'promiscuously' as they said in these days, and on testing, 18 were found to be highly coagulable and 12 had a trace of albumen. There is a table which shows 12 consecutive patients, six male and six female where a correlation between coagulable urine and diseased or non-diseased kidneys is made. A further study in 1832 is reported which had been conducted by Dr G H Barlow and Mr Tweedie, on 300 individuals and again they found one in eleven had coagulable urine suggesting a diagnosis of Bright's disease. His pupil and clinical clerk James Alderson in yet a further study in 1835 examined 141 patients and read a 'well digested paper' before the Physical Society of Guy's showing the incidence of coagulable urine to be 'above one in six'. As a result of all these various early studies Bright concludes that the incidence of albumen in the urine in hospital patients is about one in six and feels that he has proved that 500 die annually from this single disease. Kidney disease was said to be second only to tuberculosis as a major killer in the early to mid-19th century.

In the treatments section he gathers together some of the results of his contemporaries, namely Dr Osborne of Dublin, Dr Christison, 'the zealous and deeply lamented young physician Dr Gregory' and 'my friend Dr Alison' all from Edinburgh, Dr Barlow of Bath, Dr Pritchard of Bristol, and points out that the overuse of mercury is to be avoided.

He finishes the paper with a report of Case 11 who had been greatly debilitated by mercurial therapy but who illustrated that, contrary to his earlier beliefs, even patients in 'easy and comfortable circumstances' could be struck down with his disease! The technique of puncturing the skin to allow oedematous fluid to escape from the swollen legs is described, a forerunner of the use of Southey's tubes, and by this method 44 ounces of serum are removed in four hours; but the needle holes were prone to inflammation. Apart from the usual treatments the nephritic patients are encouraged to take a light diet, cut down on wine and liquors, wear flannel next to the skin, avoid riding on the outside of the carriage and if 'horse exercise' is taken eschew any 'severe exertion to the loins!'

Richard Bright's second paper entitled 'Tabular view of the Morbid Appearances in 100 Cases Connected with Albuminous Urine' is quite short as it is a tabular digest of his first 33 dissections which he says have already been published in the *Medical Reports* although only 24 case reports appeared initially, plus a further 67 previously unpublished.[22] From the Table one notes that there are 52 small hard contracted kidneys and 48 with either large white or large red kidneys. It describes the appearances of all the main organs of the body. Most of the principle lesions are in the heart, lung, pleura, arachnoid and the peritoneum while the liver, spleen, pancreas, and even the intestines were mainly spared. Perhaps the most interesting observation was that relating to the heart where he states 'The obvious structural changes in the heart have consisted chiefly of hypertrophy with or without valvular disease, and what is most striking out of 52 cases of hypertrophy, no valvular disease whatsoever could be detected in 34' although 11 showed some aortic disease probably from atheroma. So this really left him with 22 patients with marked hypertrophy of the left ventricle, with no obvious cardiac reason for the changes; this would have seemed to have kept pace with the advance in the disease of the kidney hinting again at the connection between the kidneys, the hard pulse, hypertrophied heart and cerebral haemorrhage. Interestingly 30 out of 70 died of well-marked symptoms of cerebral derangement noted under the titles of 'apoplexy', 'coma', 'convulsions' and epilepsy'. Eleven patients probably succumbed from pulmonary oedema or massive pleural effusions although many had evidence of pulmonary oedema at *post mortem* and the remainder from peritonitis, percarditis, pleurisy and diarrhoeal wasting disease relating to uraemia.

Much as we do nowadays, the mortality rate in each decade is recorded and it is noticed that those that died before their forty-fifth year comprised the biggest group—'we find that the large proportion of 50 out of 74 have sunk before the meridian of life'.

Richard Bright suspected that other forms of renal disease existed and although he felt that the high blood pressure and enlarged heart were secondary to renal damage was prepared to postulate, in a far-sighted way, how by two mechanisms high blood pressure could be sustained 'the altered quality of blood affords irregular and unwanted stimulus to the organ immediately; or that it so affects the minute and capillary circulation, as to render greater action necessary to force the blood through the distal subdivisions of the vascular system'—a very modern view which we shall see provided the foundation for further research at Guy's Hospital on essential or primary hypertension which in itself could cause pathological appearances reminiscent of the small contracted kidney but in the absence of a nephritic process.

As we have said, Dr Osman overlooked or perhaps just omitted the section on kidney disease which appeared in Volume II of *The Medical Reports*, possibly because it merely served to place the cerebral complications of advanced kidney disease in with the other disorders of the central nervous system. Bright notes that Sir Henry Halford had, in 1820 pointed out the 'Frequent termination of Ischuria Renalis in Coma and Apoplexy' and that a year later Dr Abercrombie had illustrated this in *The Edinburgh Medical and Surgical Journal*.

Bright suggests that the fits in patients with end-stage disease are the result of a high blood urea. He goes on to say how delighted he is that he has so many supporters of his views and quotes Dr Barlow of Bath, and Drs Mackintosh, Alison, Munro and Christison of Edinburgh amongst them. He mentions the importance of testing urine for albumen preoperatively as he feels surgery in the presence of renal disease is hazardous, a subject he returns to later in 'Memoir the Second'. Also there is the realistion that there was 'No direct ratio between the degree of disease and the quantity of albumen' and suggests that measuring the blood urea and the serum albumen would be a useful adjunct. He warns that quite severe kidney damage from renal calculi will not be picked up as the urine may not be coagulable. This last observation shows the depth and advanced state of Richard Bright's understanding of the intricacies of kidney disease—as we now know, proteinuria may be present in the absence of renal damage and may be absent in the presence of it. Digitalis, bleeding, cupping, leeches, purging, mercury and gentle tonics are all recommended as therapy.

The last article of any substance on renal disorders written by Richard Bright appeared in his continuing series of *Cases and Observations Illustrative of Renal Disease accompanied with the Secretion of Albuminous Urine—Memoir the Second*. The year was 1840, he was Physician Extraordinary to the Queen and a highly revered figure to whom all deferred on matters relating to the kidney.

However, major advances had been made in the understanding of nephritis, mainly in Edinburgh where Dr Robert Christison and Dr William Gregory had published their findings on the subject and in France Drs Rayer, Martin Solon and Forget had provided some formidable data challenging, to some extent, what they saw as a certain rigidity in the Bright classification. Between them they described five or six different types of kidney disease, although there was considerable overlap. Several had suggested that as time marched on, Bright was being left behind and his views had become outdated, but this is an unfair judgement; his fertile mind was already planning microscopic studies of the kidney in collaboration with Dr George Robinson the latest recruit to the team. In 'Memoir the Second' a note of exasperation creeps into the text as he defends his original work, suggesting that some of his 'Professional Brethren' had singularly 'misunderstood' and 'misinterpreted' his views. The problem was that proteinuria could occur as a result of functional disturbance of the kidney without structural damage and Bright points out that if his colleagues had taken the trouble to read his original work a bit more carefully they would see that he agreed with this! He then presents a further 23 case reports explaining succinctly that he should not be judged on his first studies carried out on mainly fatal cases of dropsy by including several cases with a good prognosis, adding that he was aware that patients could go into remission or even be cured of nephritis. He had said à propos the absence of dropsy

> 'It can never be sufficiently influenced upon the minds of practitioners that the anasarca which so often occurs in conjunction with this disease is but a symptom. The disease may exist in all its force and may be fatal with its insidious and sudden attacks without the effusion of a simple drop of fluid into the cellular membrane at any period of its course'.

We do know that Richard Bright did modify his views and recognised that coagulable urine could be present in the absence of dropsy or even other renal diseases and therefore it was indeed unjust to assess him on his original 1827 observations. There is an amusing story about the doctor who consulted him with proteinuria and was told to retire while in his forties as he had only two years to live; he survived into his eighties and indeed outlived Richard Bright! Nevertheless the latter would have been gratified that the old doctor did die of apoplexy; this illustrates the rather gloomy prognostic attitude taken by Richard Bright initially.[11]

He mentions his indebtedness to his clinical clerks Mr Noyes and Mr Blake for writing the case histories and it is obvious that Dr Bostock is approaching retirement because between 1837 and 1840 he has moved from Upper Bedford Place to Hampstead and in a rather sad letter to his old colleague dated 24 March says 'I must apologise for the imperfections of the analysis; which you must attribute to my being removed from my old laboratory and not having all my apparatus about me.' The article concludes with exhortations on treatment, bleeding, purging, strict confinement to bed, antimonial diaphoretics, warm baths, diuretics and if all else fails a voyage to the West Indies with residence on one of the more healthy islands—the last advice obviously for the benefit of his more affluent patients! Sir Benjamin Brodie his neighbour in Savile Row and one of the Founders of Urology had recommended the use of diosma crenata for irritability of

Sir Benjamin Brodie, Bart, FRS. (Portrait by Henry Room.[10])

the urinary organs which Richard Bright employed with some success.

The foregoing represents the major works on the kidney by Richard Bright; they have been compared with the great contributions of Vesalius and Laennec, and brought him fame, respect and gratitude from his medical colleagues in Britain and abroad and deservedly promoted him to the rank of those famous physicians who have been immortalised eponymously.

The nomenclature for Bright's disease evolved in the 50 or so years after his first description of the three basic types identified but not named by him and so 'albuminous nephritis' became the most satisfactory generally used term: in fact we still talk today of protein losing nephropathy prior to establishing a definite histological diagnosis from the appearance at renal biopsy.

It is a fitting postscript to Bright's work that, despite the many criticism from both his contemporaries and those that followed him about his studies and the degree of intellectual understanding that he placed on the true meaning of his findings, he has been fully vindicated. Histological examination of three kidneys from his original patients and examination of their case histories initiated by Dr Osman in 1937 and repeated on two further occasions in 1958 and 1972 have confirmed that both clinically and pathologically he was, even by present day standards, fairly close to a correct diagnosis.[12,13] Mary Sallaway, the 25-year old woman with pulmonary tuberculosis was found, predictably, to have a large white kidney infiltrated with amyloid deposits, something Bright could not have known about at that time.

Richard Bright did write on other renal pathology other than nephritis; Professor Leon Fine has reported on four further autopsies with notes in Richard Bright's own handwriting; these are held in The Royal College of Physicians, London.[14] The illustrations by Frederick Say[15] show further examples of kidney disease including calculi, tuberculosis and possibly metastatic tumour or abscesses; unfortunately in the continuing tradition of doctors Richard Bright's handwriting was often illegible.

Finally his last communication as a sole author appeared in *The London Medical Gazette* of 1841-42 as a letter concerning the pathology of the kidney and heralding the collaborative work with his colleague Dr Joseph Toynbee on the microscopic appearances of the kidney in his own disease.[16] It is difficult to understand the reason for this letter other than that he was upset that the team seemed to be fragmenting and each of them was publishing the collaborative work under their own names albeit with acknowledgement to Dr Bright, he was as usual trying to be fair in defending Dr Toynbee's right to some recognition.

'Sir,
'In consequence of having this morning received a memoir, which has been kindly dedicated to me by my very intelligent friend and pupil Mr George Robinson in which the pathology of the kidney in connection with the secretion of albuminous urine has been very diligently investigated, I have thought it almost incumbent upon me to beg of you to insert in your columns the following brief statement of what Mr J Toynbee has been doing during the last two years, in co-operation with me, upon this interesting subject: and this I do with the greater pleasure because some of the results of our labours in a great degree confirm, by actual observation, the views advanced by Mr Robinson; and our work would have been laid before the public several months ago, but from our desire of rendering the whole research complete, and latterly, from the

delay occasioned by engravings, of which many are still into the artist's hands.

'In the latter part of the year 1839, we first entered upon our investigations; and by microscopic observations made from more than a thousand specimens, obtained from the minutely injected kidneys of nearly a hundred individuals, chiefly labouring under this disease, we have been enabled to trace out the gradual change which the structure of the kidney undergoes during successive stages of the complaint, and by the aid of engravings the proof impressions of which are now before me, we shall be able to show that one of the most interesting features in the morbid anatomy of this disease is to be found in the condition of the corporal Malpighiana. Of these we possess specimens and drawings, the greater part made above a year and a half ago, illustrative of the various changes they suffer from the commencement of the disease till the kidney arrives at its most confirmed state of disorganisation; and as the specimens are all carefully preserved, should the engravings in any way fall short, the facts may be hereafter verified by any one desirous of ocular demonstration. I need scarcely say, that the observations of Mr George Robinson have been made altogether independently of the researches of Mr Toynbee and myself: our conclusions having been obtained from injections and minute anatomical observations in cases with whose histories we have been acquired; and although it has been well known at Guy's that I have been engaged in this research, I have not thought it right, co-operating as I have always been with Mr Toynbee, to make any public allusion to our results, till we could bring them forward in a form which should remove all doubts as to their accuracy.

'In conclusion I may add that our work on the Anatomy and Physiology of the Kidney, and the Pathology of that organ as connected with the secretion of Albuminous Urine will very shortly be submitted to the world.

'I remain, Sir,
Your obedient servant,
Richard Bright, MD
11, Savile Row, January 1842'

The letter was a link with the future. Sadly, the joint work was not published, possibly because of Richard Bright's attack of acute cholecystitis in 1842, but the fascinating story has been followed up and provides an excellent account of the birth and development of renal histology, illustrating the natural progression from the earlier, essentially macroscopic findings to those of microscopic appearances.[4] Ultimately Dr Toynbee did publish the findings in his own name.[17] This was the last of Richard Bright's medical writings: Dr H C Cameron concluded that 'Clinicians like Bright,

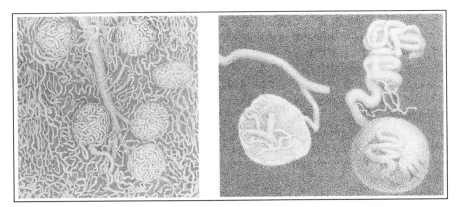

Engravings of the microscopic appearances of glomeruli from Toynbee's paper.[17]

who have made original discoveries of great value, are always apt from their very success to be forced in this way to abandon the wholehearted pursuit of new knowledge. It is a result not always to be deplored. For the researcher as for the poet, youth when vision is clearest and the imagination most easily fired is often the time for harvest. Wisdom because it is born of experience, comes later and when it comes, it cannot but bring new responsibilities and a new part to play. The call to relieve suffering is not one that can be refused, and only by answering it can the full stature of the physician be attained. Bright always looked upon these years of rewarding research as the happiest of his life but he may well have met the new call without regret.'[18] However, before examining the second phase of his medical career it is illuminating to look at his contribution to medicine beyond that of renal disease.

Chapter 11

The Medical Reports,
and Other Literature

'To connect accurate and faithful observations after death
with symptoms displayed during life, must be in some
degree to forward the objects of our noble art'

Richard Bright, 1827

Mr G A R Winston, the Wills' Librarian at Guy's said in 1958 that
'It is reasonable to assume that, during the hundred years that have
passed since the death of Richard Bright, all that could be said about
his life, work and published writings has been recorded'[1] *The
Medical Reports* nevertheless provide a fitting memorial to his life
and work and a testament to his contribution to medicine and its
literature, so let us now look at the remaining contents of Volume
I and the whole of Volume II which was devoted to the central
nervous system.

Sir William Hale-White, Consultant Physician to Guy's Hospital
in the 1920s was a dedicated Bright scholar and wrote extensively
on all matters pertaining to the Doctor's medical writings.[2,3] He
confessed to having read everything that Richard Bright had ever
written and this does not seem to have been an idle boast, certainly
his accounts of the contents of both volumes are extremely thorough
and if he sometimes embellishes the claims of originality for some
of his great hero's descriptions we can forgive him this foible as
Bright's descriptive powers could only enhance any previous account.
One gets the feeling that had he lived in the same period, he would
have become the Boswell to Bright's Johnson except that he tended
to be a little blind to the Doctor's faults—he must have had some!
Even today it is most rewarding to read the leisured and careful
observations of the past contained in the *Medical Reports*, that is,
if copies of the works can be obtained. In 1835 the author presented
both volumes, suitably inscribed, to the University of Bristol Medical
Library and happily they may be found in some other large libraries
attached to medical schools. Professor Thayer in his Bright Oration
deals extensively with the contents of both volumes and this provides
an admirable supplement to Hale-White's work.

Nowadays both Volumes I and II are rare collectors' items but do
appear occasionally at antiquarian book markets and at auction can
reach several thousand pounds. This must be compared with a
cost of three guineas for Volume I which was a high price to pay in
1827, and over seven pounds for Volume II in 1831. In fact just over

100 copies of Volume I were sold and it has been estimated that only 250 copies of the total works were purchased in all. Tragically, in 1861 the remainder were destroyed by fire.[4] However, through the auspices of The Royal Society of Medicine, Volume I has been elegantly reproduced by Gower Medical Publishers in their series of 'Library of the Medical Classics' and is a joy to handle and peruse.[5] Hopefully, Volume II may also be published in the future, in this facsimile form.

The first volume of the *Medical Reports* was 'most respectfully dedicated' to two of Bright's mentors at Guy's Hospital: to Benjamin Harrison Esq FAS with the words 'Under whose superintendence the benevolent views of the founder have been incalculably extended' and to William Babington MD, FRS, 'The early and able supporter of the medical school of that establishment'.

The Preface contains one of Bright's most memorable sayings: 'To render the labours of a large Hospital more permanently useful by bringing together such facts as seem to throw a light upon each other'. He also records his obligation to his two senior colleagues, Drs Cholmeley and Back, for allowing him access to their patients, although it is unlikely that he was on very intimate terms with the *ancien regime*; the 'young Turks' felt that the older physicians were out of touch with the needs of the hospital and students and were resistant to change such as the introduction of the stethoscope which they deemed a 'new fangled toy'. However, Dr William Babington, Bright's chief and father-in-law seems to have commanded much respect and was held in great affection by his staff.

Volume I comprises 222 pages, 90 case reports and 15 coloured plates and is best remembered for the classical section on kidney

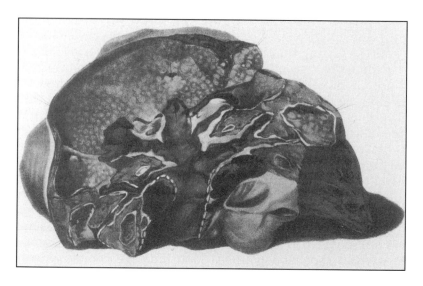

Plate X from Medical Reports *Vol. I: Pulmonary tuberculosis.*

disease; it goes on to report, and compare, a wide variety of cardiac and hepatic dropsies. There is a description of a fatty liver in one of Dr Hodgkin's patients and a large section on the lungs, finely illustrated and including patients with pneumonia, tuberculosis and other pulmonary diseases such as whooping cough followed by collapse of the lung. For those who can recall the smog in London, memories will be revived as he describes the hard winter of 1813-14 and the fatal cases of acute bronchitis and bronchopneumonia it produced, particularly in the elderly—'the almost unexampled continuance of dense fog and severe frost which followed, appeared to influence in a peculiar manner the lining membranes of the bronchi.' It is amazing that by 1830 Richard Bright was experimenting in the use of oxygen therapy in patients with a variety of complaints and that in Volume II he reports some improvement in their well-being.

It is fascinating to dip into the Reports and read of characters like Adeline, a 32 year old dancer from Astley's Theatre who died of an obstructive uropathy, secondary to cancer of the uterus with liver metastases and of Mr A B a young man of 28 with syphilis and a stricture of the rectum. The patients were almost entirely from the working classes, and as Guy's was situated in close proximity to the docks it is not surprising that a large number of sea-faring men, some from foreign parts, attended the hospital. Servants, coachmen, young children, gardeners, brassfounders, fire-engine drivers, blacksmiths, publicans, buskers, painters, druggists and very occasionally a gentleman made up the clientele. The foetor of the breath in gangrene of the lung is noted, a tape worm is found alive in the jejunum at *post mortem*, tuberculosis of the larynx is reported and a coagulum in the pulmonary artery probably describes an early example of a pulmonary embolus. Valvular disease of the heart is seen at several *post mortems* and a case of diabetes insipidus analogous to renal dropsy is discussed. Dropsy in some of the patients with advanced lung disease is clearly the result of cor pulmonale. Several of the patients who are admitted *in extremis* with ecchymoses are reminiscent of the clinical picture seen in patients with overwhelming septicaemia.

The last part of the book is devoted to ulceration of the gut in tuberculous and enteric disease, probably a mixture of typhus and typhoid fever which were not clearly distinguished at that time. Dr Bostock provides a section on the examination of the macroscopic appearance and composition of the liver and on the chemical composition of bile. It is quite encouraging therapeutically that the last eleven patients who were suffering from fever and irritable ulcerated bowel were cured, in stark contrast to the rather gloomy outcome of most of the other patients described. The very extensive medication used in the treatment of the 90 patients reported in Volume I was taken from either the *London Pharmacopoeia* or the *Pharmacopoeia of Guy's Hospital* (See Appendix 1).

Turning now to Volume II of the *Medical Reports* which was published in 1831, four years after Volume I and were in two parts both entitled 'Disease of the Brain and Nervous System' and dedicated to one of Dr Richard Bright's closest friends, James Franck MD, FRCS. In the Preface, as is his habit, he registers his pleasure in working at Guy's and pays tribute to the kindness, co-operation and support of his colleagues referring to,

> 'The great augmentation which has taken place to which I am attached; and which I am proud to say that my colleagues whether medical or surgical have, by their unremitting kindness, shown how little jealousy interferes between two professions, which as they are most properly separated in practice, should ever be united in study, in Science and in spirit.'

This very much refers to the rivalry between medicine and surgery which was fairly competitive in the 19th century and which still exists to the present day in a rather more teasing manner! However, it does illustrate that Bright was held in great esteem by surgical colleagues and was very much the surgeons' choice of physician at Guy's when a medical opinion was needed on a surgical ward.

He accepts the constructive criticisms for improving Volume II from Sir Astley Cooper who advised restricting the contents to cases illustrating morbid tissues of one system, in this case, the brain and spinal cord. However, as we have seen, Bright could not quite resist the temptation to add a small section on the kidney, albeit in relation to cerebral complications of chronic renal failure. He returns to the theme of diseased kidneys exerting morbid conditions on other organs of the body from high levels of blood urea, the classical situation in chronic uraemia. He concludes the Preface by saying

> 'Should I be fortunate enough to have followed worthily those who have distinguished themselves as labourers in the same field, both in this country and upon the Continent, and should this volume be sometimes associated with those of Dr Abercrombie and Mr Charles Bell, Mr Brodie, Dr Craigie, Dr Cheyne, Dr Munro and Dr Hooper in our own country and those of Andral, Foville, Lallemand, Magendie, Rostan and Serres and many others of our Continental brethen I shall feel in some degree compensated for the pains I have bestowed.'

Volume II in its two parts is a magnificent work of 724 pages and 40 coloured plates containing about 300 case reports which Bright sincerely hoped would be used for reference rather than for perusal. It is divided into three sections, namely 'Inflammatory', 'Pressure' and 'Irritation'; Part 1 includes the first two sections covering inflammation of the brain and its membranes, acute and chronic hydrocephalus, delirium tremens, apoplexy, paraplegia, concussion and spina bifida and Part 2 continues with hysteria, chorea, palsy from mercury, neuralgia, epilepsy, tetanus and hydrophobia.

The frontispiece is sub-titled 'Together with a concise statement of the diseased appearances of the brain and its membranes' by which one understands that the book has been illustrated with exquisite coloured plates, similar to those in Volume I. He had planned a section on 'Inanition' but felt that others including Drs Hall and Abercrombie had covered the subject adequately. Here is the art of history-taking at its best. Amongst this wealth of recorded morbid detail Bright exhibits great compassion for his patients, their misfortunes and their fortitude yet he never loses sight of the importance of advancing research or misses an opportunity to follow a patient in order to confirm, after death, his findings in life. These cameos of nature evoke not only the hardship and suffering of the patients but provide an insight into life in Victorian times. Take young Thomas Cuss, a stout 20-year old countryman who has sustained a puncture wound to his left eye inflicted by an umbrella point and who within an hour of his admission to Guy's at 1.00 pm was suffering from severe headaches. He became violent and had to be placed in a 'strait waistcoat'! By early evening he was delirious and was bled until his pulse became weak—'35 ounces were abstracted' and he 'gradually sunk' and died at four in the morning. *Post-mortem* revealed a penetrating wound of the orbit and dissolution of the brain substance.

The case reports show the wide diversity of Bright's interests with patients drawn from so many different specialities including gynaecology. Hale-White, the most meticulous chronicler of the Doctor's work, was perhaps forbidden by propriety from including the case of Mrs M, aged 74, the nymphomaniac who died sadly of what would appear to have been cancer of the cervix.

Apart from the recognised conditions of the brain and spinal cord such as cerebral haemorrhage he discusses a variety of other interesting patients suffering from diabetes, recovering hemiplegia, cerebral congestion secondary to whooping cough, advanced pulmonary disease, suffocation or the depressed respiration of laudanum or opium poisoning. Several of these miscellaneous patients were found to have granular kidneys at *post mortem* and it is revealing that the urine had not always been tested in life; it is a measure of Bright's thoroughness and tenacity that he sampled the urine for albumen taken from the bladder after death. Like all good neurologists he was an inordinately gifted anatomist with an uncanny skill for predicting, on the basis of his clinical examinations, the area of the brain where a lesion may be found and also which cranial nerve is subjected to the pressure of a tumour. He recognised the thalamic syndrome and likened the pains in a hemiplegic limb to the 'ghost pains' experienced by amputees. Several cases of lead neuropathy are reported but curiously the urine was not tested for the presence of kidney involvement. Modern day physicians have often pondered the incongruity of having to look after patients with head injuries who would seem to be more appropriately cared for by neuro-surgeons; times do not seem to have changed much as Bright not only looked after fractured skulls and recognised 'hernia cerebri' or 'coning' as a complication of raised intracranial pressure but also cared for patients with dislocated, diseased and fractured dorsal vertebrae.

Hydrocephalus, both acute and chronic, would appear to have been fairly common in the 19th century as no treatment was available for the commonest cause, tuberculosis; neither was there any means to relieve intra-cranial pressure other than by a direct tap. The ubiquitous Dr Bostock analysed the fluid from the celebrated hydrocephalic of the day, a man called Cardinal—his huge skull is well-illustrated in the book: apparently the bone was so thin that from the other side, a lighted candle or the sun could shine through his skull and cerebro-spinal fluid. Although the case reports themselves are entertaining, even more interesting are the observations which conclude each section and discuss broadly, the patients, their symptoms, diseases and treatment. Additional cases are used to illustrate a theory and to give the author's general overview of the subject. This is particularly revealing in Part 2 comprising only one section, entitled 'Irritation'; it expands on the more functional aspects of the central nervous system. He prefaces this section with:

'It is my intention to include in this division of the subject a number of diseases usually termed Nervous, some of which are strictly functional, while others occasionally owe their origin to structural changes—I shall commence with Hysteria, and pass on to Chorea, the Paralysis jactitans, and Palsy produced by mercury, Neuralgia, Epilepsy, Convulsions of children and Tetanus; and shall lastly relate a few cases of Hydrophobia;—thus ascending from the mildest and most curable to those which are more incurable or have altogether defied the effort of our art'.

Hysteria is a subject dear to Richard Bright's heart and he deals comprehensively with it. He was well aware of the dangers of taking the view that some symptoms and signs could be dismissed as hysterical without first making a careful assessment of the patient. He had said in the past 'This view has often been the unintentional cloak for ignorance and has materially retarded investigations.' Nevertheless, having been fairly scathing about labelling symptoms as hysterical or functional, he notes perceptively that the more psychoneurotic patients were less common in wards where a firm control was exercised by the Sister in Charge. Here again he shows his approach to the *esprit de corps* of his department, emphasising the importance of nursing care. One suspects that like Sir William Gull he thought that nursing was 'Sometimes a trade, sometimes a profession, ought to be a religion.' He warns particularly against labelling suspected peritonitis as hysterical. Next in importance to intemperance and cold weather as an aetiological factor in disease, is the mysterious and morbid effect that the uterus and its disorders seems to have had in causing diseases of women—a view still held by, one hopes, a diminishing number of male doctors today. There is no doubt that the sexual mores from the upper and middle classes of Victorian times led to a great deal of frustration and often, as a result, functional illness; Dr Thomas Addison was a strong supporter of this theory. All the common manifestations of hysteria are illustrated including abdominal pain, breathlessness, palpitations, painful breasts, headaches, fits, faints, hiccups, trismus, aphonia, dysphagia, painful feet, paralysis and often the ensuing hypochondriasis. The cure—drastic, but quick and effective, particularly in young women, was to shave their heads and dip them in a bucket of cold water which was kept under the bed.

Chorea as a result of acute rheumatism merits some mention as Richard Bright was accredited for much of his work on cardiac complications of the disorder describing pericarditis and possibly the mitral murmur of rheumatic valvular disease. Chorea is compared with hysteria, epilepsy and tetanus and oddly with the 'convulsive disease depending on the fumes of quick-silver'. It is a relief to know that in addition to the usual ghastly drug regimens meted out to the poor chorea patients, a cold shower or cold compresses were allowed on the day that purgatives had not been taken. Bathing in the sea to tone up, a glass or two of wine to stimulate the appetite, and a little exercise in the open air were considered beneficial.

One of Bright's most remarkable contributions to neurology, and the one by which he is most remembered, is his description of Jacksonian epilepsy. He recognised this in patients with localised fits, convulsions or epilepsy confined to one part of the body, usually the limb. He later opined 'that these fits were owing to some local disorganisation affecting the membranes and cineritious portion of the brain . . .' also that the epileptic character seemed to point to the membranes and surface of the brain as the part most affected and, more importantly, recognised that the patient rarely lost consciousness. 'My reason, then for supposing that the epileptic attacks, in this case depended on a local affection . . . was the degree of consciousness observed to be retained during the fits.' i.e. classical Jacksonian epilepsy. One can almost hear him say in his rational, perhaps rather pedantic way: 'In disease, as in other things cause and effect will be found to follow each other in pretty regular succession'.

Table 1
Some diseases and syndromes described in Medical Reports Vol. I and II

Acute yellow atrophy, cirrhosis of the liver and delirium tremens
Jaundice in liver and gall-bladder disease; gastric erosions
Glycosuria and steatorrhea in pancreatic disease
Acute appendicitis, peritonitis and hydatid disease
Tuberculous laryngitis
Acute rheumatic fever, with chorea, valvular disease and pericarditis
Heart block and Stoke-Adams attacks
Pertussis broncho-pneumonia and finger clubbing[a], pulmonary
    thrombo-embolism
Morphine, lead and mercury poisoning
Erysipelas
Herpes labialis and zoster
Localization of organic brain lesions
Nominal aphasia, dysgeusia and hemianopia
Jacksonian and idiopathic epilepsy; post-epileptic paralysis and
    somnambulism
Suppurative meningitis secondary to sinus and ear infections
Tuberculous meningitis and internal hydrocephalus
Sinus thrombosis, fractured skull and vertebra
Subarachnoid haemorrhage from berry aneurysms
Transient ischaemic attacks and narcolepsy

[a]Bright used oxygen therapy in respiratory distress.

The causes, both functional and organic, of spasmodic wry-neck are explored, the use of belladonna plasters in sciatica is discussed and post herpetic neuralgia is treated successfully with two or three scruples of subcarbonate of iron daily. Sir Henry Halford, who was known as the eel-backed Baronet on account of his deep courtly bows was physician-in-ordinary to four monarchs, namely George III and IV, William IV and Queen Victoria, felt that tic-doloreux was caused by encroachment on the nerve by spicules or abnormal growth of bone as they passed through the bony canals of the skull and Bright provides a case to support this hypothesis. He concludes Volume II with case reports depicting the horrors of tetanus and hydrophobia, both extremely serious diseases today in some parts of the world. One can envisage the anguish of realization that would follow the bite from a rabid dog and then the delay while awaiting a ghastly death: one man was even bitten by a bear as well as a dog and another underwent amputation of his arm without anaesthetic before dying. Tetanus, although not considered so lethal a condition today, was almost inevitably fatal then and was associated with appalling terminal spasm until death came as a merciful release.

These two volumes of the *Medical Reports* not only give an account of Bright's lifetime's work which, in a series of meticulously taken case notes, reflects his whole attitude to the care to his patients and his immense skill as a diagnostician, but also provide a record of the social, domestic and environmental factors within the pattern of the diseases prevalent in his time. He cannot be blamed for the fact that treatment failed so lamentably: he did at all times attempt to alleviate suffering as best he could; although when examining the lists of purges, depletions and other measures one sometimes wonders if, apart from pain killers, nature might have been a better option.

Clinical memoirs on abdominal tumours and intumescence
Richard Bright contributed many articles on abdominal diseases to the *Guy's Hospital Reports* and we have surmised that his deep interest in gastroenterology stemmed from his original concern with dropsy, characterised in some cases by ascites which is, incidentally, one of the cardinal signs of intra-abdominal michief. After Bright's death the collected papers were produced in book form and edited by his old friend and colleague of many years, Dr G Hilaro Barlow; they were published by the New Sydenham Society in 1860.[6] It is a fascinating book, very much in the now familiar 'genre' of Richard Bright, containing illustrated case reports of some 117 patients with a variety of abdominal and pelvic pathologies. Sadly, in this collected volume, the drawings are reproduced in wood by Mr Tuffen West and they do not compare with the standard of those in the original articles in the *Guy's Hospital Reports* which were cut in stone and provide a sharper image. The editorial preface provides Barlow with the opportunity to pay a sincere tribute to his old chief and the significance of his work: here we have the most famous epitaph to Richard Bright's life:

'There has been no English physician—perhaps it may be said none of any country—since the time of Harvey who has affected not only so great an advance in the knowledge of particular diseases, but also so great a revolution in our habits of thought, and methods of investigating morbid phenomena and tracing the aetiology of disease, as has the late Dr Richard Bright.'

Dr Barlow goes on to say that he

'Was indeed a man of natural clear judgement; and, as far as such a virtue can be said to have been a natural gift, of great industry. But the strongest powers of intellect languish and become feeble, if not matured by exercise, an industry which is not consistently exercised upon some definite object degenerates into a fitful restlessness.'

Barlow gives due recognition to both Drs Blackall and Wells whose earlier work on the kidney provided the foundation on which Bright's work was built and who had 'Investigated the subject in a most philisophical spirit, but missed, though narrowly, the discovery of the disease of the kidney.'

He mentions a 'singular power of observation' and 'the most trifling circumstances rarely escaped him'. What perhaps is the most significant statement of all and which passes as a thread through a lot of Bright's work, notably in the miscellaneous cases at the end of his *Medical Reports* in both Volumes I and II, is that if he describes a patient whose condition he does not quite understand he hopes that those who follow him will be able to make a diagnosis:

> 'He was in the habit of recording facts and observations on diseases and morbid anatomy apparently the most trifling, saying, that if he did not at the time perceive the importance, they might be available to himself or others at some future period.'

The other qualities for which Bright was eminently distinguished was his 'philosophical truthfulness' for

> 'He was, indeed, in all the relations of life, a man without guile and as he would have scorned an untruth, so would he not endure that the slightest bias should be given to any of his observations, in order to favour any particular views or opinions.'

Barlow's summing up of the renal findings in the editorial preface in fact is almost more concise that that of even Bright himself. He mentions not only the triad of albuminous urine, dropsy and diseased kidneys but also the low serum albumen and the raised blood urea or 'inquination' of the blood in some of the patients. Lest we underestimate Bright's contribution to renal disease he concludes:

> 'To those who have received the knowledge of the connection of dropsy, albuminous urine and disease of the kidney among the first rudiments of medicine, the facts which established that connection may appear so simple and easily ascertained that the amount of labour, the accuracy of observation and the right adherence to the inductive method which characterised the whole of Bright's researches may hardly have been suspected still less adequately appreciated.'

He ends the preface by explaining that some rearrangement was necessary to the original articles to bring the illustrations in line with the text and that a list of cases and an index have been added.

The book itself, which largely covers the same ground as the Goulstonian lectures, contains chapters on hydatid disease and ovarian, uterine, splenic, renal, hepatic and gall-bladder tumours—the word tumour being used in the old-fashioned sense of swelling or enlargement, although true growths are included amongst the cases. Once again, as with the *Medical Reports* one is struck by the meticulous detail recorded in case histories and the obvious interest that Bright showed in the background of his patients. Chapter one provides an excellent introduction to the 'explorations of the abdomen' with the use of 'ballotment' to feel viscera in an ascitic abdomen and gives a quite fascinating account of how Bright invented a device whereby an outline of the abdomen could be stamped on the case notes—a practice that most clinicians still employ today. With the assistance of his surgical colleague and friend Mr Edward Cock, who like Aston Key and Bransby Cooper was a nephew of Sir Astley Cooper and probably supplied the expertise on surface anatomy, he drew the abdomen, sub-divided into sections on which the position and size of any tumour could be drawn for future reference and in order to record any progression or regression in size.

Richard Bright instructed a Mr Bentley of High Holborn to produce a brass plate on which the outline of the abdomen was stencilled, this could then be stamped on the notes; the plates could be purchased for two or three shillings. He also suggested that it would be a simple matter, for the same price to reproduce them as a woodcut or type when, with common ink, they could be used as a seal.

The other chapters provide a glimpse back in time to the sort of gross pathology rarely, if ever, seen nowadays and certainly not in such an advanced state. The account of patients with hydatid disease is pure medical history and one is struck by the enormous size that these acephalocysts reached during the follow-up period. In this study

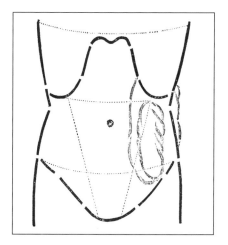

Diagram of Dr Bright's stencil outline of the abdomen showing an enlarged left kidney.

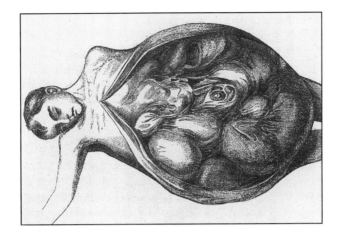

Post mortem appearance of the hydatid disease in October 1836.

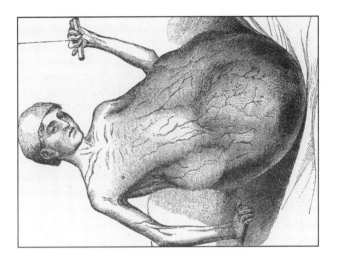

The same patient in October 1836.

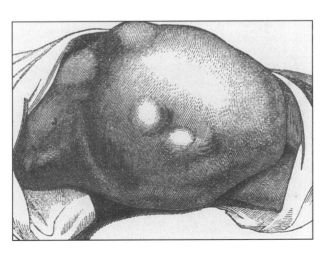

Abdominal hydatid disease in a patient Thomas D, June 1828.

Bright writes 'I examined the fluid very carefully using Dr Roget's microscope'—apparently the latter had just obtained it from Amici—and the artist, Mr Say, who had illustrated Volume I of the *Medical Reports* sketched the microscopic appearance of the cysts. Some of the other drawings were produced by Mr Canton, one of the other medical artists to Guy's who was largely responsible for the plates in Volume II of the *Medical Reports* and described by Sir Astley Cooper as an 'untidy, idle fellow, nevertheless an excellent draughtsman'. Interestingly in one of the cases of hydatid disease, haematuria and coagulable urine are noted and at *post mortem* the kidneys showed gross distension from obstructions to the ureters by the cysts. Dr Cholmeley was said to have favoured tapping the cysts and mention is made of a sucking pump to facilitate aspiration of the fluid which was then sent to Drs Rees, Bostock and Babington for analysis. Again, as in the *Medical Reports*, some patients who had been seen many years previously were recalled and included to supplement the collection, indicating that Richard Bright kept meticulous records of all his old patients. Case 12 was seen in 1813 while he was practising at the Bishop's Court Dispensary and in 1837 he wrote to Dr Laird who had retired to Bognor to obtain some follow-up details. In fact, much as with the *Medical Reports*, in a few chapters he uses some cases taken from the redoubtable Dr Hodgkin's catalogue of Guy's Museum to augment the numbers of reports. The majority of the cases had been collected roughly between 1821 and 1840 and one is struck by the fact that he rarely omits acknowledging the help of the referring physician or surgeon. In the chapter on ovarian tumours or dropsy he was called to see a five month old infant with intestinal obstruction, made a diagnosis of intussusception and was gratified to see this confirmed at autopsy—paediatrics was not a separate specialty!

In researching the section on the spleen Bright had not only studied Dr Baillie's pathological collection in the Museum of the Royal College of Physicians but also the specimens in the Royal College of Surgeons. He reports on the sad case of a nine-year old girl who has sustained a laceration of the spleen after being run over by a cart-wheel and politely contradicts Hodgkin's theories on the subject! He was obviously aware of the acute onset of a varicocoele as a harbinger of a renal tumour. He mentions an occasion on 30 October, 1836 when he visited a woman in the Borough who had been attending the Surrey Clinic and it is fascinating to read that as he left her home he made 'hasty' notes but in true Victorian understatement they are precise, elegantly descriptive, lucid and beautifully written and were probably accompanied by one of his abdominal outlines.

Such was his reputation that in the section on renal tumours Mr Hale of Guy's obviously unable to refer the patient, brought him a *post-mortem* specimen of the growth.

In the chapter on liver disease he describes a woman aged 30 who had dropsy and a large liver and at post-mortem was found to have mitral stenosis. The book contains a wealth of interesting case reports and is a pleasure to read even today, reflecting as it does the enormous care taken by Bright to record the almost infinite details of his patients during life and after death. Here we have one of the earliest descriptions of steatorrhoea and pancreatic diabetes and we shall return to these findings in the section on 'medical journalism'.

The textbook of medicine
Although Thomas Addison had been teaching for many years as an Associate Physician, following the ill-health and later death, of Dr Cholmeley, a vacancy was created on the staff at Guy's and he was appointed to join Richard Bright as a Full Physician. Thus began an association which produced one of the truly great teaching partnerships in the history of medical education. As we know, a good deal of intrigue had been going on behind the scenes regarding the sale of lectureships and the 'right to give lectures'; this dated from the time when the United Borough Hospitals split into separate medical schools. These two men seemed to complement each other and their lectures were well-attended and rivalled even those of Dr Peter Latham, Consultant Physician at St Bartholomew's Hospital who was considered to be the most outstanding clinical lecturer of his day, a man with whom Bright has often been compared and we are told, the physician who listened to Bright's chest and diagnosed his heart condition.[7] Of course, we know, *The Lancet* decried Bright and Addison as 'Dull, pompous teachers who all prospective students would do well to avoid'. Thomas Addison gradually became the more popular lecturer and his style, less avuncular and more erudite than Bright's made favourable comparison with that of Sir Astley Cooper. He was said to have raised the teaching standard at Guy's to great heights almost single-handed. He had many devotees among his past students and Dr Golding Bird, remembered for his book on 'Urinary Deposits', which was one of the first of its type, dedicated the work to Thomas Addison.

One curious incident occurred in relation to Bright's student lectures which seems rather out of character: a student felt impelled to write a letter to the *Lancet* following an introductory lecture by Dr Bright in which the latter inferred that medical students attended Guy's only 'on sufferance' and the Governors in reply had to try and pacify the irate pupil by suggesting that he would have recourse to a Court of Law should he be expelled unjustly.[8] Furthermore it is difficult to be sure whether $\Delta E\Omega$, an anonymous writer in another contribution to the *Lancet* was paying tribute to Bright or was merely being facetious about his lectures; we would like to think he was genuine in his remarks. As with the famous Welsh

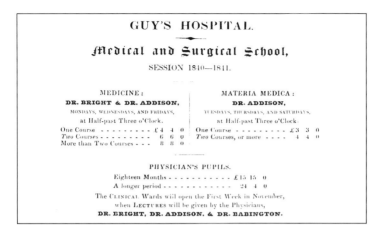

Medical students' timetable.

rugby outside-half immortalized in song by ballad singer, Max Boyce, it stated that:

'Natura lo fece, e poi ruppe la stampa'

i.e. 'Nature shaped him and then broke the mould'—a fitting tribute, we feel, to a man who has had few equals in the field of renal medicine.[9]

In 1836 Richard Bright and Thomas Addison published the results of their labours by committing their lecture notes into book form entitled *Elements of the Practice of Medicine.* Volume I appeared from the press of Longman's as did Bright's *Medical Reports* and is now a rare book partly because it was incomplete as Volume II was not published. As the preface indicates, the textbook was provided ostensibly as an elementary introduction to the history, clinical features and treatment of disease for medical students and one assumes for junior medical staff as well. It is 'properly devoid of theory and controversy' but sadly lacks also any index or references: it is written in the typically stilted literary style of the period using a vocabulary slightly alien to the present day. The text is interspersed with untranslated Latin and Greek quotes and we must thus assume that the medical profession was more proficient in these languages than it is today! Full of tautologies and semantically demanding, the book, nevertheless, gives a valuable insight into the historical details of treatment and equipment being used then, and now long-since forgotten. As we have already heard, the textbook received poor reviews from the medical press. In predictable style, Thomas Wakley of *The Lancet* pounced on the opportunity to denigrate a textbook emanating from Guy's and wrote:

'If, in any given work on the practice of medicine, facts of importance are distorted or omitted—if by a vicious process of induction false references are drawn from them—if fine spun theories are palmed on the reader as results of direct observation—if confusion and disorder prevail instead of well-ordered arrangement—if obscurity of diction render this or that chapter unintelligible—will it seriously be contended that such faults become venial because the volume disfigured by their presence was designed for, and need therefore mislead and mystify students alone?'

The *Lancet* went on to say 'We cannot help expressing our regret that so defective a product should have issued from such a source' i.e. Guy's Hospital.

Reading it today, one is struck by its rather muddled layout and the style lacks the warmth and intensity of Richard Bright; one suspects that most of it was written by Thomas Addison. Although this is a personal opinion, it has to be noted that no less an authority than the medical historians Drs Fielding Garrison and Hale-White felt the same way. Certainly it is highly unlikely that Richard Bright could have written the section on nephritis, as in 1836 his understanding of renal disease was very much more advanced than the content would indicate: the true infection of pyelonephritis is often confused with the inflammation of glomerulonephritis. Despite these reservations this is an interesting book, as scattered throughout its 560-odd pages reference is made to medical personalities and epidemiological information pertaining to that century. The authors assume, of course, that the contemporary reader knew of these people, events and sometimes, pieces of equipment—an assumption which gives the present day reader pause for thought; who was Dr Clutterbuck and what was a Mudge inhaler? Presumably it refers to Dr Henry Clutterbuck, a Cornishman who attended Edinburgh and Guy's a few years before Bright and who was an authority on fevers and agreed with the views expressed in the book.[10] Reference is made to the 'celebrated Boerhaave', the 'illustrious Sydenham' and even the 'great Hippocrates'. In the chapter on fevers one is surprised to find that the patient's temperature was not being recorded; apparently clinical thermometry was not introduced into Guy's until the latter part of the 19th century. Almost 20% of the book is devoted to fevers which is not surprising as infections constituted the largest part of medical practice then. Mention is made of Hippocrates' belief that fevers were the result of fermentation of morbidic matter and this theory had been supplanted by that of Boerhaave who postulated that it was due to an increase in viscosity or viscidity of the blood as he called it: both theories have some credence to them even today. In the chapter on influenza, fascinating epidemiological details are found

Dr Thomas Addison. (Courtesy of Guy's Hospital.)

relating to the severe outbreak in 1781-82 which swept across the Continents of Asia and Europe affecting four out of five of the population. The pattern of 'flu does not seem to have changed much down the years as several different types were described and in the year of the book's publication in 1836, it seemed to have been then, as it is now, particularly fatal in the aged.

Pulmonary disease was one of Thomas Addison's great fortes and the section on the lungs is extremely detailed. The Laennec-style stethescope was being used regularly at Guy's by the 1830s, probably because Thomas Hodgkin was a keen advocate, and in the section on auscultation the character of the breath sounds are euphonically compared with the 'croaking and squeaking voice of Mr Punch'. Further amusing and unusual similes are used, e.g. 'conveying to the ear of the auscultator a sound resembling that produced by raising a flat fish from a moist butcher's slab' or the 'whizzing and gurgling occasioned by a cow suddenly raising a flat hoof from out of a mass of mud'.

The much-quoted section, which gives one of the best descriptions of acute appendicitis and peritonitis is, of course, not the first account of the disease as that honour was rightly bestowed upon Dr James Parkinson who described it in 1812 and who will be better remembered for his masterly work on the 'shaking palsy' to which his name is attached.[11]

Each section concludes with an account of the prevailing treatments of the day. The lack of successful therapeutic measures led to an awesome degree of poly-pharmacy but on the practical side it is interesting that tracheostomy was considered in diphtheria and paracentesis thoracis in pneumothorax—quite avant-garde for the time.

Medical Journalism

In addition to his medical books, Richard Bright was a major contributor to the medical periodicals of his day. Compared with the enormous proliferation of scientific journals today, only a select few were extant in the 19th century. Very much as is the practice nowadays, communications or papers read to medical meetings and societies were published in the organisation's gazette, transactions or proceedings and perhaps at a later date reappeared either as an abstract or in an extended form. This explains much of the reduplication that we see in most of Bright's writings. Interestingly, a recent article in the *British Medical Journal* has deplored duplicate publication as 'time wasting . . . dishonest . . . and colludes with the notion that publication is in itself meritorious and desirable, instead it probably gives undue prominence to findings which are reported repeatedly'.[12] It is, however, unlikely that the Doctor was attempting to increase the bulk of his curriculum vitae as an aspiring young doctor, bent upon a hospital career, might have to do today! Most of his articles appeared in the *Medico-Chirurgical Transactions*, *The Lancet*, *The London Medical Gazette*, but of course, primarily, after 1836 in *The Guy's Hospital Reports* and it has been postulated that the title was adopted from Bright's own *Medical Reports* as a tribute to him. Sadly a few of Bright's oral presentations were not published and some have either been mislaid or lost, e.g. the Lumleian lecture. Curiously, in 1928, *Guy's Hospital Reports* reprinted a paper read before the Royal Medical Society of Edinburgh in 1813 entitled 'On Gangrene'.[13] He suggests in it that senile gangrene is met with in men advanced in age especially 'the rich and voluptuous who eat to excess'. Additionally, in the minutes of the Guy's Physical Society of October 1839 there is an account of clubbing of the fingers in pulmonary tuberculosis, empyema or chronic lung suppuration.[14]

In 1952 Russell Brock, later Lord Brock, reviewed the history of the *Guy's Hospital Reports* to mark the publication of the hundredth volume.[15] In 1798 Astley Cooper the surgeon, Haighton the physician-accoucheur and Babington the physician had produced a volume called *Medical Reports and Researches* which, although it did not flourish, was the precursor of the *Guy's Hospital Reports*. The first volume, in which Bright contributed nine articles out of 42, was published in 1836, its appearance no doubt stimulated by the fact that St Thomas's Hospital had instituted their own journal one year earlier: rivalry was still intense at that time between the two hospitals, following the split in 1825. Dr Hilaro Barlow was the first editor and continued in this role for 13 years. The journal was one of the few medical periodicals available and was taken by hospital libraries throughout the country as a means of keeping up-to-date with modern trends. The *Guy's Hospital Reports* are still published: Initially at the beginning of each journal was inscribed a quotation from Warner's *Textbook of Surgery*—'A hospital is not only an instrument of relief to the distressed who are immediately helped there, but also a means of helping others by furnishing such principles and practice as may improve the art of surgery and thus render the benefit more general.' As Warner was a surgeon working in the 18th century medicine was not mentioned! This quotation was later replaced by one of Bright's better known *bon mots* about the 'labours of a large hospital' expressing roughly the same sentiments. Comprehensive lists of all Bright's articles have been completed by several authors;[16] some of the papers became classics and are worth discussing.

In 1825-26 he contributed three articles to the same volume of *The Lancet*: the first was 'A Case of Traumatic Tetanus' under the joint care of himself and the surgeons Sir Astley Cooper and Mr Morgan; the second 'A Singular Case' about a patient with syringomelia and the third 'On the Contagious Nature of Erysipelas'.[17,18,19] After this, Bright's time was well occupied writing the *Medical Reports*, Volume I, which was published in 1827, and presiding over Guy's Physical Society, the proceedings of which appeared regularly in the *London Medical Gazette*.

In the intervening four years between 1827 and 1831 when Volume II of *Medical Reports* was completed he published very little except for a letter included in an article by Dr John Bostock on 'A Case of profuse perspiration with analysis of the fluid' in the *Medico-Chirurgical Transactions*.[20] An increasingly productive period followed from 1833 until 1840 and Sir William Hall-White postulated that one of Bright's most important articles was on disorders of the pancreas and duodenum in which he described pancreatic diabetes and steatorrhoea or, as fatty stools were then known 'alvine evacuations'. The article was abstracted from the *Medico-Chirurgical Transactions* for the *London Medical Gazette* and the *Lancet*.[21-23] This finding had been mentioned already in one of the Goulstonian lectures on abdominal viscera which also included an excellent description of scleroderma.

It was customary for papers in the *Medico-Chirurgical Transactions* or even the *Guy's Hospital Reports* to reappear in these second two journals, presumably because of their wider circulation; this applied not only to his papers on chronic proliferative peritonitis which we assume was either secondary to tuberculosis, malignant disease or idiopathic fibrosis, but also to his work on the treatment of fever.[24,25] This latter work was based on a case history which contained the excellent advice that 'It is a duty incumbent upon the physician who has ventured at any time to lay before the professional his ideas of disease and its treatment, to review from time to time his published opinions, that he may see how subsequent experience has borne out or modified his former impressions!'

A series of articles on disease of the central nervous system followed which were often modified versions of some of the cases in *Medical Reports*: those include the description of Jacksonian epilepsy with the emphasis on retention of consciousness as a diagnostic clue linked with the ability to localise the area of damage in the brain. In fact, neurologists have emphasised the contributions that Bright's perspicacity has made to the early descriptions of cerebral infarcts and haemorrhages, known then respectively as serous and sanguinous apoplexy.[26] Bright stated that cerebral infarcts or softenings were always the result of old haemorrhages and did not use the term 'cerebral thrombosis' or stroke, only apoplexy and hemiplegia.

He did, however, present examples of 'cartilaginous' or 'ossified' plaques in the arteries at the base of the brain. Although the relationship between 'ossification of blood vessels' and apoplexy was only vaguely perceived at that time; the term arteriosclerosis had only just been coined by Lobstein in 1833 and atherosclerosis, as yet, did not exist in the medical vocabulary. The reason why Bright's stroke cases were often young or middle-aged is explained by the fact that renal patients develop a raised blood pressure at an earlier age and this, coupled with biochemical distortions, mainly of the lipid metabolism, results in a rapid ageing of the arterial tree in the form of atherosclerosis. In addition, our neurological colleagues have paid tribute to Bright for his identification of narcolepsy and epilepsy secondary to a tumour of the dura mater; Mrs W aged 67 has been for 30 or 40 years, subject to a 'most remarkable drowsiness'.[27] He also describes, in a separate communication, a rather odd case of a patient with spastic paraplegia said to be secondary to a cerebral tumour with descending degeneration of the cord.[28]

Furthermore, geriatricians have recognised Bright's clinical acumen in describing 'little strokes' or transient ischaemic attacks where atherosclerotic narrowing or stenosis of the carotid and basilar arteries at the base of the brain can lead to 'drop attacks' or periods of momentary paralysis, loss of facial expression and loss of speech.[29] Up until the discovery that Richard Bright had reported such clinical phenomena it was thought that 'little strokes' had not been described properly until 1950—a further example of the old adage that many a 'man's new idea is as old as the hills'.

As we have read, the definitive articles on abdominal disease which appeared in the *Guy's Hospital Reports* between 1838-40 were gathered together in one volume and printed by The New Sydenham Society in 1860, two years after Bright's death. These provide, in addition, the substance of further contributions on the liver describing acute yellow atrophy, malignant disease and jaundice. Later, some of the collected articles and lectures were published in book form containing reprints of work on diseases of the peritoneum, kidney and misplacement of the stomach.[30] During his career he wrote several case-reports, which today might be called 'pot-boilers'; on a congenital short oesophagus with a diaphragmatic hernia, chorea and rheumatic pericarditis with a mitral murmur, renal calculous disease and a case of a 38 year old parchment worker who, following treatment with quinine and stimulants, survived an attack of tetanus; such a recovery must have been rare in the 19th century.[31-34]

Envoi

In conclusion it would be fitting to examine the contributions made by some of Richard Bright's able contemporaries and successors who did so much to consolidate and advance our knowledge of renal disease. Drs Wells, Blackall and Bright were, in our understanding of the evolution of nephritis, the first of the 'few' with the latter very much more than just the 'first amongst equals'. One might extend the Churchillian analogy; Lord Evans in the Lettsomian lectures in 1949 stated of Bright that 'Never, I think, in the history of medicine, have claims to being first to give an adequate description of a disease been more properly recognised. His writings leave us with a humble mind'.[35] Certainly the many pioneering physicians both in Britain and Europe who worked on improving our knowledge of nephritis, hypertension and, in fact, renal disease in general, owed him a great debt. Nevertheless occasionally one feels that, to begin with, he was without honour in his own country.

Obviously, it was Bright's renal work that created the greatest sensation amongst members of the profession and, valuable though some of his other work is, the unfolding story of research into kidney disease held the centre of the stage. We have seen that the microscopic appearances of tissue from the kidney was gradually supplementing examination of the whole organ macroscopically and the histological studies with which Bright was involved towards the end of his working career at Guy's were becoming available.

Progress in renal research even during Bright's lifetime was rapid; he had led the way and apart from a few doubters including Dr Graves and Dr Osborne in Dublin and Drs Copeland and Elliotson in London, had opened the medical profession's eyes to the importance of coagulable urine in dropsy. Several of his contemporaries at home and abroad, the renal team at Guy's Hospital, and those who came immediately after his death, added a greater clinical dimension to the basic three forms described by Bright in 1827 which even by the early 1830s was becoming dated, largely because of the pathological bias of his descriptions.

However, a good deal of misunderstanding and misinterpretation had followed publication of his original renal treatise and led to a kind of 'Alice in Wonderland complex'—'Then you should say what you mean . . . I do, at least I mean what I say'. The major stumbling block was the, as yet, undiscovered examples of patients with high blood pressure. The patient with hypertension leading to renal disorders and in some cases small contracted kidney exhibited no evidence of albuminuria, e.g. coagulable urine, and this caused enormous problems and debate in the light of Bright's edicts. The modern concept that kidney damage produces hypertension and hypertension produces kidney damage was unknown; an idea that Professor Kark has called the Bright Riddle.[36]

His contemporaries can be forgiven for being slightly resentful believing that the Bright theories tended to be written in stone and some colleagues felt he was a bit arrogant and aloof. In fact, Bright did not name his various types of nephritis other than numerically 1, 2 and 3 and although his own ideas changed between 1827 and his retirement from renal work in 1842 mainly in relation to prognosis and treatment, several other classifications were introduced by his fellow nephrophiles to rationalise the clinical rather than the pathological modes of presentation. It is therefore, interesting to look at some of the men who followed in Bright's wake; it was fitting that in Britain the first confirmation of his work should have originated from his old medical school in Edinburgh. Dr Robert Christison, later Sir Robert, was one of the giants in the history of medicine in Edinburgh and his extraordinarily industrious life, entertainingly and admirably related in his two-volume autobiography and edited by his sons, had much in common with that of Richard Bright, even to their shared interest in climbing and sketching![37]

Robert Christison who was, in Edinburgh, twice President of the Royal College of Physicians, a Fellow of the Royal Society there and Professor of Medicine at the University, published his book on *Granular degeneration of the Kidnies and its connection with dropsy,*

*Dr Robert Christison. (Courtesy of the Royal College
of Physicians, Edinburgh.)*

inflammation and other diseases in 1839; the spelling of kidneys is in
old Scots.[38] It contains 30 illustrative cases of nephritis, rather in the
Bright mode, but is in many ways a more readable book than the
Medical Reports, in that it starts with an historical perspective of the
state of the art in nephritis and mentions those physicians working
in that field, an area that Bright sometimes tended to overlook.

Sir Robert deserved the accolade of the 'Bright of Scotland' as in
his book he was able to confess to: 'repeating and verifying the
material parts of Dr Bright's statements'. Both men had been
weaned on the teachings of Drs Abercrombie, Gregory and Alison,
and therefore had been exposed to the same atmosphere in
Edinburgh which had a strong renal flavour: they later became close
friends. Sir Benjamin Brodie, Professor of Surgery to the Royal
College of Surgeons, an Astley Cooper-like character who was Dr
Bright's neighbour in Savile Row, had invited him to meet Dr
Christison at supper and we know that the latter wrote to Dr Bright

about the last days and death of his old friend and patient, Lord Jeffrey on 31 January 1850,[37] (see Appendix 2).

The other great contributions came from France—Dr Rayer in Paris, Dr Martin-Solon in Montpelier and Dr Forget in Strasburg, and the most outstanding renal physician of Bright's era was undoubtedly Dr Pierre Rayer working at the Hôpital de la Charité; in some ways he surpassed in his work on renal disease the man he most admired and to whom he paid the tribute 'cette belle de couvert et le fil naturelle de passe et le conclusion tire par une esprit sagace de ces propre observations.'[39]

Rayer's three volume *Traité des Maladie des Reins* is a monumental treatise with one of the most comprehensive historial accounts of research into renal disease up until 1840. By its nature it is not really comparable to Richard Bright's renal writings and is, without doubt, *the* renal textbook of the 19th century, reminiscent in some ways in its thoroughness to Professor Jean Hamburger's textbook of nephrology written in the 1960s.[40] One of the most rewarding periods during the writing of this monograph has been the translations of the historical section of Rayer's book and it is hoped that this may be published in the future. The accompanying atlas in some ways surpasses that of even Richard Bright's in its detail and Dr Rayer was fortunate in having Ambrose Tardieu as the illustrator.

Apart from his contribution to skin disease little is known of Rayer's life, although in 1931 a Dr Raoule Caveribert wrote his doctoral thesis on the life and work of Rayer and Professor Gabriel Richet has more recently contributed a further account of the latter's important position in renal medicine.[41,42]

Rayer was born at Saint-Sylvan in the Department of Calvados on 7 March 1793. He studied medicine in Paris and rather like Bright he liked to travel and went as a student to Dijon in 1812 to care for Spanish prisoners suffering from typhus. He was a prize-winning medical student and presented a scholarly thesis on the history of anatomy in 1818. By 1822 he was in Barcelona studying yellow fever and translating a monograph on this disease from the Spanish. Early in his career he fell foul of the authorities of the teaching hospital because of his protestant sympathies, but by the age of 30 he was a member of the Académie de Médicin and many honours were to follow including that of Consultant Physician to Louis Phillipe and Napoleon III.

In 1830 he began his researches into renal disease with the help of his students and his book was the fruit of these labours over a period of about nine years. The work covers not only the kidney but physiology, pathology and diseases of the urinary tract. Rayer divided nephritis into primary acute and chronic nephritis, and nephritis secondary to morbid poisons, probably pyelonephritis. He made strenuous attempts to improve the classification of nephritis but was

Dr Pierre Rayer. (Courtesy of the American Journal of Nephrology.*)*

always meticulous in honouring not only Richard Bright's contributions, but also those of his colleagues; many others felt that albuminous nephritis or albuminuria coined by Dr Martin Salon were perhaps better terms than *'Maladie de Bright'*.

Professor Menetrier who judged Dr Caveribert's thesis concluded that 'by the abundance of documents, by his richness of clinical detail, by the correctness of his ideas, the work of Rayer is the most remarkable after that of Bright'.

In addition to the work of the French School, Dublin was in the forefront of renal research. Dr Osborne's contributions merit his recognition as Ireland's first nephrologist and he recognised examples of albuminuria without kidney disease, such as lower urinary tract infections, and described renal vein obstruction. Professor Brian Keogh, Consultant Nephrologist at the Meath Hospital, where many of Ireland's most famous medical men including Graves and Stokes worked, has drawn attention to Sir Dominic Corrigan's renal interest; he is generally associated with cardiology and the 'water-hammer' pulse of Corrigan in aortic incompetence.[43] However, he noted that low urinary specific gravity was caused by a low salt and urea content in the urine of patients suffering from chronic renal diseases; he also differentiated the two separated forms of Bright's disease, the large white kidney of dropsy from the small contracted kidney of chronic uraemia. It is suggested that Dr Osborne and the Dublin school may have recognised overflow proteinuria of high plasma protein conditions such as myeloma, postural proteinuria, febrile proteinuria and in some cases, associated with a high urinary urea, the hypercatabolic state of systemic infection: it certainly makes a good story! It is surprising that Professor Keogh did not mention Dr Crampton of St Stephen's Hospital, Dublin who would have appeared to preempt some of Dr Osborne's work as early as 1818.[43]

Robert Graves in addition to his work on the overactive thyroid gland to which his name is attached, i.e. Graves' disease, was equally interested in renal disease and took issue with some of Bright's conclusions to whom he wrote 'I am much disposed to doubt'. This was regarding the inevitability of albuminous urine in dropsy denoting underlying organic renal disease. One suspects that Graves was one of those who had not quite appreciated the true meaning of Richard Bright's earlier work on the kidney (see Appendix 2).

Back in London, and particularly at Guy's, research blossomed; the two main areas of interest were hypertension and the kidney and the histological appearances of the Malpighian capsules or glomeruli. The account of the discovery and understanding of nephritis and hypertension is almost exclusively a Guy's story and can be traced through the pages of the Guy's Hospital Reports.[44] As Dr Ryles said, 'We may, I believe, justly claim that the whole story of high blood pressure including the little we know of the aetiology and the great deal we know of its consequences was written at Guy's between the years 1827 and 1881', nobody would dispute that.[46] The work of Drs Wilks, Gull and Sutton are a testament to this fact and essential hypertension causing damage to the kidneys was recognised; we have already referred to the pioneering work of Dr Frederick Mahomet in this field. He led the way to accurate and routine measurement of the blood pressure which helped to differentiate renal and essential hypertension. The new disease of nephrosclerosis was born and the investigations leading to its discovery provides some very interesting medical detective work.

Sir William Gull, one of the sharpest wits amongst the Consultant staff in the immediate post-Bright period, used to teach on one of the museum specimens of a small kidney and a large heart prepared by Bright, and was heard to remark somewhat provocatively 'I can but look upon it with veneration but not with conviction. I think, with all deference to so great an authority, that the systemic capillaries and, had it been possible the entire man, should have been included in this vase, together with the heart and kidneys; then we should have had, I believe, a truer view of the causation of cardiac hypertrophy and of the diseased kidney.'[44]

It is illuminating at this stage to examine the role that ophthalmology played in our understanding of renal disease and in this it is perhaps fortunate that one of Bright's most avid biographers was Burton Chance, an eminent American ophthalmologist; in 1927, to mark the centenary of the discovery of Bright's disease, he wrote 'an ophthalmologists appreciation.'[45]

The adage that what affects the microcirculation of the kidney can be reflected in the eye may have a modern ring to it, but by 1850 Turck had examined a *post mortem* specimen of a retina taken from a patient with albuminuria, renal failure and blindness, and described histological changes of albuminuric retinitis. This was not many years after Toynbee and Bright had examined the kidney microscopically. Liebreich was the first to examine albuminuric retinitis with an ophthalmoscope in 1859 just one year after Bright's death, and confirmed that the changes in the blood vessels of the ocular fundus were similar to those that had been seen in the kidneys as a result of renal-related high blood pressure. In fact, while visiting the Vienna School of Medicine in 1814 and meeting Drs J P Frank, De Carro and Hildenbrand, Richard Bright attended a course of lectures given by the master of ophthalmology, Professor G J Beer, whose teachings were indirectly responsible for the opening of Moorfield's Eye Hospital.[46]

The greatest classical example of nephrologist-cum-ophthalmologist of that period, of course, was Sir William Bowman who carried out so many anatomical studies on the kidney, before devoting the rest of his life to the eye. It would appear our illustrious predecessors in the medical profession could turn their hand to most things. Apparently it is on record that Richard Bright gave a paper on the ear for his friend Dr Toynbee who was indisposed![47]

It is extremely likely that Dr Lever was stimulated by Richard Bright's work to examine the significance of proteinuria in pregnant women and particularly those with eclampsia. He worked in the Lying-in-Charity wing of Guy's Hospital and was a bit of a character

and *bon-vivant* whose carriage, with its distinctive red borderings
and wheels, was known as Lever's fire-engine![47]

Work on the pathogenesis and nomenclature of nephritis entered
a frenetic period of activity over the next 50 years and in fact up
until the turn of the century albuminuric nephritis seemed a
satisfactory term and was the one generally adopted, not unlike the
present day protein-losing nephropathy. Gradually, as renal research
moved into the 20th century, it was possible to recognise different
types of nephritis or glomerulonephritis, a term used to differentiate
diseases affecting the glomerular or, as Richard Bright knew them,
the Malpighian bodies from those in other parts of the kidney such
as the tubules in the medulla, i.e. interstitial nephritis.

It is impossible to mention all the important contributors in the
history of nephritis, suffice it to say that the early classification from
the great French and German schools of pathology and medicine
supplemented the work of Drs Toynbee, Johnson and Robinson, all
of whom were from the Bright School. Notable amongst the early
German contributors were Drs Friedrick Frerichs, Ludwig Traube
and Fritz Munk and later Drs Franz Volhard and Theodore Fahr.[48]
These classifications with that of Professor Ellis from the London
Hospital, served until the introduction of the renal biopsy in the
1950s. This allowed an easy and precise tissue diagnosis to be made
during life and with serial biopsies it was possible to follow the
natural history and evolution of each type of nephritis and its
response to treatment.

The emergence of immunology, the use of experimentally-induced
nephritis in animals and better specimen staining and microscopic
techniques allowed the ultrastructure of the kidney to be examined
under electron microscopy at magnifications of 50 to 100,000 times;
fluorescent microscopy was able to detect abnormal proteins caught
up in the fine circulatory network of the glomeruli causing nephritic
reactions and all these techniques allowed a more accurate
classification to be made.

Today in the 1990s confusion still exists on many aspects of the
aetiology of nephritis. However, we know that certain people,
perhaps of an inherited 'nephritic' type can develop the condition
as a result of an abnormal or an upset immune system and that they
react to a circulating 'non-U' material normally a micro-organism,
much as the bacterium streptococcus caused scarlatina in Bright's
day. Fortunately, the body's harmful antibody response can be
altered with potent immunosuppressive drugs and other therapies.
Nevertheless one can still share the terrible feeling of frustration
and helplessness that Bright encountered when he expressed
his feelings: 'I wish that I were now able to add anything
completely satisfactory to myself with regard to the mode of treating
these diseases of the kidney'. At least these sentiments have been
tempered by the advent of therapeutic advances, and the ability

to prolong life with the use of maintenance dialysis and renal transplantation.

It is 165 years since the 'concept of the century' was born and we can say that Richard Bright set the scene for an explosion of research into renal disease which, in his own working lifetime of 20 years, overtook and improved upon his original views. This was particularly true in the establishment of a standard nomenclature and the use of the term albuminous nephritis which still describes one of the greatest therapeutic challenges in modern medicine today, i.e. protein-losing nephropathy. He was aware himself that much was still to be done in this field '. . . a disease than which there is certainly none which offers a more extended field for careful and well directed observations.'

To the end Bright always remained generous in his praise for those predecessors who had laid the foundations leading to his discovery. In the words of Sir Gilbert Blane, one of the earliest Medical Director Generals of the Royal Navy 'It is quite impossible for any single individual, however gifted, to acquire a competent knowledge of any subject particularly that which is practical, without being more or less indebted to the previous labour of others'.[49]

Foremost, Richard Bright was the paradigm of a caring physician but with that extra precious gift of an enquiring mind. It is often said, that he did not possess original thought, but whatever one calls it he was able to deduce a great deal from his simple painstaking research. Sir William Osler is quoted as having said 'that it is not the man that first describes the disease but the one who persuades the world to accept the concept, who should be remembered' and this would apply very much to Richard Bright. Dr Hale-White felt that he was a genius and Dr Wilks that his deductive ability was limited, 'he described his cases and there he left them'. The truth lies somewhere in between; like Sir Gilbert Blane 'He was undoubtedly a man of great original force of character which was not overtly displayed and became a very completely equipped physician. He blended, to an uncommon degree, adequate scholarship and considerable dialectical skill with scientific acumen and great administrative capacity.'[50]

Dr Samuel Wilks who with Drs Gull and Sutton became the next generation of famous Guy's physicians and who obtained epynomous recognition for Hodgkin was always rather critical of Richard Bright. Nevertheless he did pay tribute to him in the end when he wrote that

'He was perhaps better known abroad throughout the civilised world than any other British physician of modern times, and in his own country was particularly sought after by his professional brethren in cases of difficult diagnosis. His eminent position was fairly though tardily won by his thorough practical writings and great discoveries and was sustained by his amiable manners, by

his uniformly knowable conduct to his professional brethren, by
his sound judgement and knowledge of disease and by the pains
which he took in investigating the most intimate particulars of
every case which was brought to him.'[51]

Chapter 12

Eminent Physician to London Society

'Among influences which largely affect national statistics
of disease and death, few are of greater power than Poverty,
in its various direct and indirect ways of operation . . .'
Dr John Simon

With the accession of William IV in 1830 and the consequent
requirement for a general election the question of parliamentary
reform again became a prominent issue. The revolution in France
and the fall of Charles X caused much stir and excitement in England
and both Whigs and Tories could see that it would be dangerous
to postpone consideration of the problem of reform.

As at the time of the French Revolution of 1789 the possibility
of a similar political uprising in England was not to be ignored for
if Frenchmen could expel their reactionary government after a short
and almost bloodless contest, why should Englishmen not do the
same?

Wellington believed that the institutions already in existence were
perfect and that change could only be for the worse. With his defeat
in 1830, Earl Grey, leader of the Whigs was invited to form a
government and he asked Lord John Russell to draw up a Reform
Bill, the final acceptance of which was to be a protracted and rather
stormy affair with the First and Second Bills being defeated either
in Committee or the House of Lords. It was not until June 1832 that
the Third Bill finally won acceptance.

Unfortunately, even the Whig definition of 'the people' did not
extend beyond the middle classes. They looked at the redistribution
of Parliamentary seats at least as much in terms of vested interest
as in terms of the population as a whole. Whilst the Bill appeared
to satisfy most people, those of the working class gained nothing
and could not therefore be expected to accept it as a final settlement.

The Bristol riots
The tardiness of the House of Lords in passing the earlier Reform
Bills caused rioting in several large towns such as Nottingham,
Derby and also Richard Bright's own City of Bristol. Sir Charles
Wetherell who had been Attorney-General in Wellington's
government, was Recorder of Bristol. He opposed the First and
Second Reform Bills in the Commons and as a consequence rioting
broke out during his visit to the city on 29 October 1831. The mobs
attacked the Mansion House, burned the Bishop's palace and a

number of other buildings notably in Queen Square where Richard Bright was born—but fortunately No. 29 survived intact.

This was to be an exciting decade of change and of progress in some fields of human endeavour. It was the beginning of the great age of the railways and the steamships which brought an increase in employment and overseas trade. There was further reform when in 1833 Parliament passed an act to abolish the slave trade which, of course, met with opposition from MPs representing Bristol and Liverpool. It is interesting to note that in 1838 both Richard Bright (senior) and his son Robert received £8,092 and £3,820 respectively as part of the compensation paid out by the Government to the owners of slaves in the West Indies.

The year 1833 also brought improvement in conditions for some factory workers. The Factory Act limited working hours and set the age of nine as that below which no child could be employed in textile mills, excepting silk and lace-making; unfortunately this did not apply to mines and brick yards. It was not until 1847 that an Act was passed limiting the employment of women and children in factories to no more than 10 hours a day.

The Whig government, whilst superficially appearing to have some concern for the working conditions of the townspeople was correspondingly unconcerned for the plight of the rural poor in those areas where the Whig landowners had their estates and so in town and country alike, the inequalities persisted.

Against this backdrop of change and reform Richard Bright continued hard at work on the second volume of *The Reports of Medical Cases . . .* By 1831 he had completed some 700 pages. As we know this second volume was in two parts and described over 400 case histories covering a broad spectrum of medical subjects. In the preface to the book Bright again acknowledges his debt to Guy's and also to his medical and surgical colleagues whose co-operation and support had been invaluable not least in providing him with the cases on which his work was based.

The move to Savile Row
The second volume was dated from Richard Bright's new residence at 11 Savile Row. Earlier in the year he and Eliza had decided that owing to increasing commitments outside the hospital, it would be sensible to move to a more fashionable area. He was receiving many more requests for consultation and the development of a private practice was an inevitability and so appearances had to be maintained.

The area around Savile Row was already popular with members of the medical profession and so when a suitable house was found they were determined on the move. Richard Bright's father lent them the purchase price of £600.00 and they moved in the September of 1831. By now they had an additional family member for their first son, Follett had been born in June of that year. With them also went Jones the valet, Anna the cook, Susan and another nursemaid, two housemaids and the coachman and his wife who were housed in the mews behind the main residence.

On the whole they were well pleased with their new abode and particularly with some of the more modern gadgetry such as the cast iron stove instead of an open spit and the water heating system. There was a fine upstairs drawing room and a pleasing wrought iron balcony. They did however prefer to retain the old-fashioned candle-light rather than change to the new gas lighting. Today the ground floor of the house is occupied by a shirt maker whilst the first floor drawing room is, perhaps fittingly, used to exhibit the fine paintings belonging to an art dealer who uses it as his business premises.

The Brights were fairly comfortably off but the possibility of additional income from private practice fees was an attractive prospect for with a growing family and expenses incurred in the course of his professional duties, the monthly salary of £10 which the doctor received from the hospital in addition to his lecturer's fees was certainly well-stretched. He was also apparently something of a philanthropist in his dealings with less well-off patients for as

11 Savile Row, London home of Dr Richard Bright.

we have already seen he often contributed to the cost of their hospital keep or for extra nourishment.[1]

Elected to the Royal College of Physicians

The Spring of 1832 at last brought professional recognition for Richard Bright which was particularly pleasing for he was nominated for fellowship of the Royal College of Physicians. The exciting news was brought to him by Sir Henry Halford who wished him to accept the nomination as a 'mark of the very high esteem' in which he was held by his peers in medicine. The many long hours spent so diligently on his professional duties and in the attempt to push forward the boundaries of medical knowledge were beginning to earn just rewards.

The election took place on 25 June, 1832 and the doctor was duly admitted as a Fellow. After the ceremony he wrote to his father: 'I feel much pleasure at my new dignity and the more because I am quite sure that the feeling is unanimous as was the vote.'[1]

Cholera—problems of urban sanitation

The cholera epidemic of 1832/33 which had arisen in Asia spread with rapidity to the Continent of Europe. This again highlighted the short-comings in urban sanitation. Bright's training at the Fever Hospital had provided him with a good grounding in the principles of preventative measures and he urged those with whom he came in contact to be scrupulous in the cleansing both of their own homes and also in helping in the community as a whole with the cleaning of streets and fouled gutters. He, with other members of the medical profession called upon the authorities to provide purer drinking water. Sadly it was to take more than a decade before any serious consideration was given to the subject of public sanitation.

In November of 1831 the doctor wrote to his father of his concern regarding the impending epidemic:

'. . . now with regard to the cholera—the matter is becoming truly serious—there is no doubt in my mind that it is now in Sunderland and that it has been brought there by ships from infected places, and it is increasing . . . I have very little doubt that it will spread through the whole of England in a very short time. With regard to Pill—any means of cleansing the streets and the courts and the houses which can be enforced will be useful in giving persons attacked a better chance and probably in preventing attacks but the question is how are you to prevent its attacking Ham Green. If it appears at Pill I should exact the most complete quarantine possible and if you prepare yourselves you need have very few things brought to the house except meat for you may easily lay in stores of everything else and I should strictly interdict any of the Pill people from coming for medicines and if any thing of the

kind was to be done it should be done at one of the cottages on
the farm or some further distance . . .'

'I am doubting what to do with my family if it reaches, as
probably in a very few weeks it will, London—I am determined
that they shall not remain here to be infected by me the first attack
I have or perhaps the first patient I see . . .'[3]

Hard on the heels of the cholera the winter of 1832/33 brought
a serious form of influenza. Added to these additional professional
demands came demands on the domestic front for in the February
of 1833 his father-in-law Mr Follett died following many years of
suffering from a heart condition. Eliza rushed to Topsham to comfort
her mother and Richard Bright was summoned to attend the funeral.

The death of Dr Babington
On his return to London he again threw himself unstintingly into
the extra work involved in treating the many patients who had
succumbed to the influenza. Dr Babington, his old friend and father-
in-law from his first marriage, now seventy-seven years of age
worked with similar disregard for his own health. Unfortunately,
this was to take the ultimate toll for in April 1833 he also fell victim
to the epidemic and died two days later of double pneumonia. It is
not hard for us to imagine the terrible blow that this loss of a dear
friend and mentor represented to Richard Bright. His views on the
duty of remembering friends who are dead were made clear in his
Hungarian writings:

'We are truly no more pardonable in attempting to forget a friend
who is dead than we should be in forgetting one that is absent
. . . If putting aside all unintelligible motives, there is one which
can be felt and explained, more pure than others, leading us to
rejoice in our future prospects, it is the idea and hope of meeting
again the friends from whom we have been separated by death.'[3]

He took the opportunity of his next lecture at the College of
Physicians which had been postponed as a consequence of Dr
Babington's death to deliver a eulogy on his deceased colleague and
friend. He spoke in the most warm and glowing terms, amongst other
things, of the doctor's

'sweet simplicity of manner, his profound humility of mind, his
power of self-control, his benevolence of heart, and his patient,
pious resignation to the will of God—his was a strong perception
and an accurate appreciation of virtue and of vice.'

In addition to these exceptional character traits, Bright praised his
former father-in-law for

'an admirable skill in his profession, founded on science, supported by a great natural sagacity and power of observation, which are acknowledged to have rendered him inferior to no man that ever lived in discerning and in treating disease.'

He also noted that Dr Babington had provided an

'excellent example of that wholesome and yet comparatively rare combination of knowledge, which unites our professional pursuits with the study of the natural sciences—which connects the physician with the philosopher.'[4]

This was, of course, another area in which he would sadly miss his old friend for we must remember that it was Dr Babington who encouraged his interest in geology when he was first a student at Guy's hospital.

Goulstonian Lecturer
In the same year he found himself faced with something of a formidable professional challenge as he was chosen to give the Goulstonian Lectures at the Royal College of Physicians. These lectures date back to 1632 when Dr Goulston, a Fellow of the College left £200 to purchase a rent-charge for the maintenance of a lecture which was to be delivered annually within the College by one of the four youngest doctors in physic. The lecture to be read between Michaelmas and Easter took place over three days. On two of these days the lecturer was required to demonstrate on a cadaver the substance and facts relating to his subject. Richard Bright's lecture was entitled: 'On the Function of the abdomen and some of the diagnostic marks of its disease'.

His rather diffident nature made him extremely nervous at the thought of confronting the senior members of his profession but Eliza swept away his hesitation and pointed out that his colleagues would be fortunate in receiving such original instruction relating to the kidney.

At the commencement of his lecture Bright gave credit to his pupils, Mr Barlow, Mr Tweedie and Mr Rees whose 'intelligent and zealous co-operation' had been invaluable. The lectures were subsequently printed in the *London Medical Gazette*.[5]

A growing reputation with the student body
Richard Bright was also beginning to gain a good reputation with his students. Whilst his lectures lacked the flowing eloquence of Addison's or the impassioned vigour of Aston Keys' he communicated with clarity and succinctness. It was this that prompted a request from the student body that his introductory address given in October 1832 on Practical Medicine should be printed. With his customary modesty be wrote a letter of thanks:

'I should be wanting in sincerity were I to deny or even to disguise the satisfaction I experienced from your earnest request that the accompanying address might be printed for use: and although I am well aware that it derived its chief interest from the excitement of the moment and, therefore fully anticipate that you will be disappointed in its perusal, I have complied with your wish . . .'

The 'Introductory Address' to the subject of Practical Medicine thus became a useful initial guide to the student of medicine embarking on the long journey of commitment to a demanding profession. He gave advice regarding the pitfalls that they might encounter in their hospital work. He encouraged his students to develop delicacy in the handling of patients, 'the touch of a blind man is your duty to acquire.'

The first page of the booklet sets out for the student the heavy burden of responsibility for the patient that he must willingly accept as an essential part of his professional role:—

'To you affectionate children will look for the welfare of their parents: to you the anxious parent will turn for the rescue of his child; and on you the fond husband will depend for all that is dear to him in the hour of danger; to you perhaps may be confided the lives of numerous men led to the field of battle, or marched through unwholesome countries; to you the health and efficiency of crews destined to long and perilous navigation may be entrusted; on you the public eye is to be bent in days of plague and pestilence—for who shall now say that from such visitations even our happy climate may be free? And under all these circumstances you must be ready to give an account of what has been done, not only to those who are eagerly collected around you, but to a much more troublesome inquirer within, who will accompany you to the retirement of your closet, and with its inquisitorial voice not only ask you whether you have done your best upon the present occasion, but whether from the time you commenced your professional studies you used your utmost exertions to acquire that knowledge which would fit you for the discharge of your duties; for it is this consciousness alone which can enable you to lie down with comfort when harassed by the occasional unsuccessful issue even of your best endeavours.'

In determining the nature and function of disease he suggests that the physician must bring to bear both the knowledge he has accumulated through clinical experience and perhaps even more importantly, the fine-tuned use of all his senses:

Undoubtedly the more a man sees disease, provided he looks at it with the eye of intelligence, the better: but think not that it is enough simply to let the eye or the hand wander upon the patient: and do not flatter yourself that you possess, by intuition, the power of discerning and discriminating disease'.

He also warns the students of the danger of their feelings becoming 'too obtusely blunted against the sufferings, both mental and corporeal to which we are necessarily rendered familiar'.[6]

The death of Anna Bright
Sadly in the Autumn of 1833 the cruel hand of disease was to rob Richard and Eliza of their young daughter Anna. She had for some months been suffering from a persistent cough. Her father stayed up many nights to nurse her as Eliza was weak from lack of sleep and anxiety. Anna died suddenly in the November of 1833, at the age of five. The loss was hard for both parents and the sight of other little children engaged in happy play reinforced their desolation.

Edinburgh revisited
Some respite and diversion came in the following year for Bright decided on a visit to Scotland to coincide with the meeting of the British Association for the Advancement of Science which was to take place in Edinburgh in September 1834. He began secretly planning the trip in the February of that year for, of course, he wanted to show Eliza all the familiar places and scenes of his student days. When they set out at the end of August they were accompanied, on the instigation of Phoebe, by Bright's younger sister Elizabeth whilst the children were left behind at Ham Green in the care of aunts and nursemaids.

Their journey was marred by an unfortunate incident which took place at Warrington and which greatly upset Richard Bright. A small child ran beneath their carriage wheels but fortunately was not gravely injured. The doctor wrote to his brother Sam in Liverpool asking him to act on his behalf should there be any further requirement either for the child or his mother. He also mentioned that they had that day spent 'an hour at Newton and we saw four trains pass upon the Rail-road. We saw the whole process of stopping and putting in motion—the interchange of passengers, the carrying of pigs, of men of timber, of cotton and everything but carriages—it is very striking'.[7]

They arrived in Edinburgh on the 7th September and made their way to 43 Heriots Row, the home of Dr Alison with whom they were staying. Here they met up with the Moreheads who were also house guests. The city, crowded out with more than 12,000 associate members, was agog with excitement for the next week the Prime Minister, Earl Grey, was to be honoured with its Freedom. The programme for the British Association offered something to suit all tastes from botany to art and Bright had organised a full schedule for himself and Eliza. Mrs Alison was an excellent hostess and when time permitted she took her guests on a guided tour of the sights of the city.

One visit which afforded Richard Bright great pleasure was that to his old friend Francis Jeffrey, now Lord Advocate. This provided an opportunity to catch up on events of the past four years and also to plan the next stage of the holiday, the trip to the Trossachs. The final hours of the holiday were spent enjoying the scenery of Loch Lomond, infinitely beautiful in its changing moods and colours.

Interestingly enough the sixth meeting of the British Association was held in Bristol. Some of those attending including Barclay Fox, nephew to Hilhouse the Bristol shipbuilder, made an excursion to Portishead and on their return journey up the Avon they landed at Ham Green 'the beautiful residence of R. Bright Esq. His sons were waiting on the shore and escorted us to their house. We found the old gentleman lying on a sofa, having broken his thigh, but he received us with the utmost politeness and hospitality. They showed us into another room most sumptuously supplied with fruit and pastry and we re adjourned to the other for tea and talk.'[8]

The sojourn in Scotland had provided the doctor with some well-earned relaxation and despite his arduous workload he was gaining the corpulence of prosperous mid-life! He wrote to his father how he had just been visited by his brother Robert:

'. . . looking well but much thinner than I have seen him for a very long time—I ask him how he contrives it but he says he does nothing to produce it whereas I have been hard at working trotting one of the roughest lanes in England 14 miles a day without being able in the course of two months to make any material impression on my too solid frame . . .'[2]

Guy's Hospital Reports

The following year there was no family holiday and Bright wrote to his father regretting the limited time he had available to amuse young William 'as during a great part of the Daylight I am at Guy's where I am obliged to be every day now that I have charge of the clinical ward, as soon after twelve as possible . . .' He used the quiet time in August to continue his work on the papers he was writing on abdominal and other tumours. These papers were in fact only published posthumously in 1860 by the New Sydenham Society. It was around this time that he had the idea of resurrecting the *Guy's Hospital Reports* which had been started by Dr Babington, Astley Cooper and John Haighton, but abandoned in 1798. Benjamin Harrison, the Treasurer, was enthusiastic about the plans and the *Guy's Hospital Reports* were reborn with the first volume published in 1836 under the editorship of Richard Bright's pupil Dr George Hilaro Barlow. The doctor's latest work on the kidney appeared in the first two articles in the first volume. He revised and updated his previous work and also made new observations on the effect of chronic renal disease on the heart.

A most useful inclusion was Richard Bright's 'Tabular view of the Morbid Appearances in 100 cases connected with Albuminous Urine'. This consisted of a 'tabular digest of one hundred cases, in which the mottled and granular kidney has existed, and in most of which the renal affection was a prominent feature of the disease'.

This work is perhaps an excellent example of how the empiric approach in which tradition Richard Bright had received his training could lead to the formation of principles which would in later years be proven by more scientific methods.

Hodgkin leaves Guy's

In 1837 Dr Cholmeley's retirement left the position of Full Physician open to Dr Thomas Addison. This should have provided an opportunity for the third member of the great triumvirate to take his position as Assistant Physician. Unfortunately, although Hodgkin was one of the candidates, Benjamin Babington was the second. Again it seemed that Hodgkin's personal character traits legislated against him—as we have already seen some of his views were considered bizarre and unconventional and whilst Richard Bright was torn between the two men who were both personal friends he too perhaps felt more comfortable with Benjamin Babington, so similar in nature to his charismatic father.

Hodgkin had, of course, assisted Bright with many autopsies and had indeed been helpful in arranging for the collection of subjects so he certainly felt the loss when Hodgkin resigned from his post as curator at Guy's. Bright's reliance on Hodgkin is clearly evident in an incident in which he persuaded him to participate in the arrangements for a clandestine autopsy. He asked Hodgkin to perform a dissection 'in great secrecy', explaining that he had 'prevailed by a bribe to have the examination of our little patient'.

He gave Hodgkin precise instruction for the preservation of kidneys, spleen, liver and especially the heart. Hodgkin was apparently none too keen on taking part in the autopsy but Bright was most insistent:

'Though it would not be very difficult in case of absolute necessity to get a substitute for you—yet I should myself prefer you as I shall not be present myself and I know you are not apt to overlook and I expect whatever may be found will be minute.' He asked Hodgkin to bring his own instruments and to arrive surreptiously: 'do not drive up exactly to the door as we want everything as quiet as possible.'[9]

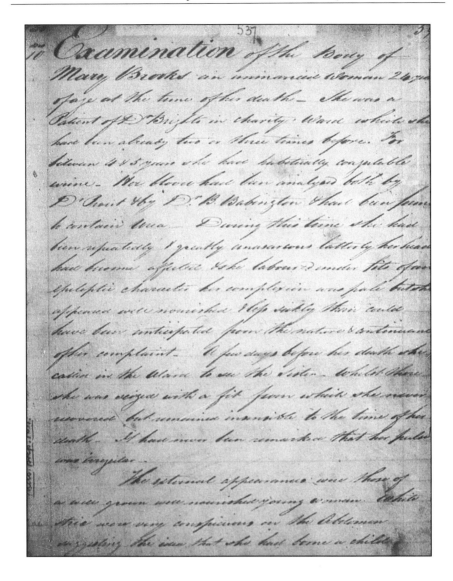

The Green Book—entry of post mortem details made by Dr Hodgkin.

His powers of persuasion prevailed for Hodgkin performed this and other such services for him, including many autopsies involving the kidney. It is interesting to see how Bright, like so many of his contemporaries was obliged to involve himself in these rather under-hand methods of procuring the material which would provide concrete evidence for his medical theories.

Bright and Addison: *The Elements of the Practice of Medicine*

The retirement of one of the 'old guard' and Addison's appointment as Full Physician paved the way for the younger men to raise the standard of training in the Guy's Medical School. Bright and Addison collaborated on the writing of a textbook entitled *The Elements of the Practice of Medicine* which was finally published in 1839.[10]

In the preface to the book the authors stated that 'they had frequently felt the want of a work at once elementary and practical to which they might refer their pupils as a companion and assistant during the period of their studies'.

Again stress is placed upon the importance of the employment of all the senses in arriving at a correct diagnosis of disease—its progress in particular must be carefully monitored for today's swollen knee or hand might tomorrow be replaced by a heart beating 'its laborious stroke in a thick crust of coagulable lymph . . . or, restless activity of the inflamed brain shall be changed into the death-like coma'. Bright's deep interest in patient care is revealed in the advice on treatment. He feels that the physician should also be initiated into the role of the nurse and know something of how to cope with bed-sores, how to relieve the pressure on protruding bones and how to utilise the healing power of dilute brandy and laudanum.

Both Richard Bright and Thomas Addison expressed some dissatisfaction with the organisation of the content of the book; certainly it lacked a systematic approach and, without an index, cross referencing was difficult.

The curious case of Richard Bright the Lesser

Thomas Wakley of *The Lancet*, ever active in his criticism of certain members of the medical profession and the establishments they represented seized the opportunity for vituperative comment:

> 'A compendium really fitted for the guidance of learners is of necessity adapted for a work of reference for practitioners and this because the volume ought in either case, to contain all the well-established facts of science, methodically arranged, expressed with perspicacity and unemcumbered with any purely theoretical matter. If, in any given work on the practice of medicine, facts of importance are distorted or omitted—if by a vicious process of induction false inferences are drawn from them—if fine spun theories are palmed on the reader as results of direct observation—if confusion and disorders prevail instead of well-ordered arrangement—if obscurity of diction render this or that chapter unintelligible will it seriously be contended that such faults become venial because the volume disfigured by their presence was designed for, and need therefore mislead and mystify, students alone?'[11]

Interestingly, in 1846, it was again Thomas Wakley who sought to discredit Bright by quoting in *The Lancet* the details of the case of Dr Richard Bright of 25 Ely Place who was involved in dealings of blatant quackery with one self-styled Professor Thomas Holloway as if it were indeed Dr Richard Bright of Savile Row who was the culprit. The Dr Richard Bright of Ely Place exploited Richard Bright's fame by writing on female disease and on the treatment of dropsy. Bright never sought to clear his name of this unfortunate association—this was something which Wakley could not understand:

> 'Let Dr Bright proceed a little longer in his untoward course, and his brethren instead of seeking him as the consulting physician, may avoid him as the ally or the willing victim of the quack. We promise Dr Bright that we shall follow the matter so closely and doggedly that unless he alters his line of conduct he shall be more remembered as the utensil of Holloway the quack, than as a distinguised physician.'

Perhaps he genuinely feared that the doctor might be involved in quackery—be that as it may, it is interesting to reflect that this currently highly respected journal of the medical profession was at that time so damning! Professor Robert Kark investigated the case of Dr Richard Bright of Ely Place in minute detail and made it the subject of his inaugural lecture to the Dr Richard Bright Society in 1981 entitled: 'Dr Richard Bright and Richard Bright the Lesser'.[12]

Physician Extraordinary—a growing private practice
On the accession of the young Queen Victoria in 1837 Richard Bright had been apppointed Physician Extraordinary to Her Majesty. This was, indeed, a great honour but he was wise enough to know that he was one among many—previous monarchs had surrounded themselves with eminent doctors who had no official court position.

It was pleasing, however, to realise that his name and reputation were gaining wider recognition. His private practice too was growing rapidly. Some of his patients were, of course, from the higher echelons of society yet this did not seduce Bright from his work amongst the poor of the parish or those who made up the patient body at Guy's—all those that represented the hard-pressed workers that kept 'that mighty heart' beating what was for most a cruel quotidian rhythm and an exposure to all 'the difficulties and temptations of the lower classes'.[13]

Poor sanitation—a major cause of disease
Public health was still a grossly neglected area of concern. The Boards of Health set up during the cholera epidemic of 1831-3 had been allowed to lapse and their revival in the late 1830s was due to Edwin Chadwick and the Poor Law Commissioners. They employed a number of doctors to enquire into the causes of

destitution and death in the City of London. The conditions they
described in their report were so horrific that one Cabinet Minister,
Lord Normanby refused to give them credence. The reports
illuminated a situation of grave danger to the community as a whole
and the remedies as one might expect, given the appalling conditions
in which most people lived, were expressed in terms of sanitary
engineering rather than purely medical intervention.[14]

As we know, Bright was a caring man and he often spoke about
the inequalities he found in the course of his work. He took great
pains to try and influence the more wealthy to play their part in
attempting to redress the social imbalance, for whilst systematic
efforts had been made to widen streets, remove any obstruction to
air circulation and to extend and improve drainage and sewerage
in more salubrious areas, nothing had been done to improve the
poorer districts for:

> 'These neglected places [were] out of view and not thought of,
> their condition known only to the parish officers and the medical
> men whose duties oblige them to visit the inhabitants to relieve
> their necessities and to attend their sick; and even these services
> are not to be performed without danger'.[14]

The problem was in part caused by a too rapid population growth
in the city. At the beginning of 19th century the population of London
totalled around one million but by the end of the century it had
reached 4½ million. People were crammed into the honeycomb of
tenements, the cheap lodging houses where men and women mingled
promiscuously together.[15] In some places the excrement lay
scattered about rooms, cellars and yards so thick that it was barely
possible to move. One official report describes the death of a woman
who had been living in Bermondsey in a small unfurnished room
with her husband and son:

> 'She lay dead beside her son upon a heap of feathers which were
> scattered over her almost naked body, there being neither sheet
> nor coverlet. The feathers stuck so fast over the whole body that
> the physician could not examine the corpse until it was cleansed,
> and then found it starved and scarred from the bites of vermin.
> Part of the floor of the room was torn up, and the hole used by
> the family as a privy'.[16]

It was a common belief that the pestiferous airs that emanated from
these areas of gross poverty bore with them the very seeds of disease.
Such sewers as existed were in a state of advanced decay and the
street gutters served as channels for carrying excrement and urine
until they were blocked up in a courtyard or alleyway. As if this
were not problem enough most of the sewage ended up in the

Thames, the water of which was then pumped back into domestic cisterns or to water stand pipes.

Equally hazardous to the health of the urban population was the overcrowding of burial grounds—another link in this crippling chain of what was essentially man-made destruction. Bodies were piled high upon each other and sometimes broke through the ground to emit noxious, even poisonous gases to strangle the already foetid air. When the reality of this appalling social scene is revealed then the situation as far as progress in the field of medicine is concerned comes into clearer focus.

Treatments—to kill or cure?

Richard Bright's attention to detail and the meticulous cataloguing of every indication of disease he observed during the process of autopsy was extending the whole body of medical knowledge in terms of anatomy and the recognition of possible causes of disease. The treatment of disease, on the other hand, was still very much a question of trial and error with cupping, blistering, coldwater dousing, the use of the seton, to say nothing of a dubious concoction of herbal draughts, comprising the physician's repertoire of prescription.

Reports of Medical Cases Volume II provides a catalogue of the use, often with disastrous effects, of such treatments. On the other hand Case VII 'Arichnitis, with excessive Irritability in an intemperate Man', fortunately provides a lighter moment in an otherwise dark world and shows the amazing recuperate powers of the humble mutton chop and porter:

'In the year 1823 I was requested to see a gentleman who had unfortunately contracted habits of intemperance, and had become suddenly delirious the day before. Leeches had been applied to his temples; and his delirium, so far from being relieved, seemed to be greatly aggravated, so that he passed the night in most violent agitation, requiring the strength of two or three persons to restrain him; and on one occasion he had nearly leaped out of the window, but when I arrived two or three hours afterwards, a most striking alteration had taken place for on his expressing a strong desire in his delirium for a mutton-chop and some porter, the medical man who was attending him thought it not improbable that it might do him good to have some solid food on his stomach and at once granted his request; the effect was instantaneous. His mind became calm and collected and when I saw him, little but general nervous agitation and a hurried manner of speaking remained; and a few doses of opium with calomile was all that I saw occasion to recommend'.[17]

Perhaps some of the other patients might have derived greater benefit from some solid sustenance rather than the excessive purging to which they were subjected. It seems that even new-born babes did not escape such 'treatment' for in a letter to his father informing him of the birth of baby Emily the Doctor writes that whilst Eliza is as 'tranquil and quiet and all that we could wish six hours after confinement—I cannot describe the little lady in the same terms for she is most noisy and turbulent and the nurse says is anxiously looking about for what she may devour, but I believe at present her chief beverage has been castor oil according to nurse's custom.'[2]

The Monthyon Medal

The Doctor's life became increasingly busy and, apart from hospital and private patients who took so much of his time, he had the additional worry about his brother Benjamin who, it seems, was suffering from cancer of the throat. He could scarcely find time to write the promised lecture: 'Cases of Spasmodic Disease accompanying Affections of the Pericardium'[18] which had been promised for the Medical Chirurgical Society.

But again amidst all this hard work it must have been gratifying to receive further recognition of his contribution to the understanding of disease this time from his Continental colleagues for in July 1838 he was awarded the Monthyon Medal by the Institute des Sciences in Paris. The prize, which may be seen as a kind of Nobel Prize of that time, had been set up by Monsieur Antoine-Jean Baptiste Robert Auget baron de Monthyon (1733-1820). In his will he left the sum of 10 million francs for the award of an annual prize for the perfecting of Medical Science or the Art of Surgery and it was obviously a great honour for the award for 1838 to be presented jointly to Richard Bright, Pierre Olive Rayer and Martin Solon for their work on diseases of the kidney—'a previously little known disease but now recognized under the name of "Maladie de Bright, albuminuria or albuminous nephritis". As one of the names indicates, Doctor Bright of London is the first to recognize these characteristis and to show the relationships which connect these morbid changes in the kidney to dropsy on the one part, and on the other, to the albuminous state of the urine which is the most usual accompaniment.' The prize was presented to Richard Bright in London by the French Consul.[19]

It is interesting to note that in 1835 he had already received an honorary Diploma from the Academy of Science of Hungary. With typical modesty he recorded the award in a letter to his father:

'. . . I have nothing particular to tell you except that I have received a Diploma from the Academy of Science of Hungary with the following address: To the most honourable Sir Richard Bright Doctor —Physician in the Guy's Hospital, Member of the Royal Society and Correspondent Member of the Hungarian Academy of Sciences —with the Diploma of the Hungarian Academy of Sciences.'[2]

Ironically the Hungarians had also invested him with the knighthood which he never received in his own country.

Anxious parent

His son William was about to start at Rugby and he was pleased that a brief visit to Ham Green afforded the opportunity to discuss the school with his brother Robert whose two sons were already there under the care of Dr Arnold the Headmaster. He was evidently something of an anxious parent as revealed in a letter from Mr Mills, the Headmaster of the preparatory school in Hampton in reply to Richard Bright's request that he accept Follett as a pupil:

'Hampton, October 3, 1838.
'I am naturally tempted to wish for your second son as a pupil. I should expect to find him a good clean child, but at the same time I am fearful to enter into connections again with a parent so painfully anxious as yourself.

'The best of my energies are unceasingly devoted to my pupils and anxious parents can push me no further. I am only paralyzed thereby. A father who would act a wise parent both for the child and himself must show his confidence over a wide space and not contemplate the end and the result in such a manner as to fret all the period between.'[1]

The wrench of leaving William at Rugby school was hard to bear particularly for a father who wondered if his son might be 'somewhat unmanly'. Would he cope with the rough and tumble of the public school? Would his quiet personality gain him the friends be craved? Fortunately a reassuring letter from William soon arrived to dispel these fears for 'Merivale's house contains as nice boys as any in the school'.

The Lumleian Lecture

With an easing of this domestic strain Richard Bright could again give his more-or-less undivided attention to his work. He was busy preparing his paper for the Lumleian Lecture which he was invited to give in the year 1839. The Lumleian Trust was set up in 1581 by Dr Richard Caldwell, a Fellow and former President of the College, in conjunction with Lord Lumley. It was set up to fund the Lumleian Lecture in Surgery. It was commonly known in the annals as the Chirurgical Lecture and endowed with a rent charge of £40 a year on their lands and those of their heirs in perpetuity. At first there was a very ambitious programme of Surgical Lectures but this became an impractical proposition and currently the lecture is in Medicine with the Lecturer being appointed by the Censors' Board.

Award made to Dr Bright by the Société de Biologie of Paris.

Richard Bright's Lecture was on 'Disorders of the Brain', including the studies he had made on circulatory disturbances resulting from pulmonary changes.[26]

During the next few years the Doctor attracted further honours and professional responsibilities which added to an already overburdened work load. He was President of the Medico-Chirurgical Society, Consilarius and Censor of the Royal College of Physicians and Fellow of the Royal Society. He was also an honorary member of most European Medical Societies. In 1848 he was elected Associate Member of the 'Société de Biologie' of Paris; his Certificate of Membership was signed by Rayer and also by Rayer's student Claude Bernard.[2]

Scarlet fever—kidney damage can be avoided

In the Spring of 1840 a sudden increase in cases of scarlet fever provided Bright with a curiously high and unprecedented occurrence of anasarca with albuminous urine. The doctor saw case after case displaying these additional symptoms but he was pleased by the opportunity this 'epidemic' afforded to substantiate his former affirmation that any permanent damage to the kidney could, through rest and proper medical care, be avoided. His old friend, John Davy, who had just returned from abroad was very interested in his findings since some years previously he had lost two of his own children to the disease. Davy was very fond of Bright and held him in high esteem—he asked the Secretary of the Royal Medical Society of Edinburgh if, on his death, his portrait might be hung next to that of his friend.

The death of Richard Bright (senior)

The meeting with an old friend must have brought some cheer to the Doctor, too, for at this time he was still in mourning for his father who had died in the January of 1840. He had for some time been suffering from paralysis of the left side of his body resulting from the effects of a stroke but at 84 he was otherwise in possession of all his faculties. On his death his vast and valuable geological collection was donated to Bristol Museum and an obituary for the Geological Association was one of the few that appeared for Richard Bright (senior) remained an essentially private man.[21] He requested a funeral without pomp, his coffin to be followed only by his sons, his executors and his trustees.

He was laid quietly to rest beside his beloved wife Sarah. After his death his daughter Phoebe observed that had he not been so involved with his family he could have been a great man in the field of science. His doctor son must have felt the loss most keenly for, as we know, there had always been a very close relationship between the two.

Friends become patients

In the late Spring of 1840 Bright made a sudden and unexpected trip to Paris but unfortunately there is no account of the reason for his visit. One may suppose that one possibility is that he went to attend his brother-in-law, Webb Follett, who was suffering from consumption and thus always in poor health. On his return, Lord Holland was added to his list of private patients and the Doctor made daily visits to the fine Jacobean Manor house which was home to Lord and Lady Holland. They were renowned for their hospitality and here Bright found himself in the company of many important and influential people, representatives of the literary world too for Charles Dickens was also a frequent visitor. Some of the popular reformers such as Lord John Russell and Lord Ashby were often at Holland House and here too the Doctor met Macaulay the historian who later also became one of his private patients.

In the October of 1840 Lord Holland died but Lady Holland, who was very interested in all medical matters, continued to consult the Doctor. She introduced other private patients to him such as a Mrs Elphinstone of the Albany and George Anson the Keeper of the Privy Seal. In those days before the telephone, requests for visits were hand delivered. Amongst the Bright papers a note from Lady Palmerston provides an example of such a request:

'Lady Palmerston presents her Compts to Dr Bright and would be obliged to him if he would mention some morning when it would be convenient to him to call on her as she is anxious to consult him.'[2]

Lord Jeffrey, his friend from Edinburgh days, now nearly seventy years old, also consulted Bright in a medical capacity whilst at the same time retaining Henry Holland as his official London doctor. He wrote to Bright from Edinburgh setting out in detail the treatment prescribed and the progress of his illness. He also included a touching note marked 'Private':

'If it at all depend on your choice or election, may I beg you my dear Bright, to offer to take the duty of caring for me on yourself? You see so much more of the course of my malady, that I cannot but be more confident in the effects of your inspection, than in Holland—it afflicts me to ask you to take any trouble which you might wish to avoid—But I really consider this as important. I look upon you as having *saved my life*, by your skill, promptitude and energy—I shall never think myself so safe in any other hands—F.J.[2]

Again the pressure of work meant some neglect of family and family affairs. The August of 1840 found Eliza holidaying alone with the children on the Isle of Wight—the Doctor could only spare a few days with them. Neither could he devote much time to assist his brother Robert in sorting out the 53 closely written pages of their father's will. The family estates, stocks and shares amounted to a small fortune but little was in easily realisable cash which all the brothers seemed to require as the raising and educating of a young family was an exceedingly expensive business. Feeling guilty at his brother's admonishment Richard Bright made a swift visit to Ham Green to lend support. He also set aside a few personal belongings of his father's including a miniature of his mother, which he would treasure as a remembrance of the parents who, throughout their lives, had shown him such love and support.

Bright was also involved during the summer of 1840 with professional attendance upon his former tutor and friend, Sir Astley Cooper who was suffering from emphysema and who died in the February of 1841. In accordance with his wishes an autopsy was performed and the results written up for the *Guy's Hospital Reports*. The autopsy was carried out by Dr John Hilton the anatomist, in attendance were two surgeons Aston Key and Edward Cock and the two physicians, Dr Chambers and Dr Richard Bright.

It had been hard for the doctor to witness his old friend's suffering and death was obviously a happy release. The autopsy confirmed the diagnosis of emphysema and it also showed him to be suffering from an inguinal and umbilical hernia, the latter being kept in position by an ingenious device of the great surgeon's own design—a piece of cork held in place with adhesive plaster!

A few years earlier Bright had received a gift from the famous surgeon accompanied by a charming note:

'My dear Bright,
'As you are a voluminous and most excellent Author as well as an accomplished and kind physician I have been thinking that a material for instructing and curing the public might not be unacceptable and therefore request your acceptance of the accompanying trifle as a memento of my gratitude.
'believe me yours always
Astley Cooper'[2]

In response to a letter from Sir Astley Cooper's nephew thanking him for 'the skill' he had 'bestowed' upon his friend and colleague during his final illness, Bright took the opportunity to express his own fondness and admiration for the great surgeon:

'. . . ever since I entered upon my professional career I have not ceased to look upon your Uncle as the object most worthy of our praise and imitation. There is no man from whom I have experienced more uniform friendship and very few for whom I have felt an equal regard.
'His death has been to me a loss both in the daily and in the professional intercourse of life which cannot be replaced . . .'[2]

Wards set aside for renal patients

At Guy's Hospital a new arrangement of wards made work slightly easier for the 'renal team'. They had been labouring under great difficulties with patients scattered throughout the hospital. Such everyday tasks as observation, record keeping and swift attendance in cases of emergency were all seriously hampered by this problem. In 1842 however, two wards, one female and one male, were set aside exclusively for the use of Bright's renal patients and for the intensive study of the eponymous disease. We must remember that all medical research at that time was of necessity carried out with the most primitive of instruments. The doctor did not possess his own microscope but borrowed one from his friend Dr Roget. There was no such thing as a sphygmomanometer to allow for accurate charting of blood pressure, only a glass tube which could be inserted into the carotid artery to measure the pulse pressure.

The 'renal team'

Bright now used his team with great efficiency: Barlow, Owen Rees and Pavy were to work in the laboratory on the study of albuminous urine whilst he instructed his students in the *post mortem* room. He wrote that the laboratory 'was fitted up and decorated entirely to [their] purpose,' and he also saw the new arrangement as 'the first experiment which as far as [he knew had] yet been made in this country to turn the ample resources of a hospital to the investigation of a particular disease by bringing patients labouring under it into one ward properly arranged for observation.' The wards 'Lydia' and 'Job', including ground plans, have been described by Eason.[22]

The Doctor personally invented a mechanical figure which was designed to help students place the organs in their correct abdominal positions. Students, were of course, as lacking as their tutors in terms of aids to their tuition—we must, however, remember the important work of Joseph Towne, so skilled in creating wax models of dissected specimens. These were indispensible teaching materials, reminiscent of the wonderful models which the doctor had seen in Dr Prochaska's cabinets in Vienna, simiarly, Towne took with him to the grave all the secrets of his intricate modelling and the procurement of colours. And so with a vastly improved working environment the Doctor continued his researches whilst the rest of the hospital remained largely in ignorance of the extent of his work or indeed of the treatments that were being provided in the 'renal unit'.

At home, life was now a little easier for Eliza, with all but the youngest, Charles and Henry, receiving some form of schooling. She was able to devote more time both to her household duties and to supporting her husband in his work. There were happy moments, too, spent with the Folletts at their home at Hampton. There the children of both families could enjoy the freedom of the fine, rambling garden, much as Bright and his siblings had enjoyed the rolling meadowland of Ham Green so many years before.

If there was a disappointment in Bright's life it was the fact that his son William, now at Balliol College, Oxford, wished to take holy orders rather than, as his father had wished, follow a career in medicine. William wrote to his father setting out the reasons for his decision and asking his forgiveness for the pain he caused him:

'My dear Father,
    'I have taken courage to write to you upon the most serious subject I ever wrote about. I have before been strongly inclined to mention it, but a few words in your last letter have confirmed my resolution. I hope that God has suggested the thoughts to me and that he will bring good out of it.
    'I think I need hardly say how fully I feel that you have been beyond every thing a most kind good Father to me. I love you indeed for it, and I believe there is nothing that I would not do to please you, which I did not think inconsistent with the one higher duty to God. If I have for the last two or three years given

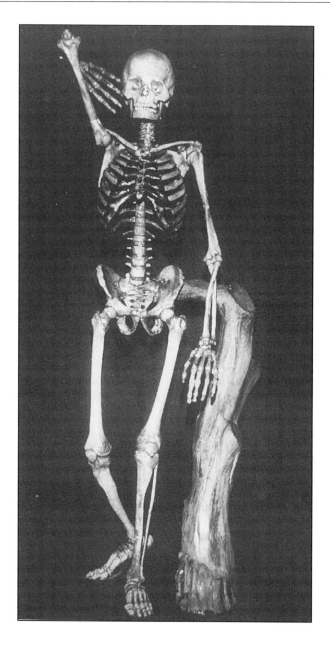

Wax skeleton by Joseph Towne.

you pain in opposing your wishes I sincerely believe it has never been without a real conviction, (though I now think often a mistaken one) that my duty to God required it.'[23]

The doctor's thoughts went back to the time when he had broached the subject of his chosen career with his own father—how could he now fail to understand and support his son's wishes? In the end he was wise enough to accept William's decision without further question.

The Doctor's health gives cause for concern

The unremitting devotion to his medical work began to take its toll and the Doctor's health gave cause for concern not only to himself but also to Eliza. He found the hot summer of 1842 particularly trying, since excessive professional commitments meant that he had to curtail his annual holiday.

It was in the Spring of 1843, however, when his health really began to deteriorate, culminating in an acute bout of cholelithiasis. One can imagine his anxiety, even fear, as he was struck down by a disease he knew so intimately and the thought of submitting to the surgeon's knife would surely have evoked terror in the stoutest of hearts. But he was fortunate as the blockage cleared itself thus obviating the need for surgery: some of his own team helped to nurse him back to health. Then, when he was stronger, a problem arose as to where he should go to convalesce. Fortunately he and Eliza received an opportune offer of the use of 'Alverbank', the country residence of an old family friend and patient the Hon J W Croker, the historian and Secretary to the Admiralty who should perhaps go down in history as the man to whom Wellington presented his Waterloo cloak—unfortunately Croker managed to lose it!

In a letter dated June 30th the Doctor wrote to thank Croker for his kind offer:

'I cannot sufficiently express my thankfulness for your kind offer, for as I am absolutely obliged to abstain from practice it is my great wish to get away from London as soon as I am pronounced capable of undertaking a journey, and how to find a suitable and comfortable retreat has been a real anxiety . . . we hope to take possession of your house on Tuesday or Wednesday next.'[24]

Situated in Alverstoke village near Gosport, 'Alverbank', now an hotel, provides fine views of the Solent to the Isle of Wight. At that time the house was also popular with Queen Victoria who often stayed there on her way across to Osborne House. Below the house the uprights of the old pier and landing stage are still visible.

Richard Bright and Eliza found the house delightful in every way, surrounded by trees and with a fine terrace where the doctor could sit and gaze at the ships or watch the children at play on the beach below. After their sojourn at Alverstoke they travelled on to Dorset where they spent some weeks in a lodging house in Swanage. Whilst there news came of the death of the Doctor's brother Benjamin, but sadly he was still not strong enough to attend the funeral.

In early September, however, he went to Ham Green to be with his sisters for there was need for a family discussion as to what was

to happen to the house. Benjamin had taken up the option provided
in his father's will which gave each son an opportunity to purchase
the house and he had spent much money on extensions and the
purchase of further land. Benjamin had been in debt and now his
fine library collection was to come under the hammer at Sotheby's.
It seems likely that this was the last time that Richard Bright would
visit the house as the family home.

Retirement from Guy's
The Doctor was now 54 years old and although he returned to London
with his health much restored he felt that it was time to think about
cutting down on his work and so, in the early part of 1844, he
resigned from his post at Guy's Hospital although he remained as
honorary medical consultant. It had been some 34 years since Bright
first entered the courtyard of Guy's Hospital: it would have been
unthinkable to turn his back on it completely.

Chapter 13

The Final Years—
International Recognition

'Let our medical attendants be of compatible years,
Who will think of us as in certain ways their peers,
Who know what we possibly still have to live for,
Why we are not unfailingly poised to withdraw.'

Anon

Sir Robert Peel's second ministry brought further limited reforms such as the Mines (1842) and Factories Act (1844); the setting up of Royal Commissions to look into the health of towns and the reduction of import tariffs. The working classes benefited from all these reforms; their working conditions were slightly improved, prices fell as a result of the tariff reduction and the chance of employment grew.

The reduction in tariffs similarly benefited the industrialists, the farmers and landowners since business expanded and the increased incomes of the urban population brought greater spending power, which allowed for the purchase of the wider variety of foodstuffs which were transported to the towns via the new railway system.

Improvements in health conditions in the cities progressed rather more slowly for, as we have already seen, it took the work of Edwin Chadwick and the Poor Law Commissioners and a further outbreak of cholera which occurred in 1848 before Dr John Simon was appointed as Medical Officer of Health for London.

Bright's work in medicine after his retirement from Guy's was no longer so involved with the urban poor for now he was paying much greater attention to his quite substantial private practice. His professional relationship with society physician Dr Chambers was good and of course his friend Henry Holland referred many patients to him. The next few years however would inevitably bring much sadness as he watched members of his own family, as well as old friends who had become patients fade into 'the unfathomable deep'. His brother-in-law Webb's health continued to deteriorate but he struggled on with his duties as Attorney-General to which position he had just been reappointed under Peel's second administration. The Doctor did all in his power to help him regain some modicum of health but any improvement was short-lived. Despite the doctor's best endeavours the 'art of physic' was of no avail.

A continental holiday

In the August of 1844 it was proposed that both families, the Brights and the Folletts, should make a visit to the Continent, an idea which was particularly appealing to Eliza who longed to have time with her husband. Plans were made and within two weeks they were ready to embark. All the Bright children were included apart from William and the two youngest boys. They journeyed through Holland, Switzerland and Germany and into Italy. We can imagine that Bright found many scenes to capture with sketch-book and paints, although, sadly, we have no evidence of such work.

The death of Webb Follett

Richard and Eliza returned in October to England leaving Webb and Lady Jane in Italy. Sadly Webb barely survived another year—having returned to England in mid-winter his condition grew worse and he died the following July. His position as Attorney-General meant for the family the ordeal of a public funeral.

A great crowd assembled to watch the cortège pass for Webb Follett had been a very popular man. Eliza was overwhelmed with an almost pathological grief from which it took her many months to recover. They spent some time in September in the Lake District at a farmhouse lent to them by one of Bright's patients.

Despite his retirement from Guy's Hospital the Doctor did not find himself with the free time he had so badly needed; he was seeing both Francis Jeffrey and Sydney Smith who had also been a founder of the *Edinburgh Review*. John Morgan, Surgeon to Guy's also claimed his time but rather more in the capacity of a friend than physician, although by this time he was sadly suffering all the symptoms of nephritis. Morgan's skill as a surgeon had made him the first to remove a diseased ovary and also to perform section of the cornea. All his life he had been a keen collector of wildlife specimens and he had a fine collection of stuffed birds now housed in Cambridge University Museum. Morgan told his friend of his symptoms but it was already too late for the doctor to attempt any treatment.

The Royal Society—the need for reform

An affair which exercised Richard Bright considerably during this period was what he and others considered to be the need for reform in the Royal Society. At this time Dr Roget, now more than 70 years old, was Secretary of the Society and inflexible in his ideas. A disagreement was raging around the Physiology Committee's decision regarding the award of the Royal Medal. The chosen candidate was Thomas Beck for his work on the nerves of the uterus.[1]

There were many who considered the choice unfair since they considered it to have been Robert Lee's pioneering work which resulted in Beck's discoveries. Bright strongly supported this view and was thus instrumental in setting up a special committee of enquiry. After careful amassing of evidence they set their case before the Council of the Royal Society in the February of 1847. Eventually public outcry demanded a reform; Dr Roget was removed from office—the 'revolution' had been a success!

The death of William Bright

Cruel fate had yet another personal blow in store for the doctor. William left Balliol College in the autumn and went on to Great Yarmouth to train with a well known Churchman, Henry MacKenzie. Within a few months he was offered a curacy in Wiltshire and he was later ordained in Salisbury Cathedral in September 1847. William, however, had never been physically strong, in fact Eliza had had to nurse him at home in Savile Row during the Spring of the previous year and his future as a priest was to be all too short. In January 1848 William conducted his first marriage ceremony—sadly he died the following April and was buried in the Brights' parish church of St James, Piccadilly.

In the September of 1849 the Brights spent a holiday in Scotland stopping off to visit the Jeffreys on their way north. The Doctor was keen to visit Argyllshire again, having had a brief introduction to its beauty the previous year. The family received warm hospitality from the local minister Mr Menzies and from Mr MacDonald the laird whom Richard Bright had met in London some years previously.

Physician to Queen Adelaide

The Doctor was recalled from his holiday in order to attend the Dowager Queen Adelaide who was suffering from advanced cancer of the lung. Bright was called in at the instigation of Sir David Davies, the Household Physician and within a short space of time he had gained the Queen's confidence and they conversed on a range of subjects of mutual interest such as the German language, painting and architecture. The visits to Stanmore became more frequent as the Queen's illness progressed—the bulletin announcing her death on Sunday 2 December, 1849 was signed by Sir David Davies and Dr Richard Bright:

'The Priory, December 2, 1849
'Her Majesty the Queen Dowager expired at seven minutes before two o'clock on Sunday morning, the 2 December, without any apparent suffering, and retaining her composure of mind to the last.

'David Davies M.D.
'Richard Bright M.D.'[2]

INTERMENT OF HER LATE MAJESTY

THE QUEEN DOWAGER.

Admit Dr Bright to

St Georges Chapel

Norfolk

EARL MARSHAL.

*Invitation to Dr Bright to attend the interment of
the Dowager Queen Adelaide.*

The doctor received an invitation to attend the interment of 'Her
Late Majesty, the Queen Dowager' in the Royal Chapel of St George
at Windsor on Thursday 13 December. It was a surprise for Bright
to find that he had been remembered amongst others of the Dowager
Queen's legatees: he received an item of furniture, an illuminated
Bible and a canteen of gold and silver plate.

A Physician's salary

It is interesting to note and to make some comparison between the
doctor's income at this time and that which an eminent physician
might expect to earn some 150 years later. Apparently he was
surprised to find that in the year 1850 he had made £6,000 but of
course his expenses with school and university fees were high. He
was also aware that as he advanced in years his earning capacity
would decrease so he was perhaps anxious to set money aside for
his retirement.

Richard Bright had other colourful and interesting patients at this
time and professional visits often turned in to social occasions. He
went frequently to the house of the Misses Berry, now in their
eighties. Mary, the diarist, keen on political economy and a student
of the theories of Malthus and Free Trade was a lively
conversationalist and her sisters Miss Agnes and Lady Charlotte
Linsay were equally charming.

Emily Eden, the novelist was also one of his favourites—she was
not one to suffer fools gladly and even the Monarchy did not escape
forthright comment; on the accession of William IV she was heard
to remark, 'He is an immense improvement on the last unforgiving
animal . . . this man at least wishes to make everybody happy.'[3]

The Epidemiological Society

In 1850 the first meeting of the London Epidemiological Society was held Benjamin Babington was the President and Thomas Addison, Richard Bright, John Simon and John Snow were all founder members.[4] Bright was extremely interested in epidemiology and particularly in the incidence of his disease in relation to scarlet fever; it was estimated that there were 500 deaths per year from nephritis in the London population of one million.

This makes an interesting comparison with present day statistics which indicate that 80-100 patients per million of the population with terminal renal failure require artificial kidney treatment. His fellow member Dr John Snow, one of the fathers of modern anaesthesia was also one of his patients. As he had always been a total abstainer and vegetarian, Richard Bright, however, recommended not only a complete change of diet to include red meat but also a modest intake of wine! Dr Snow is also famous for having removed the handle from the Broad Street Pump in an attempt to quell the cholera epidemic of 1853.

The year 1850 also brought its burden of sad news with the death of Francis Jeffrey and the generally weakened condition of J W Croker who showed all the symptoms of heart block and who seemed to hover in a state of semi-consciousness—there was little that the doctor could do apart from provide stimulants for his weakened heart muscle.

The edifice designed to house the Great Exhibition in Hyde Park was growing apace but when it was opened pressure of work meant that the Doctor could not find time to visit it but had to wait instead until it was moved to the Crystal Palace.

The death of Follett Bright

The Spring of 1851 plunged the family into mourning once again for news came of Follett's death at Cambridge. This combined, with the continuing pace of work and the anxiety he often experienced regarding his inadequancy as a father, all took its toll and within months Bright was experiencing symptoms which led him to a self-diagnosis of aortic valve disease; he was overwhelmed by a heavy languor, he found himself unable to sleep and be experienced severe nose-bleeds yet he was unwilling to submit to examination by any of his colleagues. He rested in bed until the worst had passed and then on the insistence of his first cousin Sir Benjamin Heywood, he went with Eliza to spend some time in the Heywood home in Blackpool. Here it was quiet and peaceful and the fine beaches provided delightful walks and bracing air. All too soon, however, be became anxious to return to his work, to ascertain that his patients were making progress and of course to make certain that he maintained an income. That Summer he tried to spend more time with his children and managed to accompany them on some of their outings, to the National Gallery, the Temple Gardens or even on shopping expeditions; his daughters were delighted to have his company.

In September they went again to Argyllshire where they received the same warm welcome as they had done on their previous visit; the Reverend Menzies was in thundering good voice and David MacDonald invited the doctor to fish his waters. It was not until the last day of the holiday that a salmon found its way onto his hook! The return journey led them across to Aberdeenshire, to the hillsides overlooking Loch Erich and so to Braemar.

On his return to Savile Row, Bright was urgently called to the bedside of Lord Macaulay whom he had been attending in a professional capacity since mid-July. Macaulay was highly suspicious of all doctors but be appears to have tolerated Bright's company for the latter visited him often and sometimes sat with him during the night when his condition gave cause for particular concern. Finally, the doctor recommended that Macaulay go to Clifton to recuperate, yet despite this period of rest away from London his patient made little real progress and Bright was appalled to see, on his return, that Macaulay looked much older than his 50 years.

A further outbreak of cholera

This deep concern for those in his care meant that Bright continued to neglect his own health and the winter of 1852 brought little respite before the new outbreak of cholera which threatened to reach epidemic proportions in the February of 1853. He was anxious for the health of his sons and sent letters of advice to the housemaster at Rugby and one to Franck at Oxford with pills for his bowels and medicine to counteract any possibility of contagion from the drinking water.

The Doctor's face betrayed his exhaustion, he was pallid and the swelling of his feet led some to believe that he was suffering from the disease which he had so faithfully catalogued; he had not mentioned his heart condition so all remained in ignorance of the real cause for these alarming symptoms. Amongst family papers relevant to this period is what appears to be an unwitnessed will or general request regarding the fate of certain of the doctor's books:

11 Savile Row
March 3, 1852

'I leave a small collection of books which I have collected with a view to illustrating the history and progress of the art of engraving on wood—they have in the course of many years frequently afforded me much harmless amusement and I should be sorry that they should be immediately got rid of all though they have probably lost me at various times nearly a hundred pounds.'[5]

The parental role
On the domestic front there were also again demands on the doctor's time for his daughters were growing up and needed to be escorted to various social events. Fortunately Lord Gainsborough, who seems to have been a good family friend, was often on hand to take them about and their next-door neighbour Mrs Grote made a great fuss of the girls, inviting them to all her soirées.

Franck, away at Oxford, was also much in his father's thoughts although he nearly forgot his birthday:

'My dearest Franck,
'Your mother told me just now that it was your birthday today, God bless you and give you a great many happy returns. If there is anything we can do to make it so you know our willingness, but you have long known that and I need not repeat it. There is one thing I wish you fully to understand—that it is my particular desire that if you can by any possibility derive advantage from any private help or tuition to forward you in your studies you will not hesitate to pursue it . . .'[5]

Many visitors came to the house, including post-graduate students sent from Paris by Professor Rayer. Members of the younger generation, like cousin Henry Arthur, brought friends such as Nathaniel Hawthorne whose novels the *Scarlet Letter* and *The Blithedale Romance* were eagerly sought after, particularly amongst those liberal-minded intellectuals who could appreciate his avant-garde notions of the experimental socialist commune. Hawthorne's ideas were rather in the spirit of the earlier Pantisocrats such as Coleridge and Southey who, as we have already seen, when Richard Bright was a young boy in Bristol at the height of the Napoleonic wars, had dreamed of commune life on the virgin lands of the Susquehanna. Their dreams were sadly now firmly buried beneath the sterner face of reactionary conservatism; Coleridge for one had long since 'snapped [his] squeaking baby-trumpet of Sedition'.

The Brights received countless invitations of a professional and social nature but rarely were they accepted—occasionally they went to musical evenings for the doctor found them restful; he particularly enjoyed listening to Jenny Lind who often sang at Mrs Grote's evening gatherings.

The doctor is honoured with a DCL
In the June of 1853 Bright received another public honour for he was invited to New College, Oxford to receive a Doctorate of Civil Law. Whilst he looked forward to the opportunity of seeing Franck the ordeal of the ceremony he found quite unnerving for being of a rather reserved nature he preferred to avoid such public affairs. On June 8th the family set off for Oxford where they were met by

a very proud Franck who wasted no time before bringing along the many friends who were eager to meet his father. The next day Bright received his Doctorate, then be spent some time with Sir Henry Acland, the Professor of Medicine, who showed him the new Ashmolean Museum and the Radcliffe library. Despite his former misgivings the Doctor later admitted to having quite enjoyed himself!

Very shortly after his return to London he was summoned to attend the royal children who were suffering from measles. He was called in as a consultant to ascertain that the correct treatment was being administered and that there were no dangerous complications.

Britain enters the Crimean War

Britain's entry into the Crimean War in March of 1854 was not only upsetting for the doctor but it also increased his workload even further for his membership of so many European Medical Societies brought requests for professional advice. It seemed the war lacked direction, the troops were ill-equipped and once again appalling conditions prevailed in the military or field hospitals where an attempt was made to treat the many casualties. Florence Nightingale challenged the army's cavalier attitude to the sick and wounded and with a group of nursing nuns and other women with nursing experience she set up the first efficient military hospital. Based at Scutari it set standards of organisation and hygiene which gave the men a much better chance of survival; now they were far less likely to die of infected wounds or from the fevers which had in the past swept through hospitals claiming many lives.

At Guy's Hospital, Benjamin Babington offered to cover the work of any medical colleague who volunteered to go to the Crimean and Richard Bright dismayed by the shortcomings so evident in his profession gave all his energy to advising those who would undertake such work.

Isambard Brunel came to Savile Row to discuss the war and to show the doctor his plans for the transportation of large numbers of troops and for his 'floating siege gun'—he despaired of a government that ignored the possibilities provided by the engineering resources now available to it.

Brunel was involved in the design of an improved hospital for the Crimea which was to be built in England then shipped out for assembly on a predetermined site. The hospital was eventually built at Renkioi and close on 1500 sick and wounded men were treated there before peace was declared.[6]

A visit to Bristol

The following year Bright's brother Robert was seriously ill and in the summer of 1855 the doctor went by train to Bristol to visit him. His brother's appearance gave great cause for concern; he managed to raise himself sufficiently to greet his visitor but soon lapsed again into a state of semi-delirium. Bright consulted with Mr Harrison and Dr Bernard from the Bristol Infirmary to decide on a suitable course of treatment. As soon as he felt his brother to be out of immediate danger and that all was in order the doctor returned to London. Sadly he had missed his opportunity to visit the Science Exhibition at the Crystal Palace but he did manage to see Turner's pictures at the Royal Society of Arts.

The recuperative powers of the Isle of Wight

By the Autumn of 1855 the Doctor's own health was beginning the slow process of deterioration. He was constantly in a state of fatique and although be refused to consult any of his colleagues he did consent to bed rest. When he was somewhat recovered he went to Brighton to recuperate. He returned to find Eliza exhausted by the constant stream of visitors so now it was her turn to try the recuperative powers of Brighton! When Eliza returned they spent some time trying to decide on the venue for their summer holiday. It seems that the decision was made when Tennyson offered to lease them his house at Farringford on the Isle of Wight for the months of August and September.

They gladly accepted the offer and were delighted with what they found. The house was as charming as 'Alverbank', in a superb situation overlooking Freshwater Bay; its garden sheltered by ilex, pines and magnolias. Richard Bright siezed the opportunity to make use of his artists materials; he apparently sketched and painted many local scenes including the Needles and Portland Bay. Sadly he found he could not cope with too much exertion and was unable to accompany the family on their walks and picnic parties.

Back in London in November Tennyson himself appeared at Savile Row wishing to consult the Doctor. Apparently it was his habit to go from doctor to doctor; one had successfully weaned him off both opium and alcohol but tobacco he would not give up.

The winter of 1856/7 was again hard and brought the usual increase in cases of pneumonia and bronchitis to keep the Doctor busy. He still visited Lord Macaulay and J W Croker until the latter's sudden demise. On Saturdays Bright went to see Isambard Brunel, as busy and pre-occupied as ever, this time over the imminent launch of the SS 'Great Eastern'. It was hard for the Doctor to see his old family friend moving into an advanced stage of renal failure; he knew he had not many months to live.

Declining health

His own health continued to deteriorate over the next couple of years and it seemed that it was only the thought of his annual holiday which kept him going. It was in the summer of 1857 that he managed sufficiently to master the worst symptoms of his increasing ill-health to undertake his last holiday in Europe. Plans were made to leave

Dr Richard Bright—a daguerreotype. (Courtesy of the Royal College of Physicians of London.)

on the 1st August—the planned itinerary to include Vienna, Berlin, and possibly Italy. Eliza was anxious until the last moment that something would occur to prevent their departure. She longed for him to give up all his work and to take greater care of his own health.

It seems that their holiday in fact took them down the Loire Valley and on to Avignon—here Franck left them to return to Oxford. His going left a great void: his father missed him sorely and his mother was anxious without him.

When they reached Cannes the Doctor's health improved a little and he took the opportunity of renewing his acquaintance with Lord Brougham and reminiscing about the old days in Edinburgh. They moved on to Genoa, then to Venice whose magical charm they found utterly captivating. All too soon it was time to return to England, this time by a different route which took them through Verona, Milan and Berne.

Bright returned to his professional duties but the bitter cold of January 1858 found him breathless again and suffering from severe angina. Yet he struggled on despite pleas from Eliza and his children that he should give up his work. He still took on more patients and continued to see those like Brunel, whose sufferings he found hard to bear. Brunel had little time to live and had been advised to winter in Egypt—he was reluctant to go; he jokingly suggested that the Doctor should accompany him.

The death of Doctor Bright
In the Autumn of 1858 Richard Bright experienced a period of high spirits, his health seemed for a while to be improving and friends remarked on his cheerfulness. Ironically, within a week or two he was dead. The end was unexpected in view of the seeming improvement but it appears that it was an internal haemorrhage which finally caused his death on the 16th December, 1858. The *Medical Times and Gazette* reported the details of the Doctor's last hours:

> 'Dr Bright was in the enjoyment of his usual health until Saturday, December 11, when, about midnight, he was seized with haemorrhage from the bowels, with great prostration of strength and difficulty of breathing, assuming the form of angina pectoris. He was attended by Dr Babington and Dr Latham, and Dr Watson was subsequently called in in consultation. From these three physicians, in conjunction with his friend and neighbour, Mr H C Johnson, he received the most unremitting attention, until the night of Wednesday, December 15th, when he was visited about 12 o'clock by Dr Babington, whom he recognised, and about half past 12 o'clock by Sir Charles Locock in whose presence he breathed his last.'[7]

In his will he had asked for a private funeral; he was buried in Kensal Green but sadly the family grave was destroyed by enemy action in 1940 during a bombing raid on London.

Professor Stewart Cameron has most aptly named the Church of St James Piccadilly, 'The Cathedral of the Renal Physicians' as it commemorates not only Dr Richard Bright but also Sir William Bowman, the 'Father of the Kidney' and Dr George Johnson who worked with Richard Bright's team. On the staircase at the back of the church there is also a plaque to the memory of James Baillie, eldest son of Matthew Baillie, the man who perhaps provided the catalyst which stimulated the study of clinico-pathological relationships.

The church of St James Piccadilly, London.

The inscription on the memorial plaque to Dr Bright reads:

'He contributed to medical science many discoveries and works of great value; and died while in full practice of his profession after a life of warm affection, unsullied purity and great usefulness.'

We might also wish to record that Richard Bright was a talented, dedicated and above all an unassuming man—qualities which are perhaps most succinctly expressed in the words of the poet Wordsworth:

'Strongest minds
Are often those of whom the noisy world
Hears least.'

It is a relatively simple task to describe a man's professional achievements in his life and work for these things are usually well-documented. To construct a true picture of the man himself and his character may prove rather more difficult. In physical terms we are told that Richard Bright was a robust man, short in stature with a fine head of hair and twinkling eyes. We have seen that he was a good husband and father though at times he felt this area of his life to be sadly neglected; certainly his family would have wished to see more of him.

Testimony from colleagues and patients alike would confirm that his warm, magnanimous nature endeared him to all who shared his life in whatever capacity.

We know that apart from his undeniable success in his chosen profession, the Doctor was a gifted man in many other fields of endeavour. Hobbies such as geology, travel, the study of foreign languages, writing, sketching and water-colour painting might have led Coleridge to claim that had he not been a great doctor he would have made an excellent geologist, linguist, author or artist so broad were Richard Bright's talents.

Many tributes to the man and his work

As he did not receive a knighthood like many of his contemporaries, we may feel that the doctor did not receive during his lifetime as much formal recognition as his work clearly merited. There have, nevertheless, been many tributes to him since his death, leaving us in no doubt of his greatness. Even the erstwhile scathing 'old enemy' Thomas Wakley was swift to praise both the man and his lifetime's work in medicine:

> 'The sudden and unexpected demise of Dr Bright has created a deep impression of grief and regret, such as only a sense of irretrievable loss could occasion. In him all feel that the medical profession of England has lost one of the most original, observant and philosophical minds that have ever contributed to the glory and the usefulness of the body. A man of peculiar independence of thought, of high morale, and untiring energy, he had contributed more than, perhaps, any other to form the medical opinion of his day.'[8]

Many excellent accounts of his life and work have been published including a biography by his great-great niece Miss Pamela Bright. In 1983, Dr Robert Kark delivered the Fitzpatrick Lecture to the Royal College of Physicians, London dedicated to Bright's memory. Earlier, he had, in the continuing tradition of American Medical historians such as Burton Chance, Fielding Garrison, and of course, Dr W S Thayer, commemorated the centenary of Bright's death in an editorial comparing his achievements with those of William Harvey.

The Guy's Hospital Commemorative Medal. (Courtesy of Guy's Hospital.)

Perhaps the greatest commemorative occasion was the celebration of the centenary of the discovery of Bright's disease which took place at Guy's Hospital in July 1927. Presiding over the meeting was the Right Honourable the Earl of Balfour.

As we already know, the Bright Memorial Oration was delivered by Dr W S Thayer, Emeritus Professor of Medicine at the Johns Hopkins University of Baltimore, USA. It remains the most interesting and succinct account to date both of Richard Bright's work in medicine and of his life.[9] It was therefore fitting that Professor Thayer should be the first recipient of the Bright Centenary Medal. Others similarly honoured at the meeting and also receiving gold medals included Dr Ludwig Aschoff, Professor of Pathology at Freiburg University, Professor Widal of France *in absentia*, Sir John Rose Bradford, President of the Royal College of Physicians and post-humously, Professor Starling. Professor Lemiere collected the prize for Professor Widal, and Dr Hurst on behalf of Professor Starling.

In his oration, Professor Thayer paid tribute to the doctor's personal qualities and compared him with Laennec adding that although not brilliant, Bright had steadfastness of purpose , an equanimity which was more precious than brilliancy; that he was straightforward, kindly, charitable, honest, tolerant and serene, and through conscientiousness and painstaking work, became a learned and wise man earning himself a well-merited and honourable immortality.

One of the greatest tributes to Dr Richard Bright however, came in 1861 from his old friend, pupil and colleague, Dr George Hilaro Barlow who said:

'There has been no English physician—perhaps it may be said none of any country—since the time of Harvey who has effected not only so great on advance in the knowledge of particular disease, but also some greater revolution in our habit of thought and methods of investigating morbid phenomenon and tracing aetiology of disease as the late Dr Richard Bright'.[10]

Our account of Richard Bright's life and his work started with the social and industrial revolution which helped form the world into which he was born. By the end of his lifetime he had witnessed the advent of reforms long overdue.

It is perhaps fitting that we should end with a mention of the medical revolution in which the doctor was clearly instrumental for when talking of medicine, as with the flood, there is a natural watershed before Richard Bright and after Richard Bright.

Comparisons tend in a sense to derogate and although he has been likened to Harvey, Laennec, Vesalius and Latham, in our opinion Richard Bright was very much his own man, idiosyncratic in the approach he took to the study of disease and in that idiosyncrasy lay his true greatness.

Chapter 1
Bristol—City of Merchant Venturers

1 Latimer J. *The Annals of Bristol*, Vol 2. Bristol: Georges, 1970.
2 Plans for improvement to Bristol Docks drawn up by Richard Bright (Snr) are held at Bristol Records Office.
3 McGrath P. *The Merchant Venturers of Bristol*. Bristol: Society of Merchant Venturers of the City of Bristol, 1975.
4 Family letters. Property of Mrs E Lloyd of Colwall—available on microfilm at Bristol Records Office.
5 Cave C H. *A History of Banking in Bristol* Bristol, 1750-1889.
6 Latimer J. *The Annals of Bristol*, Vol 2. Bristol: Georges, 1970.
7 *Ibid.*
8 Hazlitt W. In: Blythe R, ed. *Selected Writings*. Harmondsworth: Penguin Books, 1970.

Chapter 2
Growing up in an Age of Revolution

1 Treneer A. *The Mercurial Chemist—A Life of Sir Humphry Davy*. London: Methuen & Co, 1965.
2 Stansfield D A. *Thomas Beddoes MD, 1760-1808, Chemist, Physician & Democrat*. Dordrecht: Reidel Publishing, 1984.
3 Christiansen R. *Romantic Affinities—Portraits from an Age 1780-1830*. London: Bodley Head, 1988.
4 Porter R. *Thomas Beddoes—Doctor of Society*. Routledge, 1992.
5 Little B. *The City & County of Bristol*. Bristol: Werner Laurie, 1954.
6 Family Letters. Property of Major Athill, Holt, Norfolk.

Chapter 3
Student Days in Edinburgh

1 Joyce M. *Edinburgh, the Golden Age*. London: Longman, Green & Co, 1951.
2 Christison Sir Robert. *The Life of Sir Robert Christison, Bart*, 2 Vols. London: William Blackwood & Sons, 1835.
3 Craig W S. *History of the Royal College of Physicians of Edinburgh*. Oxford: Blackwell, 1976.
4 Rosner L. *Andrew Duncan (1744-1828) FRSE.—Scottish Men of Medicine*. In: Scotland's Medical Heritage, 1981.
5 Cooper Bransby-Blake. *Life of Sir Astley Cooper*, 2 Vols. London. John W Parker, 1843.
6 Mackenzie Sir G S *Travels in the Island of Iceland*. Edinburgh: Archibald Constable, 1811.

Chapter 4
Iceland—
From Arthur's Seat to Snaefellsjokul

1 Wawn A, ed. *The Iceland Journal of Henry Holland 1810.* London. The Hakluyt Society, 1987.
2 Mackenzie Sir G S. *Travels in the Island of Iceland.* Edinburgh: Archibald Constable, 1811.

Chapter 5
Guy's and Edinburgh—
From Student to Doctor of Medicine

1 Southey R. *Letters from England.* London: The Cresset Press, 1951.
2 Hill W. Richard Bright—A Bio-Bibliography. *Guy's Hospital Gazette* 1950-51; **65**: 373-483.
3 Cooper Bransby-Blake. *Life of Sir Astley Cooper,* 2 Vols. London: John W Parker, 1843.
4 Sakula A. Gentlemen of the Hammer: British medical geologists in the 19th Century. *Journal of the Royal Society of Medicine* 1990: **83**, No. 12, 788-794.
5 Christison Sir Robert *The Life of Sir Robert Christison, Bart,* 2 Vols. William Blackwood & Sons, 1835.
6 Bright P. *Richard Bright.* London: The Bodley Head, 1983.
7 Joyce M. *Edinburgh—The Golden Age.* London: Longman, Green & Co, 1951.
8 Hurwitz B, Richardson R. Inspector General James Barry MD: putting the woman in her place. *British Medical Journal* 1989; **298**: 299-304.
9 Bright Family manuscripts and letters. Property of David and Charles Bright, Melbourne, Australia.

Chapter 6
Beginning to Observe—
Traveller, Author and Artist

1 Honti J. Richard Bright, Edward Brown, and John Paget's Travels in Hungary. *Proceedings of the International Congress of the History of Medicine* 1974.
2 Bright R. *Travels from Vienna through Lower Hungary; with some remarks on the state of Vienna during the Congress of the Year—1814.* Edinburgh: Archibald Constable, 1818. All quotations from Richard Bright's book unless otherwise stated.
3 Neuberger M. British Medicine and the Old Vienna Medical School. *Bulletin of the Institute of the History of Medicine.* Baltimore: Johns Hopkins University, 1942; **12**: 486-528.

4 Rooney P, Szebenyi B, Balint G P. Richard Bright's 'Travels from Vienna through Lower Hungary': A glimpse of medicine & health care in the early nineteenth century. Unpublished.
5 *Guy's Hospital Gazette* 1962; **76**: 513.
6 *The Times* No 9554. London: Thursday June 22nd, 1815.
7 *The Edinburgh Review* 1818; **13**: 214.

Chapter 7
Physician and Family Man—
A Brief Moment of Happiness

1 Bailey P. *Whose Cities?* Harmondsworth: Penguin, 1991.
2 MacCormac H. At the Public Dispensary with Willan and Bateman. *British Journal of Dermatology and Syphilology* 1933; **45**: 385-95.
3 Abel Smith B. The Hospitals 1860-1948; a study in social administration in England and Wales. London: Heinemann 1964.
4 Munro-Smith G. *A History of the Bristol Royal Infirmary*. Bristol: J W Arrowsmith, 1917.
5 Bright P. *Richard Bright*. London: The Bodley Head, 1983.
6 Rooney P, Szebeny B, Balint G P. Richard Bright's 'Travels from Vienna through Lower Hungary': A glimpse of medicine & health care in the early nineteenth century. Unpublished.
7 Enright D J, ed. *The Faber Book of Fevers and Frets*. London: Faber & Faber, 1989.
8 Cameron H C. *Mr Guy's Hospital—1726-1948*. London: Longmans, Green & Co, 1954.
9 Bright R. *Reports of Medical Cases*, Vol 2 part 1. London. Longmans, Green & Co, 1954.

Chapter 8
Dr Richard Bright of Guy's—
Physicians Challenge Surgical Supremacy

1 Woodward Sir L. *The Oxford History of England: The Age of Reform*, 2nd Ed. Oxford: Clarendon Press, 1962.
2 Porter R. *Thomas Beddoes, Doctor of Society*. London: Routledge, 1992.
3 Thayer W S. Richard Bright: the Bright Oration delivered at Guy's Hospital on 8th July, 1927 on the occasion of the Centenary of the publication of the first volume of Bright's Reports on Medical Cases. *Guy's Hospital Reports* 1927; **77**: 253-301.
4 Cameron H C. *Mr Guy's Hospital—1726-1948*. London: Longmans, Green & Co, 1954.

5 Bright R. *Reports of Medical Cases selected with a view of illustrating the symptoms and Cure of Diseases with a Reference to Morbid Anatomy* (Vol 1). London: Longman, Rees, Orme, Brom & Green, 1827.
6 Addison T, Bright R. *Elements of the Practice of Medicine* Vol 1. London: Longman, Orme, Brown, Green & Longmans, 1839.
7 Bright P. *Richard Bright*. London: The Bodley Head, 1983.
8 Family letters. Property of Major Athill, Holt, Norfolk.

Chapter 9
The Medical Writings—
A Legacy of his Life's Work

1 Bright R. *Reports on Medical Cases selected with a view of illustrating Disease with a reference to Morbid Anatomy*, Vol I. London: Longman, Rees, Orme, Brown and Green, 1827.
2 Bright R. *Reports on Medical Cases selected with a view of illustrating Disease with a reference to Morbid Anatomy*, Vol II. London: Longman, Rees, Orme, Brown and Green, 1831.
3 Christison R. *The Life of Sir Robert Christison*, Bart, Vols I & II. Edited by his sons. London. W Blackwood & Sons, 1886.
4 Cameron H C. Richard Bright at Guy's. *Guy's Hospital Reports* 1958; **107**: 263-93.
5 One Hundred Years Ago. *British Medical Journal* Sept 13, 1913; 683-6.
6 Thayer W S. Richard Bright. *Guy's Hospital Reports* 1927; **77**: 253-301.
7 Munk W. *Roll of the Royal College of Physicians of London*, 3 Vols. London, 1878.
8 Cooper Bransby-Blake. *Life of Sir Astley Cooper*, 2 Vols. London: J W Parker, 1843.
9 Kark R M. The First Dr Richard Bright Memorial Lecture: Dr Richard Bright and Richard Bright the Lesser. Unpublished, but held by the Dr Richard Bright Society.
10 Taylor Selwyn (Sir) *Robert Graves—The Golden Years of Irish Eponymists in Medicine*. London: Royal Society of Medicine Services Limited, 1989.
11 Bostock John (1773-1806). Physician and Chemist; his work on the urine and blood urea and albumen content, fatty stools and bile composition on Richard Bright's patients earned him a place as one of the founders of modern clinical biochemistry.
12 Barlow G Hilaro (1806-1866). Physician and another member of the team; he took over the supervision of the renal unit after Richard Bright's retirement.
13 Rees George Owen (1813-1889). Physician, physiologist and chemist. Dr J Boss in an article 'Richard Bright's Reports of

Medical Cases (1827)—A sesquicential note'. *Bristol Medical Chirurgical Journal* 5-6, 1978, recognises the importance of Richard Bright and Owen Rees as renal physiologists. The latter published his own text book on *Diseases of the Kidney* in 1850.

14 Toynbee Joseph (1815-1866). Otologist and microscopist, he extended the work of the team to the microscopic examination of the minute structure of the glomeruli on Malpighian corpuscles.

15 Babington Benjamin (1794-1866). Physician and son of Dr Bright's old chief Dr William Babington whose daughter, Martha, was Richard Bright's first wife. Benjamin was appointed to the staff of Guy's Hospital in preference to Dr Thomas Hodgkin.

16 Robinson George (1821-1875). Physician and member of the team. He also wrote on the microscopic appearance of the kidney.

17 Johnson George (1818-1896). Professor of Medicine at St George's Hospital; although not a member of the Bright team was a great supporter of that school and became a leading renal physician: Sir William Bowman, Richard Bright and he have memorial plaques in St James's Piccadilly.

18 Morgagni G B. *De Sedibus et Causis Moriborum*. Venice, 1761.

19 Baillie Matthew. *The Morbid Anatomy of some of the most important parts of the Human Body*. London: Bulmer, 1793.

20 Sherrington C C (Sir). *The Endeavour of Jean Fernel*. Cambridge University Press, 1946.

21 Fine L G. William Bowman's Description of the Glomerulus. *American Journal of Nephrology* 1985; **5**: 439-40.

22 Bright R. *The Medical Reports*. Vol 1, 1827.

23 Wells William C. Observations on the dropsy which succeeds Scarlet Fever. *Transactions of the Society for the Improvement of Medical and Surgical Knowledge* 1812; **3**: 167-86.

24 Blackall John. *Observations on the nature and cure of dropsies, and particularly on the presence of the coagulable part of the blood in dropsical urine*, 3rd Ed. London: Longman, Green, 1818.

25 Fothergill J M. *Vaso-renal change versus Bright's Disease*. London. Baillière Tindall and Cox, 1887.

26 Wright V. In defence of eponyms. *British Medical Journal* 1991 **303**: 1600-2.

27 Cruickshank AG, Kinninmouth Sir W, eds. *Notes of Portraits of Presidents Hanging in the Royal College of Physicians, Edinburgh*. Edinburgh: September 1981.

28 Dobson J. *Anatomical eponyms*. Edinburgh: Livingstone, 1962.

29 Pettigrew T J. *Biographical Memoirs of the Most Celebrated Physicians and Surgeons*, Vol II. London: Fisher Son & Co, 1840.

30 Forget M C. Letter on Albuminuria (Maladie de Bright) addressed to Dr Rayer. *Medical Gazette, Paris* 1837; **6**: 609-18.

31   Eknoyan G. Origins of nephrology: Hippocrates, the father of
     clinical nephrology. *American Journal of Nephrology* 1988; **8**:
     498-507.
32   Eknoyan G. Galen, the founding father of experimental renal
     physiology. *American Journal of Nephrology* 1989; **9**: 66-82.
33   Jivaka (6BC) writing about the Atharva Veda, an ancient Hindu
     medical text dating back to 2000 BC, written by Arteya
     Punarvasus.
34   Major R H. *Classical Descriptions of Disease*, 3rd Ed. Springfield,
     Illinois, USA: Charles C Thomas, 1945.
35   Major R H. Notes on the history of nephritis. *Bulletin of the
     History of Medicine* 1948; **23**: 453-60.
36   Cameron J S. A historical review; The nephrotic syndrome. 3-56,
     In Cameron J Stewart & Glassock Richard J, eds. New York:
     Marcel Dekker Inc, 1988.
37   Rayer P F O. *Traité des Maladies Des Reins*, 3 Vols. Paris:
     Baillière, 1841.
38   Klemperer P, Federn W. The dilemma of Johann Jacob Wepfer;
     the history of the contracted kidney. *British Journal of History
     of Medicine* 1959; **33**: 50-66.
40   Brian T. *The Pisse Prophet or Certain Pisse-Pot Lectures*. Thrale
     E P & R, London—(1637), Facsimile edition published by Riker
     Laboratories—(1968).
41   Foster W D. The early history of chemical pathology in Great
     Britain's medical history. *Medical History Journal* 1959; **3**:
     173-187.
42   Reil J. *Uber die Erkentiss und Kur der Fieber* Book 5, Halle,
     Curtsche, Buchhandlung, 1799-1815; 123-125.
43   Harris Delpratt J. *The Royal Devon and Exeter Hospital*. Exeter:
     Eland Bros, 1922.

Chapter 10
The Renal Portfolio—Bright's Disease

1   Osman A A. *Original Papers by Richard Bright on Renal
    Disease*. Oxford University Press, 1937.
2   Bright R. Cases and observations. Illustrative of Renal disease
    accompanied with the secretion of albuminous urine. Memoir
    the Second. *Guy's Hospital Reports* 1840; **5**: 101-61.
3   Bright R. *Reports of Medical Cases. Vol II. Diseases of the Brain
    and Nervous System*. London: Longman, Reese, Orme and Green,
    1831.
4   Bright R. Concerning the pathology of the kidney (letter).
    London Medical Gazette 1842; **29**: 707-8.
5   Mann W H. Bright's disease: the changing concept of a century.
    Guy's Hospital Reports 1958; **107**; 323-47.

6 Lowry S, Smith J. Duplicate publications. *British Medical Journal* 1992; **304**: 990-1000.

7 Bright R. On the function of the abdomen and some of the diagnostic marks of its disease. The Goulstonian Lectures. *London Medical Gazette* 1833; **xii**: 281, 312, 345, 378, 411.

8 Mahomed F A. Chronic Bright's disease without albuminuria. Thesis—University of Cambridge, 1881.

9 Bright R. Cases and observations, illustrative of renal disease accompanied with the secretion of albuminous urine. *Guy's Hospital Reports* 1836; **1**: 338-79.

10 Bright R. Tabular view of the morbid appearances of 100 cases connected with albuminous urine. *Guy's Hospital Report* 1836; **1**: 380-400.

11 Hawkins F. Two cases of Chronic Albuminuria, One of 25 years and the other 43 years' duration. *Transactions of the Clinical Society of London.* 1893; **26**: 216-22.

12 Cavanagh J B. A note on the histological appearances of the three kidneys originally described by Dr Richard Bright. *Guy's Hospital Reports* 1958; **107**: 390-98.

13 Weller R O, Nester B. Histological reassessment of three kidneys originally described by Richard Bright in 1827-36. *British Medical Journal* 1972; **3**: 761-3.

14 Fine L G. Pathological specimens of the kidney examined by Richard Bright. *Kidney International* 1986; **29**: 779-83.

15 Say F. Although five artists were involved in illustrating Richard Bright's books. Frederick and William Say, father and son drew and engraved the majority of the plates from his own sketches in the post-mortem room. George Scharf, Thomas Fairland, William Hurst and C J Cantor completed the quintet; the latter was said to be 'too fond of liquid refreshment'. He and Hurst were the official artists to Guy's Hospital.

16 Cameron J S, Becker E L. Richard Bright and observations in renal history. *Guy's Hospital Reports* 1964; **113**: 159-71.

17 Toynbee J. On the intimate studies of the human kidney, and on the changes which its several component parts undergo in 'Bright disease'. *Transactions of the Royal Medical Chirurgical Society, London* 1846; **29**: 303-24.

18 Cameron H C. Richard Bright at Guy's. *Guy's Hospital Reports* 1958; **107**: 263-93.

Chapter 11
The Medical Reports and Other Literature

1 Winston G A R. Richard Bright and his published writings—a review. *Guy's Hospital Gazette* 1958; **72**: 483-8.

2 Hale-White William (Sir). Bright's observations other than those on renal disease. *Guy's Hospital Reports* 1921; **71**: 143-57.

3 Hale-White William (Sir). *Great Doctors of the Nineteenth Century: Richard Bright*. London: Butler and Tanner, 1935.

4 Peitzman S J. Bright's disease and Bright's generation—toward exact medicine at Guy's Hospital. *Bulletin of the History of Medicine* 1981; **55**: 307-21.

5 *Reports of Medical Cases of Richard Bright*. Facsimile Report Jointly published. London: Gower Medical Publishers Limited and the Royal Society of medicine, 1985.

6 Barlow G Hilaro. *Clinical Memoirs on Abdominal Tumours and Intumescence*. London: New Sydenham Society, 1861.

7 White Franklin, A. *Medicine in the Eighteenth and Nineteenth Centuries in The Royal Hospital of Saint Bartholomew 1123-1973*. Medvei V C, Thornton J L, eds. London: W S Cowell Ltd, 1974.

8 Letter to the Editor. The right of students to attend the practice of endowed hospitals, after payment of fees. *Lancet* 1837; **i**: 95.

9 Δ.Ε.Ω. *Lancet* 1826-6; **ix**: 135.

10. Pettigrew T J. *Biographical Memoirs of the Most Celebrated Physicians and Surgeons. Henry Clutterbuck MD Vol 11*. London: Fisher & Son, 1840.

11 Gardner-Thorpe C. *James Parkinson 1755-1824 and a reprint of 'The Shaking Palsy'*. 1st Ed. Exeter: A Wheaton & Co, 1987.

12 Lowry S, Smith J. Duplicate publications. *British Medical Journal* 1992; **304**: 990-1000.

13 Bright R. On gangrene. *Guy's Hospital Reports* 1928; **78**: 23-24.

14 Bright R. The clavated nail and finger which is generally supposed to be indicative of a strumous diathesis. *Minutes of the Guy's Physical Society*, Oct 5th, 1839.

15 Brock R (Lord). The Guy's Hospital Reports. *The Guy's Hospital Gazette* 1952; 252-261.

16 Hill W. Richard Bright—A Bio-Bibliography. *Guy's Hospital Gazette* 1950-51; **64-65**: 373-483.

17 Bright R. A case of traumatic tetanus. *Lancet* 1825-26; **9**: 268.

18 Bright R. A singular case. *Lancet* 1825-26; **9**: 653.

19 Bright R. On the contagious nature of erysipelas. *Lancet* 1825-26; **9**: 717.

20 Bostock J. A case of profuse perspiration with analysis of the fluid. *Medico-Chirurgical Transactions* 1828; **14**: 433-6.

21 Bright R. Cases and observations connected with disease of the pancreas and duodenums. *Medico-Chirurgical Transactions* 1833; **18**: 1-56.

22 Bright R. The same. *London Medical Gazette* 1833; **11**: 324.

23 Bright R. The same. *Lancet* 1832-33; 396.

24 Bright R. Cases and observations illustrative of diagnosis when adhesions have taken place in the peritoneum, both remarks on some other changes of that membrane. *Medico-Chirurgical*

Transactions. 1835; **19**: 176-216. *London Medical Gazette* 1834-35; 697.

25   Bright R. Observations on the treatment of fever. *Guy's Hospital Reports* 1836; **1**: 1-8. *London Medical Gazette* 1835-36; 576.

26   Bruetsch W L. Richard Bright (1789-1858) and Apoplexy. *Transactions of the American Neurological Association* 1971; **76**: 213-15.

27   Cave H A. Contribution to the history of narcolepsy. *Archives of Neurology and Psychiatry* 1937; **38**: 136-9.

28   Bright R. Permanent contraction of all extremities and numerous cartilaginous deposits in the arachnoid of the spinal marrow. *Guy's Hospital Reports* 1836; **1**: 33-6.

29   Alvarez W C. A pioneer in geriatrics—Editorial. *Geriatrics* 1965; **20**: 433-44.

30   Thelwell's library held three bound volumes entitled: Dr Bright's Miscellaneous Memoirs; Dr Bright's contributions to the Guy's Hospital Reports 1836-38; 4 Lectures and 2 Cases, originally in the posession of Dr George Charles Bright of Cannes.

31   Bright R. An account of a remarkable misplacement of the stomach. *Guy's Hospital Reports* 1836; **1**: 598-603.

32   B right R. Cases of spasmodic disease accompanying affections of the pericardium. *Medico-Chirurgical Transactions* 1839; **22**: 1-19.

33   Bright R. Internal concretion of phosphate of lime. *London Medical Gazette* 1839-40; **ii**: 76.

34   Bright R. Case of tetanus in which quinine and stimulants were administered very extensively with success. *Guy's Hospital Reports* 1836; **i**: 111-18.

35   Evans H (Lord). Richard Bright—Before and after: Lettsomian lectures. *Transactions of the Medical Society, London* 1951; **66**: 129-147.

36   Kark R M. Physician Extraordinary: Dr Richard Bright (1789-1858). The FitzPatrick Lecture. Montpelier, Vermont: Horn of Moon Enterprise, 1986.

37   Christison Robert (Sir). *The Life of Sir Robert Christison, Bart.* Edited by his sons. Edinburgh & London: W Blackwood, 1885.

38   Christison Robert (Sir). *On granular degeneration of the kidnies and its connection with dropsy, inflammations and other diseases.* Edinburgh: Black, 1835 (his original article was published in 1829).

39   Rayer P F O. *Traité des Maladies des Reins*, 3 Vols, with atlas. Paris: Baillière J B, 1839.

40   Hamburger J. *Nephrology.* Philadelphia: W B Saunders & Co, 1968.

41   Caveribert R. La Vie et L'oeuvre de Rayer. Thesis—University of Paris, Vigne, 1931.

42   Richet G. From Bright's disease to modern nephrology: Pierre Rayer's innovative method of clinical investigation. *Kidney International* 1991; **39**: 787-92.

43　Maher J F, Keogh J A B. Osborne of Dublin and the origin of Nephrology in Ireland. *Irish Journal of Medical Science* (in press).

44　Mann W N. Bright's disease. The changing concept of a century. *Guy's Hospital Reports* 1958; 323-47.

45　Chance Burton. Dr Richard Bright An Ophthalmologist's Appreciation. *Annals of Medical History* 1927; 332-336.

46　Neuburger M. British Medicine and the Old Vienna Medical School. *Bulletin of the Institute of the History of Medicine* 1942; **12**: 486-527.

47　Keith N M, Keys T E. Contributors of Richard Bright and his associates to renal disease. *Archives of Internal Medicine* 1956; **94**: 5-21.

48　Ritz E, Zeier M, Lundin P. French and German Nephrologists in the Mid-19th Century. *American Journal of Nephrology* 1989; **9**: 167-72.

49　Gilbert Blane (Sir). *Elements of Medical Logick*. London: 1825.

50　Jenkinson S. Biography of Sir Gilbert Blane. *Journal of the Royal Naval Medical Service* 1937; **23** (4, Part 1): 293-7.

51　Wilks Samuel (Sir) *Biographical reminiscences*. London: Adlard & Son, 1911.

Chapter 12
Eminent Physician to London Society

1　Bright P. *Richard Bright*. London: The Bodley Head, 1983.

2　Family letters. Property of Major Athill, Holt, Norfolk.

3　Bright R. *Travels from Vienna through Lower Hungary; with some remarks on the State of Vienna during the Congress of the year—1814*. Edinburgh: Archibald Constable, 1818.

4　Bright R. The Character of the late Dr Babington. *London Medical Gazette*. 1833; **12**: 264-5.

5　Bright R. On the Function of the abdomen and some of the diagnostic marks of its disease, The Goulstonian Lectures. *London Medical Gazette* 1833; **12**: 281, 312, 345, 378, 411.

6　Bright R. Address delivered at the commencement of a course of lectures on the practice of medicine. London: Richard Taylor, 1832.

7　Bright family manuscripts and letters. Property of David and Charles Bright, Melbourne, Australia.

8　Brett R L, ed. *Barclay Fox's Journal*. London: Bell & Hyman, 1836.

9　Kass A M, Kass E H. *Perfecting the World—The Life and Times of Dr Thomas Hodgkin*. Boston/San Diego/New York: Harcourt, Brace, Jovanovich, 1988.

10　Addison T, Bright R. *Elements of the Practice of Medicine*. London: Longman, 1839.

11　*Lancet* 1838-9; **36**: 620.

12 Kark R M. The First Dr Richard Bright Memorial Lecture: Dr Richard Bright & Richard Bright the Lesser, 1981, unpublished; held by the Dr Richard Bright Society.

13 Bright R. *Reports of Medical Cases selected with a view of illustrating the Symptoms and Cure of Diseases with a reference to Morbid Anatomy*, 2 Vols. London: Longman, Rees, Orme, Brown and Green, 1827.

14 Simon J. *English Sanitary Institutes*, 2nd Ed. London: Smith, Elder & Co, 1897.

15 Quenell P, ed. *Mayhew's London*. London: Pilot Press, 1949.

16 Ackroyd P. *Dickens*. Place: Sinclair-Stevenson Ltd, 1990.

17 Bright R. *Reports of Medical Cases*, Vol 2. London: Longman, Rees, Orme, Brown & Green, 1831.

18 Bright R. Cases of Spasmodic disease accompanying affections of the pericardium. *Medico-Chirurgical Transactions* 1839; **22**: *London Medical Gazette* 1838-9.

19 Monthyon Medal. Details from The Archivist of the Academy of Science, Paris, France.

20 Lumleian Lecture: Disorders of the Brain—no details of publication.

21 Buckland W J. Mr Richard Bright (Obituary): *Proceedings of the Geological Society of London* 1841; **3**: 520-2.

22 Eason H L. The situation of the clinical wards of Guy's Hospital in the time of Richard Bright. *Guy's Hospital Reports 1927;* **77**: 302-6.

23 Family letters & papers: Property of Pamela Bright, London.

24 Family letters on loan in exhibition, 'Aspects of Bright'—Royal College of Physicians of London, 1983.

Chapter 13
The Final Years—International Recognition

1 Emblem D M. *Peter Mark Roget*. London: Longman, 1970.

2 Invitation and instructions for the interment of Queen Adelaide sent to Dr R Bright—the property of Miss Pamela Bright, London.

3 Longford E. *Wellington—Pillar of State*. Book Club Associates, 1972.

4 Lilienfeld D E. The Greening of Epidemiology; Sanitary Physicians and the London Epidemiological Society (1830-1870). *British Institute for the History of Medicine* 1978; **52**: 503-28. The first meeting of the London Epidemiological Society was held in 1850: Benjamin Babington was President and Addison, Bright, Simon and Snow were among founder members.

5 Family letters and manuscripts. Property of Major Athill, Holt, Norfolk.

6   Rolt L T C. *Isambard Kingdom Brunel.* London: Longman &
    Green, 1957.
7   *Medical Times & Gazette.* Memoir of Dr Bright, December 25th,
    1858. The post mortem carried out on Dr Bright confirmed the
    presence of gall stones but death resulted from calcific congenital
    bicuspid aortic valve disease combined with acquired
    angiodysplasia of the gut causing gastro-intestinal haemorrhage,
    an association known as William's Syndrome. This was reported
    in 'The Fitzpatrick Lecture' given by Dr Robert Kark.
    Montpelier, Vermont: Horn of the Moon Enterprises, 1986.
8   *Lancet,* December 1858.
9   Thayer W S. Richard Bright. The Bright Oration delivered at
    Guy's Hospital, July 1927.
10 Barlow G H. Introduction to the New Sydenham Society's
    reprint of his papers on Abdominal Tumours: *Clinical memoirs
    on abdominal tumours and intumescence.* London, 1861.

Ackroyd P. *Dickens*. Sinclair-Stevenson Ltd, 1990.

Basham W R. *On Dropsy connected with Disease of the Kidneys (MORBUS BRIGHTII) and on some other diseases of those organs associated with Albuminous and Purulent Urine*. London: John Churchill, 1842.

Bynum W F, Porter R, eds. *Living and Dying in London*. London: Wellcome Institute for the History of Medicine, 1991.

Bright P. *Dr Richard Bright, 1789-1858*. London: Bodley Head, 1983.

Cameron H C. *Mr Guy's Hospital, 1726-1948*. London: Longmans, Green & Co, 1954.

Cave C H. *A History of Banking in Bristol, 1750-1899*. Bristol, 1899.

Christiansen R. *Romantic Affinities—Portraits from an Age, 1780-1830*. London: Bodley Head, 1988.

Christison Sir Robert. *The Life of Sir Robert Christison, Bart*. Edinburgh and London: William Blackwood & Sons, 1885.

Cooper Bransby-Blake. *The Life of Sir Astley Cooper*, 2 Vols. London: John Parker, 1843.

Craig W S. *History of the Royal College of Physicians of Edinburgh*. Oxford: Blackwell Scientific Publications, 1976.

Enright D J, ed. *The Faber Book of Fevers and Frets*. London: Faber & Faber, 1989.

Fisher R B. *Edward Jenner, 1749-1825*. London: Andre Deutsch, 1991.

Garrison Fielding H. *An introduction to the History of Medicine*. Philadelphia and London: W B Saunders Co, 1914.

Gray J (Guthrie D, ed.) *History of the Royal Medical Society 1737-1937*. Edinburgh University Press, 1952.

Hazlitt W. *Selected Writings*. Harmondsworth: Penguin, 1970.

Hobsbawn E J. *The Age of Revolution*. London: Weidenfeld & Nicolson, 1964.

Holmes R. *Coleridge: Early Visions*. London: Hodder & Stoughton, 1989.

Joyce M. *Edinburgh—The Golden Age*. London: Longmans, Green & Co, 1952.

Kass A M, Kass E. *Perfecting the World—The Life and Times of Dr Thomas Hodgkin*. Harcourt, Brace, Jovanovich, 1988.

Latimer J. *Annals of Bristol*, Bristol: Georges, 1970.

Little B. *The City and County of Bristol*. Bristol: J'Werner Laurie, 1954.

Longford E. *Wellington—Pillar of State*. London: Weidenfeld and Nicolson Ltd, 1972.

Mackenzie Sir G S. *Travels in the Island of Iceland during the Summer of the Year 1810*. Edinburgh: Archibald Constable, 1811.

McGrath P. *The Society of Merchant Venturers of the City of Bristol.* Bristol, 1975.

Nicholls J F, Taylor J. *Bristol Past & Present*, Vol III. Bristol: J W Arrowsmith, 1882.

Porter R. *Doctor of Society—Beddoes and the Sick Trade in Late Enlightenment.* London: Routledge, 1992.

Quennell P, ed. *Mayhew's London.* London: Pilot Press, 1949.

Rayer P F O. *Traité des Maladies des Reins et des Aleterations de la Secretion Urinaire.* Paris: J B Baillière, Libraire de l'Academie Royale de Medicine, 1841.

Rhodes P. *An Outline History of Medicine.* London: Butterworths, 1985.

Rolt L T C. *Isambard Kingdom Brunel.* London: Longman & Green, 1957.

Simon J. *English Sanitary Institutions.* London: Smith, Elder & Co, 1897.

Snellen H A. *History of Cardiology.* Rotterdam: Donker Academic Publications, 1984.

Southey R. *Letters from England.* London: The Cresset Press, 1951.

Stansfield D A. *Thomas Beddoes M D, 1760-1808.* Dordrecht: Reidel Publishing, 1984.

Thomson D. *England in the Nineteenth Century—Pelican History of England.* Harmondsworth: Penguin Books, 1950.

Treneer A. *The Mercurial Chemist—A Life of Sir Humphry Davy.* London: Methuen & Co Ltd, 1963.

Wawn A, ed. *The Iceland Journal of Henry Holland 1810.* London: The Hakluyt Society, 1987.

Woodward Sir Llewellyn. *The Age of Reform 1815-1870*, 2nd Ed. Oxford: The Clarendon Press, 1962.

Richard Bright's Therapeutic Options

Dr Richard Bright's own clinical acumen and diagnostic abilities, derived from a gifted and skilled use of the five senses, formed an essential part of the 'Art of Physic' and he attempted to impart these skills to his students on almost every occasion whether in the lecture room, by the bedside or in the *post mortem* room.

Apart from the desultory use of the stethoscope he had no access to the 'tools of the trade' of his 20th century counterpart such as the ophthalmoscope, the sphygmomanometer or even the clinical thermometer, nor, apart form his biochemical team, did he have the support of haematology, microbiology, X-rays, scans, electro-cardiograms or pathology services to give him a tissue diagnosis from *post mortem* material; biopsies and fine needle aspirations were unheard of.

Sadly, diagnostic ability vastly outweighed therapeutic success. The Doctor had only the vast armamentarium of Galenical-type remedies with which to treat his patients and during much of his working life at Guy's Hospital he relied, of necessity, on the recommendations for 'curative' preparations from the lists in the *London Pharmacopoeia* and the *Pharmacopoeia of Guy's Hospital*. This was, of course, some years before the launch, in 1841 of the Pharmaceutical Society in which Jacob Bell saw for the pharmaceutical chemist a role involving 'the application of chemical science to the preparations of remedial agents'.

For many years the 'chemists' and 'druggists' were free to practise medicine under this title. In such an unprofessional climate and without the benefit of scientific study, drug trial and evaluation by medical audit, it is small wonder that a 'muddle of polypharmacy' was the only choice available to both physician and surgeon alike during the middle decades of the 19th century: this was an age of therapeutic destitution. Pliny the Elder's *Naturalis Historis* written around 60 AD devotes several books to medicine and divides remedies into those from the mineral world and those from plant and animal categories of both marine and earth kingdoms: he even gives advice on the treatment of renal disease, including the use of diuretics in ascites. Remarkably, this remained the basis of most pharmacopoeia until the first quarter of the 20th century.

The *Guy's Pharmacopoeia* was divided into two sections, firstly the Materia Medica and secondly the Preparations and Composition of Purges, Enemas, Plasters, Infusions, Pills and Powders, Spirits, Tinctures, Syrups and Ointments. The list of herbs and minerals

PHARMACOPŒIA

IN USUM

NOSOCOMII

A

THOMA GUY, ARMIGERO,

PROPRIO SUMPTU

Ante Obitum Fundati,

ET

Maxima ex Parte Conditi;

HENRICO JACOBO CHOLMELEY. M.D.
GULIELMO BACK, M.D.
RICARDO BRIGHT, M.D.

HUJUSCE NOSOCOMII

MEDICIS,

THOMA ADDISON, M.D.

PRO-MEDICO,

ASTLEY PASTON COOPER, BARONETTO,

CONSILIARIO CHIRURGICO.

CAROLO ASTON KEY,
JOHANNE MORGAN,
BRANSBY BLAKE COOPER,

CHIRURGIS,

THOMA CALLAWAY,

PRO-CHIRURGO,

JACOBO STOCKER,

PHARMACOPŒO.

PHARMACOPŒIA

IN USUM

NOSOCOMII

A

THOMA GUY, ARMIGERO.

A. D. MDCCXXI

FUNDATI.

————

LONDINI:

PROSTAT VENALIS AD NOSOCOMIUM IPSUM,

ET APUD OMNES BIBLIOPOLAS.

at the back of the volume includes many items familiar to us and some still employed to this day, hopefully in a more controlled and better formulated composition! Included are such things as digitalis, hyoscyamus, ipecacuanha, magnesia, terebinthina, scilla, sulphur, opium, quinine and salicin—some of these now notably contraindicated in renal patients.

It is naturally of great interest to our study to consider some of Dr Richard Bright's both general and more specific observations regarding the treatment chosen for the patients under his care, particularly in respect of kidney disease. Whilst the Doctor points out that 'after the decided organic change has taken a firm hold on the kidney' he doubts the possibility either of affecting a cure or providing much relief, he does, however, in cases where 'the mischief is less rooted' believe much may be done to produce a beneficial outcome. The treatment has a double objective, the one to restore 'healthy action of the kidney', the second to 'guard continually against those dangerous secondary consequences which may destroy the patient at any period of the disease'.

Richard Bright considered the 'two great sources of casual danger' to be found in the 'inflammatory affections, more particularly of the serous, sometimes of the mucous membranes, and in the effusion of blood or serum into the brain, and the consequent occurrence of apoplexy'.

He points out that whatever the chosen mode of treatment, these 'impending dangers' should be of prime consideration and thus in the 'early stages of the disease it will generally be necessary to have recourse to active depletion, even as a preventive measure; but still more we should be ready at every stage of the complaint to combat the first symptoms of inflammation on the one hand, or of cerebral congestion on the other, by the free abstraction of blood the moment we have our fears awakened'. He found that in many cases 'the abstraction of blood generally' to have been 'productive of speedy effects', in other cases a local cupping from the loins was to prove efficacious. 'As our Science has advanced, medical men have learned to apply their remedies, not to the name but to the disease; hence it might occur that bleeding should be necessary in one instance while bark and stimulants are indispensable in another: and it is the power of distinguishing these that stamp the merit of the practitioner'.

He had no means of treating infection, nor, apart from bleeding and depletion, of reducing blood pressure but he did use diet to some good effect in diabetes, and possibly nephritis, reducing the intake of carbohydrate and animal produce respectively.

In retrospect we may consider that, as an established physician, Richard Bright's adherence to this ancient practice of blood-letting to be rather curious, particularly since one of his own earliest papers warned of the excessive use of such treatment. Stephen Hales in his classic animal experiments on blood pressure knew that bleeding could lower pressure catastrophically, indeed Pierre Louis, a French contemporary of Bright's who was a pioneer of clinical measurement, used a watch to time the pulse and showed statistically that blood letting was harmful, thus emphasising the paucity of shared knowledge. It is also worth noting that Dr Marshall Hall, his colleague from student days in Edinburgh certainly recognised the dangers of these sanguinary outpourings! Hall's book *Researches principally relevant to the morbid and curative effect of loss of blood*, outlines the severe symptoms such as syncope, convulsions, coma and delerium which may be directly traced to an over-zealous application of the lancet, leeches or scarifier. He points out that a timely cessation of such acitvity may be enough to effect recovery; this particularly in the case of children, who, already weakened by a bout of diarrhoea, are further depleted through the well-intentioned offices of the physician: 'Of the whole number of fatal cases of disease in infancy a great proportion occur from this inappropriate or undue application of exhausting remedies. This observation may have salutory effect in checking the ardour of many young practitioners, who are apt to think that if they have only bled, and purged and given calomel enough they have done their duty when in fact they have excited a new disease, which they have not understood, and had led to a fatal result'—the common iatrogenic disease of today.

Significantly, by the time that Dr Hilaro Barlow had published his
Manual of the Practice of Medicine in 1855 the quantity of blood
withdrawn had diminished from sometimes over a pint, to a token
few ounces.

It seems to be a sad fact, as we have already noted, that the
communication of valid and useful information between those
practising the art of medicine was woefully inadequate for, as Dr
Thomas Beddoes had shown some half a century earlier 'To lose a
single fact may be to lose many lives. Yet ten thousand, perhaps,
are lost for one that is preserved; and all for want of a system among
our theatres of disease, combined with the establishment of a
national bank of medical wealth, where each individual practioner
may deposit his gains and knowledge, and draw out, in return, the
stock accumulated by all his brethren.' We may see this as the
forerunner of today's medical audit.

In such a climate the physician's response was to administer
treatment on an essentially empiric, or should we say neo-empiric,
basis and we should not therefore be surprised to find Bright
adopting similar methods. Treatments, as today, could be divided
roughly into general and specific—the former such as fluid balance,
bed rest, flannel next to the skin, cooling, pain-killers, bland diets
and the odd 'dram', and the avoidance of chills were directed at the
general improvement of the patient's well-being while the latter was
used to relieve the specific disease, e.g. dropsy.

Depletion seemed of prime importance and could be achieved by
bleeding both locally and generally, cupping, purging, applying
leeches and with diaphoretics, diuretics, emetics; puncturing the
swollen legs or scrotum with a lancet or needle to release an
oedematous fluid was also employed and occasionally rollers were
used to squeeze the fluid up the legs. Ascites was often relieved by
abdominal paracentesis. The fact that some of these treatments could
be lethal to his dropsical patients, some of whom would already have
a small circulating blood volume, i.e. hypovolaemia, despite their
water-logged appearance, was unknown to him. The addition of salts
of potash as a saline diuretic may well have been the 'coup de grace'
to other renal patients; a high potassium level in the blood must
at that time have been a fairly common terminal event!

Therapy seemed totally to lack discrimination, was of a
blunderbuss nature and broadly followed the same lines whatever
the primary disease, differing only in that applications, leeches,
blisters and poultices were often sited over the diseased organ.
Richard Bright favoured certain combinations in his renal patients
but overall no consistent regimen emerges. He did gradually move
away from industrial doses of mercurials until erethism or salicysm
occurred, to a more discerning policy in their application as a
diuretic. Digitalis seemed in his later studies to become more popular
but it is interesting that Dr William Withering, the great advocate

of the foxglove, i.e. Digitalis folias, recognised a group of digitalis-resistant dropsies which were to become identified later as of renal origin. If digitalis was effective, cardiac failure was probably present as well. The use of oral internal remedies was often limited by the patient vomiting and no doubt many a renal patient was saved by the emetic effect of an unsuitable remedy. Intramuscular or intravenous administration of drugs was not developed at this stage. Epicacuanha and tartar emetics were used to deplete patients and jalap and senna enemas were used to supplement purging.

The movement of the bowels seemed paramount to any regimen and consequently the patient was subjected to either strong purging or, in the presence of wasting diarrhoea, chalk and epicacuanha derivatives to limit gastrointestinal 'hurry'. However, one gets the feeling that punitive catharsis was good for the soul as well as the body.

The horror of being ill and having to suffer these treatments is difficult to imagine and little was known about anti-emetics or antacids to relieve gut symptoms although magnesia was used for diarrhoea. Elaterium seemed to be the favoured purgative coupled with a saline laxative such as supertartrate of potash which had the added benefit of a diuretic effect; jalap, castor oil, rhubarb, ginger, gamboge, taraxacum, scammony and Gregory's powder were also employed. Squill and hyoscyamus or henbane were first-line diuretics and, if mercury had been used before and was contraindicated, a little digitalis or a broom top or Spartium scoparium infusion was added. If mercury was being tried it was often as a calomel and opium mixture or as the 'blue pill': but several 'hydragyri' or mercurial preparations were available. It is fascinating that Dog grass (or Triticum repens) infusion was an effective diuretic as it is not unlike mannitol which we use today in acute renal failure. The supertartrate of potash, however, seemed to be the main saline diuretic. Antimonials, sometimes as James' Powder, seemed to have had both a diuretic and diaphoretic effect and were added occasionally and hydragium with chalk and epicacuanha was used for reducing fevers. To get a good sweat going diaphoretic measures were applied including warm steam baths, hip baths, Dover's powders, arrow root and a variety of beef and other hot teas, the general aim being antiphlogistic or anti-inflammatory. Richard Bright prescribed diosma crenata for inflammation of the renal tract on the recommendation of Sir Benjamin Brodie.

Opium seemed to be the main pain killer although salicin was used as a sort of early 'aspirin' preparation which was also antipyretic.

Tonics were popular and included iron and zinc preparations, which are still commonly used as dietary supplements in renal patients today. Uva ursi or bear berry, pyrolla umbellata and various alcoholic beverages including porter, gin, port and light wines seemed to improve the patients' spirits, especially when accompanied by a little Peruvian balsam or quinine.

Counter irritation was considered valuable and could be achieved by inserting a thread through the skin with a seton or bristle needle to cause an inflammatory response usually at the back of the neck but also by applying hot fomentations or poultices. Rubifacients such as turpentine and cantharides capsium, linseed and belladonna plasters were used to produce a skin reaction and scarifying blisters and glysters were employed for the same purpose. Interestingly if the skin did become inflamed or infected following puncturing or as a result of the above measures, Goulard's water or Lotio plumbi was applied, a modern practice which has only just been discontinued. Richard Bright wrote all his prescriptions and instructions for treatment in Latin e.g. Repetatur Medicamenta or Detrahatur Sanguinis e Regione Lumborum, but tended, when discussing treatment to write in English. The final words must be his and he must have written them with a mixed feeling of frustration and impotence: 'The ordinary medicines exhibited with unusual care and skill have failed in making any favourable impression on the disease': the disease in this case being his own. It is gratifying that within 10 years of Bright's death the more discerning physicians at Guy's Hospital such as Drs Gull and Sutton, had shown that patients with rheumatic fever, treated with a multitude of remedies, did just as well with a 'little mint' water; these findings, more or less, sounded a death knell for the old worthless treatments—therapeutic nihilism, good nursing and nature remained the preferred approach, until the introduction of chemotherapy in the 20th century. In fact, as early as the mid-18th century, Sir John Fowler said that 'in a large proportion of cases treated by physicians, the disease is cured by nature not by them'.

Letters Illustrative of an Age

Family letters and manuscripts provide a valuable wealth of socio-historical material and the vast collection of Bright family letters is no exception. We have, therefore, chosen a few examples which are printed mainly in their entirety. These letters demonstrate, firstly, the strength of filial and matrimonial duty and respect common to that period, whilst the second group provide an insight into Dr Richard Bright's professional life, illustrated by letters from four contemporary eponymists.

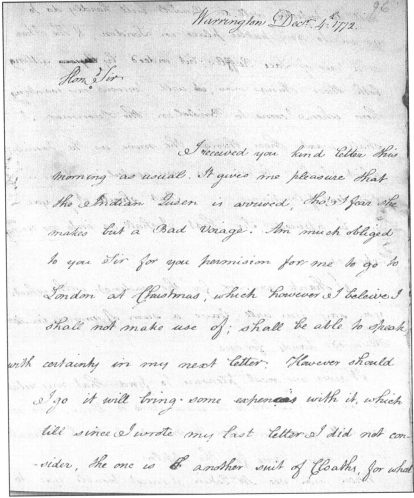

Letter 1

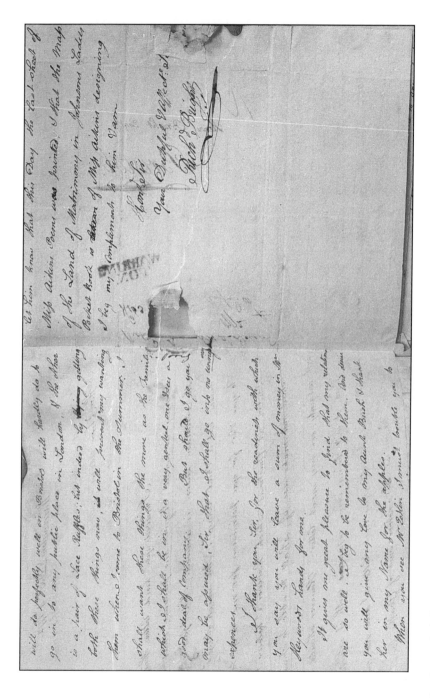

Letter 1 contd. A letter from Richard Bright (senior) to his father, Henry Bright, in which he displays concern both for his sartorial elegance and also for pecuniary restraint!

Dear Sir

I feel that I stand in need of your forgiveness when I borrow your name, without permission, to adorn my Thesis; and I feel this the more when I consider that it is a truly unworthy performance, and calculated to give nothing in return for the weight and ornament it derives from you. The existence of a Thesis is however so ephemeral, that I conceive myself as offering you a private, rather than a public testimony, of my esteem, and as such, originating in the sincerity of my heart, I hope you will accept it — I need not enumerate circumstances which gave rise to this esteem — but I will say that transferring my respect for yourself to the profession which you had long and successfully exercised, I was first induced to select that path of life which I have now begun seriously to pursue; and which every day

Letter 2

Extract from Dr Richard Bright's letter to his father expressing his deep respect and asking forgiveness for using the family name to adorn a thesis which he considers is 'a truly unworthy performance'.

Letter 3

A letter from Richard Bright to his father written three months after his marriage to Eliza, in which he sets out details of his current unfortunate financial situation.

Letter 4
A letter from William Bright to his father Dr Richard
Bright asking for acceptance and understanding of his
decision to enter the Ministry.

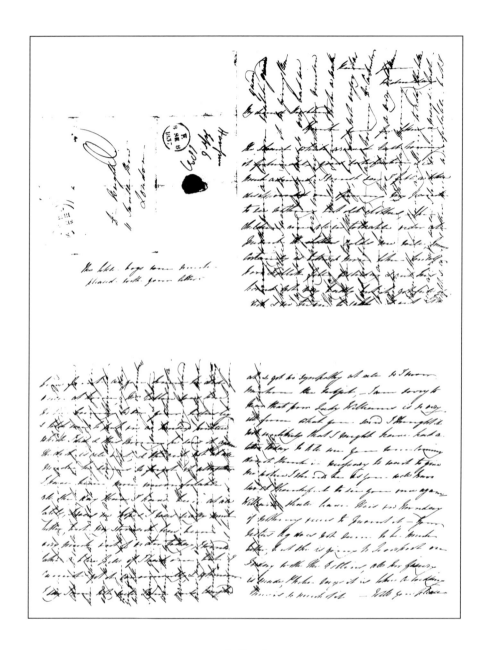

Letter 5
*An interesting, albeit almost illegible cross-written letter from Eliza Follett to her
husband Dr Richard Bright. She apparently wrote to him twice daily when she was
away from home and the prohibitive cost of paper necessitated cross-writing.*

Letter 6
A letter from Sir Astley Cooper accompanying a gift he sent to Dr Richard Bright in recognition of his professional excellence.

> 9 Harcourt St. Dublin
> 31st December 38
>
> Dear Sir
>
> Your letter gave me much
> pleasure indeed, and that for several reasons.
> First, I rejoice at the opportunity of making
> an acquaintance by letter with one from
> whose writings I have derived so much
> instruction and profit — Secondly I
> still more rejoice at finding that we
> do not differ much, if at all, concer
> =ning the Connexion between albumi
> =nous urine & structural disease
> of the Kidney — I think you would
> do well to publish in the Medical
> Gazette a short exposé of your
> opinions on the subject, for certainly
> your views have been very generally
> misunderstood both here & in America —

Letter 7
A letter from Dr Robert Graves to Dr Richard Bright discussing renal disorders
and the pandemic of cholera.

The matter is one of much practical
importance for ~~actually~~ the idea is
now too prevalent that albuminous
urine, invariably denotes in dropsy organic
renal disease —
I am much disposed to doubt — but
what use in repeating that I have printed —
Let us break new ground — Can you,
or can any of your friends aid me in
making a good map of the progress
of Indian Cholera — I want dates of
its arrival at each important city or
point &c &c — Such a map I know
was published on the continent, but it
was at an early period — I am much at a
loss for data for America, Portugal
Spain & Italy —
I believe Geneva, & Switzerland
generally, escaped!
Another special point is to ascertain
the instinctual effort it made to

Letter 7 contd.

get to the mediterranean by the
way of the Persian Gulf, or rather
the Shores of the Red Sea —
I am not going to write more than
an essay on this Subject, to be read at
a Soirée of the College of
Physicians here — So if
You can get me references
to books where the information I
seek is to be found, you will
confer a very great obligation
on me ——

Yours faithfully

Robt. J. Graves

Letter 7 contd.

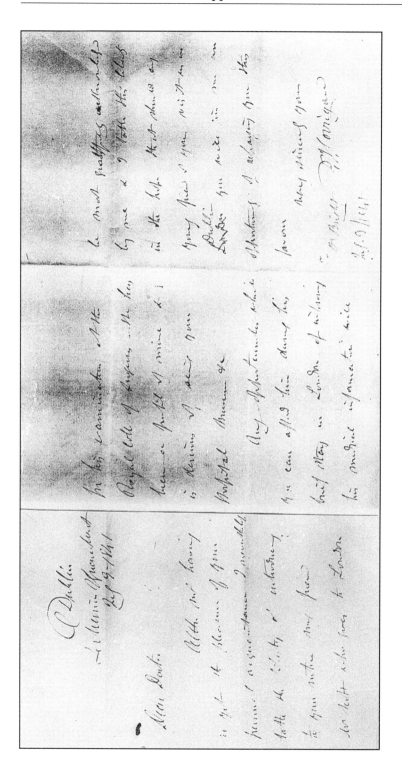

Letter 8

A letter from Dr Dominic Corrigan introducing one of his pupils, Mr Scott, who has come over to London to sit his examinations at the Royal College of Physicians.

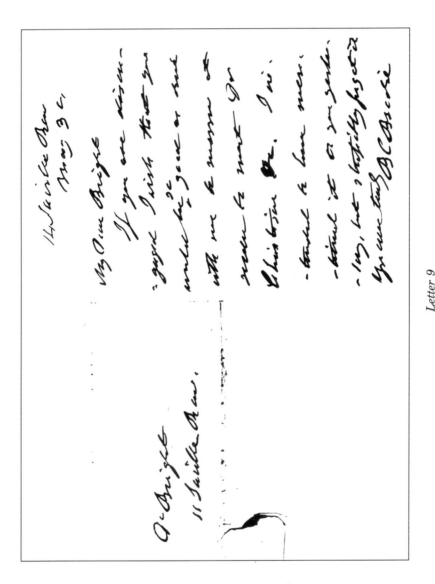

Letter 9

A letter from Dr Benjamin Brodie inviting Dr Richard Bright to supper to meet Dr Robert Christison.

Index

271

HENRY BRIGHT, second son, merchant in Bristol. **b.** 12 March 1715. Baptised at Ledbury. Sherrif of the city of Bristol, 1753. Mayor thereof, 1771. Purchased Welland Court, Worcester, of his brother Allen, **d.** 25 Nov. 1777, buried in St. Nicholas's Church, Bristol.

RICHARD BRIGHT, of Ham Green, Somersetshire, Esq. Merchant at Bristol, only child, **b.** 21 July, 175 **m.** 24 March, 1782, at St. Thomas's Church, Liverpool. Heir to his cousins, Lowbridge Bright, Es and Richard Meyler, Esq. MP for Winchester. **d.** Jar 1840.

HENRY BRIGHT, **b.** in Queen's square, Bristol, 18 Jan. 1784. Barrister-at-Law, MP for Bristol, 1820 to 1830, succeeded to the Estate of Colwall, Herefordshire, and of Crawley Manor, Hampshire, at his father's death. **d.** unmarried, 26 March, 1869. Buried at Colwall.

ELIZABETH, daughter of Nathaniel Heywood, of Manchester, banker. **m.** 6 Nov. 1818. **d.** May 1819.

BENJAMIN HEYWOOD BRIGHT, second son, **b.** in Queen's Square, Bristol, 14 Aug. 1787, **d.** at Ham Green, 7 Aug. 1843.

MARY ELIZABETH, daughter of Rev. J. Rowe, Minister at St. Michael's in Bristol, 20 June, 1822. **d.** 26 Oct. 1829, buried in Hackney.

MARTHA LYNDON, third daughter of Dr. Babington. **m.** 14 Aug. 1822 **d.** 30 Dec. 1823. First wife.

PHEBE, **b.** in Queen's Square, Bristol, Aug, 1785.

SARAH, **b.** 26 March, 1792. **d.** 16 July, 1792.

SARAH ANNE, **b.** at Ham Green. 3 Sep. 1793. **d.** 1866, buried at Cornwall.

WILLIAM RICHARD BRIGHT, **b.** in Bloomsbury Square, in the city of Westminster, 30 Dec. 1823. Was ordained and died 1848.

ANNA, d. 1832.

WILLIAM WEBB FOLLET BRIGHT, **b.** London. 11 June, 1831. **d.** 1851.

JAMES FRANCKBRIGHT, **b.** 29 May, 1832. Ordained 1856 Master in Malbro' College. **m.** 1864. Emmeline Theresa, daughter of Rev. E. D. Wickham Possessed of Manor of Brockbury, by will of his uncle, Henry Bright.